CHARLOTTE MEW (1869–19
of the four children of an upper-
was educated at Lucy Harrison'
and attended lectures at Unive
was twenty-nine her father, an architect, died, leaving the family in severely reduced circumstances; Charlotte remained, with her mother and sister Anne, living in Bloomsbury.

Charlotte Mew's literary career began with the publication of a short story in *The Yellow Book*. She went on to publish stories and poems in *Temple Bar*, *The Egoist*, *The English Woman*, *The Nation* and other journals. She produced two books of verse, *The Farmer's Bride* (1915) and *The Rambling Sailor* (1929), both of which were published by Harold Monro at the Poetry Bookshop. Charlotte Mew was a close friend of May Sinclair and was admired by numerous literary figures of the day. In 1923 she was awarded a Civil List pension at the instigation of John Masefield, Walter de la Mare and Thomas Hardy. In the same year her mother died, followed in 1927 by her sister Anne. Charlotte Mew lived only one year longer, committing suicide in a nursing home in London in 1928.

CHARLOTTE MEW

Collected Poems and Prose

Edited and with an Introduction
by VAL WARNER

VIRAGO PRESS
in association with CARCANET PRESS

Published by VIRAGO PRESS Limited 1982
Ely House, 37 Dover Street, London W1X 4HS
in association with CARCANET PRESS
330 Corn Exchange Building, Manchester

Printed in Great Britain by The Anchor Press
and bound by William Brendon & Sons
both of Tiptree, Essex

British Library Cataloguing in Publication Data

Mew, Charlotte
Collected poems and prose.
I. Title
828'.91209 PR6025.E8

ISBN 0-86068-223-4

CONTENTS

Poems

The Farmer's Bride (1916)

Additional poems included in *The Farmer's Bride,* 1921 edition

The Rambling Sailor (1929)

Early poems printed at the end
of *The Rambling Sailor*

Unpublished or uncollected poems

Stories

apparently unpublished

Essays

Play

Appendix

INTRODUCTION

CHARLOTTE MARY MEW was born on 15 November 1869, the third child of Frederick Mew (1832-1898), who was the son of a farmer on the Isle of Wight. Frederick Mew came to London to train as an architect; in 1863 he married the daughter of his partner, the well-known H. E. Kendall the younger. Anna Kendall (1837-1923), Charlotte's mother, came to feel she had married beneath her and partly because of her concern 'that appearances must be kept up at all costs' impressed many who met her as a silly, superficial woman. Of the seven Mew children, two died after a few months, and a third at the age of five. A brother and a sister both became insane in later life, and were confined to institutions. Charlotte was very close to her remaining sibling, Anne (1873-1927), who took up work restoring antique furniture.

Charlotte was born at 10 Doughty Street, Mecklenburgh Square, where the Mew family lived until 1888; they then moved to 9 Gordon Street, Gordon Square, where Charlotte lived for most of her life. Her article 'An Old Servant', about her old nurse, Elizabeth Goodman, gives an account of the Mew nursery. The nurse was a dominant figure in middle-class Victorian childhood, and Miss Goodman continued to work in the Mew household until her death in 1893. Lottie was a passionate and wilful girl. Once, on arrival for a holiday on the Isle of Wight, she insisted on riding in the cart from the station beside the driver; when tapped with her nurse's parasol in reprimand, she snapped it in two. There is, too, the story that she banged her head against a brick wall when informed of her headmistress's forthcoming retirement.

Charlotte attended Lucy Harrison's School for Girls in Gower Street, and with a few other pupils spent some time as a boarder in the home of the headmistress, Lucy Harrison. Although the school curriculum was broader than that of many girls' schools at the time, Charlotte did not take full advantage of it. She insisted on learning only what appealed to her—English literature, and a little about art and music.

Later, she attended lectures at University College, London. She played the organ and the piano. She read widely in French and English. She also used the British Museum Reading Room: her essays 'Mary Stuart in Fiction' and 'Men and Trees' reveal her extensive reading. Among her papers, an impressive list of quotations from George Eliot's work has survived.

There is a dearth of information about Charlotte's earlier life. 'An

Old Servant' mentions 'sheets of pathetically laboured MSS,' as the nursery inmates grew older. In 1894 Henry Harland, literary editor of *The Yellow Book,* published her story 'Passed' in the second issue of the magazine: Charlotte's first recorded publication. Harland also admired 'The China Bowl', but deemed it too long for publication in *The Yellow Book.* Ella D'Arcy, the magazine's assistant literary editor, listed Charlotte Mew among the literati who attended Harland's Saturday evening gatherings at his Cromwell Road flat, along with Kenneth Grahame, Max Beerbohm, George Moore, Richard Le Gallienne, Arthur Symons, Henry James, occasionally Edmund Gosse, and many others.

When she left the Gower Street school, Anne Mew attended the 'Female School of Art' in Queen's Square and the Mew sisters' circle of acquaintance included artistic friends made by Anne. Charlotte was considered advanced in her behaviour, visiting where she wanted unchaperoned, smoking and swearing. She was also very good at embroidery.

Her article 'Notes in a Brittany Convent' and the related poem 'The Little Portress' were sparked off by a visit to Brittany in 1901, as one of a party of six women staying at the convent in St. Gilda de Rhuys. Subsequently—and perhaps before, too—she made a number of visits to Paris and Brittany, probably in the company of her aunt Mary Leonora Kendall. She used a French setting for many of her poems and stories and was clearly much attracted to France and to the Roman Catholic Church.

Through the first decade of this century, Charlotte Mew published prose pieces and some poems at a modest rate. In March 1913 she mentioned in a letter that she was now called 'Charlotte' by 'Sappho', Catherine Amy Dawson-Scott, the novelist and founder of PEN. Soon afterwards Charlotte got to know the novelist May Sinclair, whom she had already met briefly, after sending her an admiring letter about her novel *The Combined Maze,* just published. A friendship developed between May Sinclair, then approaching the height of her career, and the relatively unknown Charlotte. May Sinclair was at the heart of literary London—had even been responsible for first introducing Ezra Pound to Ford Madox Ford. She was active in the suffrage movement, too. Largely self-taught, she was trained in philosophy; her deep interest in psychology led to her involvement in establishing the Medico-Psychological Clinic of London. One of Charlotte's letters to her includes an offer to address envelopes for the Clinic.

May Sinclair admired Charlotte's prose as well as her poems, and Charlotte read much of her work, including an unfinished version of 'Madeleine in Church', aloud to her. May Sinclair helped Charlotte by bringing her work to the attention of Edward Garnett, Austin Harrison of the *English Review* and Ezra Pound of *The Egoist.*

Pound was enthusiastic about Charlotte's poetry and in turn forwarded copies to *Poetry* in Chicago. *Poetry* rejected them, but *The Egoist* printed 'The Fête'.

Charlotte's friendship with May Sinclair coincided with an awakening of interest in her poetry in another quarter. Alida Monro, Alida Klemantaski before her marriage to the Georgian poet and publisher Harold Monro, describes how, in 1912, she 'was electrified' to find 'The Farmer's Bride' printed in the *Nation:* 'This poem I immediately committed to memory, and a year or two later repeated it with enthusiasm to Harold Monro, who had recently opened the Poetry Bookshop, with the avowed intention of publishing the work of young poets and presenting them to a large audience.' Thus, in 1916, a collection of seventeen poems by Charlotte appeared under the title *The Farmer's Bride.*

Though only five hundred copies were printed, this was a big edition by the standards of the Poetry Bookshop. The book sold poorly. It was not widely reviewed, despite the efforts of May Sinclair, who sent copies to a number of well-known reviewers and received most response from H.D. and Rebecca West. Harold Monro championed Charlotte's work, later amply representing it in his anthologies *Some Contemporary Poets* and *Twentieth-century Poetry.* Alida Monro did the same in her anthology *Recent Poetry.* In 1917 when Edward Marsh asked him to suggest work by a woman poet for inclusion in *Georgian Poetry III,* which was expected to be as popular and prestigious as the previous volumes, Harold Monro argued for 'The Farmer's Bride'. For a second opinion of the poem, Marsh appealed to Walter de la Mare, who judged the poem unsatisfactory, and no woman poet was in fact included. When, two years later, Marsh was again seeking a 'poetess' for *Georgian Poetry IV,* Monro again urged Charlotte Mew, without success. Marsh favoured Fredegond Shove instead. Monro wrote to Marsh that 'the absence of Charlotte Mew is of course again a conspicuous flaw'.

Sir Sydney Cockerell, Director of the Fitzwilliam Museum at Cambridge, read *The Farmer's Bride.* He made himself known to Charlotte, and a long friendship between the Mew sisters and Cockerell and his wife followed. They met in London and on visits to Cambridge. Cockerell introduced Charlotte's work to many of his wide circle, including the poet Wilfred Scawen Blunt, T. E. Lawrence and Dame Laurentia McLachlan, Abbess of Stanbrook, friend of Bernard Shaw, and pioneer in the restoration of the Gregorian chant in England. In 1919 Cockerell brought Siegfried Sassoon to tea with Charlotte, who became one of his 'spiritual benefactors'. He championed her work at home and in Germany.

Charlotte Mew's extensive correspondence with Cockerell gives a vivid picture of the last decade of her life in London, with outings to lectures and art galleries and the like—'Bach is beyond me'—and the odd weekend in the country. The letters also show Charlotte's keen interest in personalities, such as Dame Laurentia, who caught her imagination. Concerning her life in an enclosed order, Charlotte wrote: 'Do not "defy" me to find a more wonderful lady—I shall not try; but as for saints, this same lady would agree that the grey cloisters here and there hide—how many? to whom perhaps we owe it that this wicked old Earth is not yet in ashes.'

Charlotte learned from Cockerell that Hugh Walpole was among her admirers. So also was the Poet Laureate, Robert Bridges. Lady Ottoline Morrell invited her to visit: Robert Gathorne-Hardy described how he was introduced by Lady Ottoline to the poetry of Charlotte Mew, whom 'she believed to be among the best of poets alive then'. The sentiment was shared by Virginia Woolf, who in 1920 found *The Farmer's Bride* 'very good and interesting and unlike anyone else'; in 1924 she wrote to Vita Sackville-West that she had just met, among others, 'Charlotte Mew, (the greatest living poetess)'.

Thomas Hardy's admiration probably meant more to her than anyone else's. He described her as 'far and away the best living woman poet—who will be read when others are forgotten'. After reading *The Farmer's Bride,* he invited her to visit at Max Gate. The visit was made in December 1918, and followed by at least one more visit in 1926. Quite a friendship sprang up between Florence Hardy and Charlotte, who met in London. Charlotte seems to have revered Hardy more than any other living writer, referring to him as her King of Wessex.

Despite the discriminating acclaim that greeted *The Farmer's Bride,* after 1916 Charlotte seems to have written little, poetry or prose. In 1921 an expanded edition of the book came out with eleven new poems. It was published as *Saturday Market* in America, where Louis Untermeyer reviewed it enthusiastically. Sassoon introduced Charlotte to Untermeyer and his wife when they visited London. In 1923 she was awarded a Civil List pension of £75 a year, on the recommendation of John Masefield, Walter de la Mare and Thomas Hardy, but later she wished to give it up because she was no longer writing enough to justify it. Alida Monro pointed out that 'Few of the poems which were published posthumously in *The Rambling Sailor* (1929) were written after 1916'.

The 1920s were clearly a very difficult period for Charlotte Mew. In 1922, when the lease of the Gordon Street house expired, the Mews rented a house in Delancey Street, Regent's Park. Both Anne and Mrs Mew were unwell. Mrs Mew died in May 1923. The sisters gave up the Delancey Street house and moved into Anne's studio in the Hogarth Studios, Charlotte Street. Alida Monro recalled, 'Often in the past Charlotte and Anne had received friends there if they did not want to have them at their home at tea time; but after they went to live there, although it was only a temporary measure, Charlotte decided that no one could possibly be asked to visit'.

Anne's health began to decline seriously from Christmas 1925. She finally died of cancer in June 1927. A week later Charlotte wrote to Cockerell, 'how exquisite a spirit it was or how dauntless only I can know who know what she had to fight and how she fought it—and so much more of that grace of thought and deed than her oldest friend could know . . .'. According to Alida Monro, 'Charlotte was so overcome by Anne's death that she was inconsolable, and after a short time her nerves became very bad. She was unable to sleep and so tortured herself with the idea that as she had not had a vein opened in Anne's wrist her sister might have been buried alive, that medical help had to be sought.'

On 15 February 1928 Charlotte went into a nursing home in Beaumont Street for treatment for neurasthenia. On 24 March she killed herself there by drinking half a bottle of lysol. At the inquest her doctor said that after Anne's death, 'she became obsessed with the idea that her room and belongings were infected by the germ which she thought had killed her sister'. Two local papers reported the verdict of 'suicide whilst of unsound mind' of 'Miss Charlotte Mary New [sic]', 'a writer of verse'.

In her will, Charlotte left instructions that a headstone should be erected over Anne's grave in Fortune Green Cemetery with this inscription: 'To the beloved memory of Caroline Frances Anne Mew who departed this life on June 18, 1927. "Cast down the seed of weeping and attend." Here lies also her sister Charlotte Mary Mew who departed this life on — 19—.' The quotation comes from Canto XXXI of Dante's *Purgatorio,* Beatrice's answer when Dante is finally able to confess what turned his steps from ideal love.

The 'mystery' of Charlotte Mew began in her lifetime when she jibbed at supplying biographical notes for an anthology. People who knew her in later life often found her very reserved. There has been speculation, too, about her private life, focusing on the identity of the unnamed dedicatee of *The Farmer's Bride.* One of her cousins recalled that in the early 1890s, Charlotte was 'walking out' with a young man. T. E. M. Boll, later May Sinclair's biographer, argues that Charlotte attempted to have a lesbian relationship with May Sinclair some time before their friendship ended abruptly in the autumn of 1916. Boll quotes a letter to Rebecca West from the novelist G. B. Stern (Gladys B. 'Peter' Stern), recalling an account by May Sinclair of her attempted seduction by 'a lesbian poetess named Charlotte M.'. There may be no proof positive, but throughout her work Charlotte Mew's romantic interest generally focuses on women.

Her reserve is easily explained by her family circumstances. Throughout her long friendship with Alida Monro, Charlotte kept from her the information that she had an insane sister in hospital on the Isle of Wight (where she died in 1958) and that a brother had died in mental hospital after a stay of some years. It is clear from the money inherited by Charlotte's mother and from her own will, in which she left a personal estate valued at £8,608, that she was in fact far better off than was believed by many of her acquaintances, who saw her life as 'a long struggle . . . with poverty'. The insanity of Freda Mew and Henry Herne Mew, who had his own private nurse in a London hospital, was a heavy if clandestine drain on the Mew family resources. In 1921 the maintenance and support of Freda was costing about £130 per year out of Mrs Mew's net income of about £300 from trust property. Charlotte Mew left the bulk of her estate in trust for the care of Freda.

In default of evidence about the identity of the unnamed dedicatee of *The Farmer's Bride* ('To —'), it is likely that Charlotte dedicated the volume to her brother, Henry (1865-1901). His insanity began only when he had nearly completed his training as an architect, articled to their father. His breakdown must have been a great shock to Charlotte, who had grown up with him. The epigraph itself has a strong Mew family connection. It is a verse from Psalm 21, 'He asked life of thee, and thou gavest him a long life: even for ever and ever', which was adapted by Charlotte's great-grandfather to 'She asked life of thee, and thou gavest her . . .' and used as the epitaph on the grave of his wife, Anne, in Fortune Green Cemetery, where Charlotte would have been familiar with it.

Henry Herne Mew was buried in Nunhead Cemetery. Charlotte's poem 'In Nunhead Cemetery', included in *The Farmer's Bride,* is written with a male persona about a dead woman. This is a characteristic transformation: in a letter about the 1916 collection, she described 'The Quiet House' as 'perhaps the most subjective to me, of the lot', and there too she made considerable changes in autobiographical detail; for instance, the father in 'The Quiet House' has long survived the mother of the four children.

The over-all arrangement of the 1916 *Farmer's Bride* is interesting when taken in conjunction with the epigraph. Despite the doubts expressed in the penultimate poem in the collection, 'Madeleine in Church', still unresolved in its final 'Or, if, for once, He would only speak', the collection ends with a short lyric, 'Exspecto Resurrectionem', whose title speaks for itself.

Mental illness is a theme which recurs throughout *The Farmer's Bride.* One of Charlotte's best poems, 'Ken', is a portrait of insanity in which she tries to obscure 'the tragic side by a tenderness of treatment'. The 'tragic side' comes out in 'On the Asylum Road' in which she describes madness in the context of society at large: the insane are 'the incarnate wages of man's sin'.

Charlotte Mew told Alida Monro that 'She and her sister had both made up their minds early in life . . . that they would never marry for fear of passing on the mental taint that was in their heredity.' Whether or not Alida Monro's statement is accurate, it accounts for the themes which dominate Charlotte's work: denial and renunciation, themes which in turn affect her portrayal of love as confined to brief, passionate encounters, or yearnings, always negated, often quite arbitrarily.

Renunciation of marriage entailed renunciation of motherhood. Several passages in Charlotte Mew's writing, for example in 'The Shade-catchers', suggest that she was fond of children, and she wrote in a letter about 'Sappho' Dawson-Scott that she 'largely appreciated my new acquaintance because of the children in her home'. Yet in 'Madeleine in Church', the woman seems to be thinking more of misery endured by others than by herself in her agonized 'If there were fifty heavens God could not give us back the child who went or never came', and perhaps closer to Charlotte herself is the loneliness behind the only half-believing cry later in the poem:

> There must be someone. Christ! there must,
> Tell me there *will* be someone. Who?
> If there were no one else, could it be You?

If Charlotte Mew was lesbian, then this too signified repression, both because of her own divided nature, and because of the time in which she lived. In 1895 the Oscar Wilde judgment helped to close *The Yellow Book*. In 1921 only the House of Lords prevented from becoming law a bill, already passed by the Commons, to apply the Criminal Law Amendment Act ('the blackmailer's charter') of 1885 to female as well as male homosexuals. In 1928, the year of Charlotte's death, in *The Well of Loneliness*, Radclyffe Hall portrayed the position of lesbians in society and their relation to the Church:

> And what of that curious craving for religion which so often went hand in hand with inversion? Many such people were deeply religious, and this surely was one of their bitterest problems. They believed, and believing they craved a blessing on what to some of them seemed very sacred—a faithful and deeply devoted union. But the Church's blessing was not for them. Faithful they might be, leading orderly lives, harming no one, and yet the Church turned away; her blessings were strictly reserved for the normal.

There is no sign in her work that Charlotte Mew accepted her sexuality, and given her concern for appearances, it can hardly be expected of her. Just as she never describes happy, continuing love in heterosexual marriage, so there is nothing in her work of Radclyffe Hall's ideal of 'union', the homosexual ideal of 'my friend', 'someone to last your whole life and you his', as in E. M. Forster's *Maurice,* written in 1913-14 but withheld from publication during the author's lifetime. Charlotte was never able, either homosexually or heterosexually, to integrate the passion she expressed so piercingly in her poems and prose with the life she lived. She lived in a time when patriarchal taboos upon female sexual desire were at their strongest: yet her unresolved sexuality helped to produce the poems, stories and essays which illuminate problems peculiar to women.

Her fear of hereditary insanity frustrated her existence, making her unable to fulfil herself in any way as a woman—as lover, wife or mother. It has been suggested that she killed herself because, having been obliged to enter a nursing-home, she feared she too was on the verge of insanity. Her suicide vividly raises the question of her attitude to religion. In 'An Old Servant', she describes how as a child she was brought up by her nurse in conventional religious observance: 'In early years the rite and reality of daily prayers were for us strictly insisted on, and "Forgive us our trespasses" was no idle phrase when after it, each night at bedtime, we had to specify them.'

More characteristic, though, at least of her mature attitude, is the rhetorical question of 'In the Fields' and in the parallel poem 'Old Shepherd's Prayer'. 'In the Fields' opens with 'Lord, when I look at lovely things which pass' and leads on to 'Can I believe there is a heavenlier world than this?' Her ambivalent attitude towards Christianity is striking. An unbeliever would celebrate this world in the assurance that it is all we have. She seems to *feel* this, yet she retains a kind of religious belief.

According to Alida Monro, whose judgement may here be affected by her own attitude, organized religion never 'took any place' in Charlotte's adult life. Charlotte's letters make clear, though, that she attended religious services at least on occasion in both England and France. Writing to Cockerell, she called herself a 'poor infidel', but after her death he wrote to Dame Laurentia, 'She longed to join your faith but could not bring herself to accept its dogmas. When she stayed with us here she sallied forth to the R.C. church.' While Charlotte's letters show that she appreciated the quiet of a Quaker household, she was fascinated too by the sumptuous trappings of the Roman Catholic church in the 1890s, though she ridiculed superstition in the priest in 'The London Sunday' and in 'Notes in a Brittany Convent'. Anne Mew died an Anglo-Catholic, and one of Charlotte's cousins, herself a nun, stated that but for confession, Charlotte would have become a Roman Catholic.

There is no worked-out, rigorous structure of thought behind Charlotte Mew's work. It is impossible to abstract from it, for example, a defined sense of her political attitudes. In this respect, little more than a sense of a quirky and individualistic personality emerges from her work. In 'Notes in a Brittany Convent', she describes herself as 'a dilettante', and the small quantity of her work in prose and in verse to some extent bears this out. According to Alida Monro, 'She herself attributed her small output to the difficulties of domestic life, doing the housekeeping and looking after "Ma", and the constant interruptions when she sat at her desk—Jane, the factotum who was with her for years, knocking on the door'. Domestic chores are part of the subject matter of her work, in the stories. Alida Monro also recalled that Charlotte 'always spoke of stacks of MSS. salted away in trunks, but after her death very little was found'. She tells a story of Charlotte making spills out of old MSS.

In her writing, Charlotte seems fairly conformist in her attitude to society, including the family, and she was certainly dominated by her own, of whom only Anne took her writing seriously. Alida Monro wrote that Charlotte 'would always say, when speaking of her mother, that family ties meant everything to her; but it is probable that she adored the idea of a mother rather than the woman herself, for there was little in common between them.'

Alida Monro's preface to the 1953 *Collected Poems,* 'Charlotte Mew—A Memoir', may be inaccurate in some details and lacking in information withheld by Charlotte. All the same, it paints a vivid portrait. While insisting that Charlotte's 'temperament was naturally keyed very low', Alida Monro stresses how lively she could be, and there are several accounts of her impassioned readings of her own work to groups of two or three friends. Charlotte could be good company, gay, witty, enchanting the circle 'who loved and valued her dearly'. Her work expresses this aspect of her personality as well as the darker side. The prose and verse are often suffused with flashes of humour and a penetrating, ironic wit. Her temperament would swing from high to low, perhaps a version of the family temperament that in its extreme form produced the insanity of her brother and sister. Whatever her sexual proclivities, her passionate nature made the impossibility of marriage, forced upon her by arbitrary circumstances of environment and heredity, cruelly hard to bear; she was unable to commit herself completely to her sexuality, to the sensual world, to the Roman Catholic church. It is not surprising, therefore, that her work is a celebration of passion deeply felt, but always denied.

Virginia Woolf wrote that 'human nature had changed . . . in or about 1910', and the novel had to shift from the socio-descriptive type to focus more on the inner character. In 1915 Dorothy Richardson published *Pointed Roofs,* written in 1913, and the first volume of *Pilgrimage.* The term 'stream of consciousness', borrowed from William James to apply to a literary method, originated in an article about Dorothy Richardson published by May Sinclair in 1918. May Sinclair used the technique in her next novel, *Mary Olivier,* 1919, but even in her first novel, *Audrey Craven,* 1897, she had used something of this technique in a modified form. Her subsequent interest in it, of course, is inseparable from her desire to express insights from psychology in writing.

Charlotte Mew must have picked up many of May Sinclair's intellectual interests during the years of their friendship (1913-16). It is no coincidence that Charlotte's best work was done during this period—notably her longest poem, 'Madeleine in Church', which like most of her poetry relies on the same free association as her short story 'Spine' does.

Ultimately, however, she is interested in expressing *moments* of heightened emotional response, and 'stream of consciousness' is by its nature not the right vehicle. She was very much a spiritual child of the 1890s, in more ways than her Roman Catholic imagery and the tendency to glamourize prostitutes suggest. In parts of 'Madeleine in Church' she brought dramatic monologue near to interior monologue, but the associations she makes are always intensely emotional, *intense,* rather than the chance detritus of the everyday. There is association in this sense in 'The Fête', written in 1910 before Charlotte had any contact with May Sinclair and her exciting intellectual ideas, and even as early as the word-associations of the title of her *Yellow Book* piece 'Passed'. Yet 1913, the beginning of her relationship with May Sinclair, was something of an *annus mirabilis* for Charlotte's poetry, and as she wrote in a letter of July that year, 'I've things now in my head rather unmanageable and possibly too big to pull off as in this form I am really a beginner'.

The kind of free association present earlier in Charlotte's work developed rapidly at about this time in her poetry and prose pieces. She did not aim for the low-key, conversational tone of voice that Eliot achieved in 'Prufrock' in 1917. What she articulated was an extended *cri de coeur,* and she developed a style ideal for that.

Throughout her writing, she focuses on women. This particular interest is neither that of a woman writer writing about what she knows best nor that of a feminist writer, because Charlotte Mew's interest in women is romantic and passionate. But she has a strong sense of the limitations placed upon women by the particular circumstances of female experience. She focuses on women who are themselves objects of passion or romance, and on women who yearn after it: in both cases their male counterparts are rather colourless personifications. But her main concern is to articulate physical passion and its denial, though there is a shift from the early prose in which the polarities of passion and negation result from the situation, to the later dramatic monologues where the polarities derive more from character. Passion unfulfilled, by the loss of youth, by death, by the workings of a malign fate, by the dictates of conventional morality, by renunciation and even by the glorification of the renunciation of all love into itself a kind of passion—these are Charlotte Mew's variations on the theme basic to all her writings. The negative effects of the dictates of religiously sanctioned morality also relate to her renunciation theme, but her most intractable figure of renunciation is Elinor, in the story named after her. This is apparently Charlotte Mew's fictionalized picture of Emily Brontë.

Charlotte Mew submitted to Elkin Mathews an introduction for a volume of Emily Brontë's poetry which she projected, without success. In her essay on 'The Poems of Emily Brontë', as published in *Temple Bar,* she praises her work in the highest terms: 'The two most prominent women poets of the century, Mrs Browning and Christina Rossetti, among whose writings passion, exotic or mystical, plays so conspicuous a part, have never surpassed, if they have ever equalled, this love-song of a woman who never loved'. She was clearly infatuated with the figure of Emily Brontë. Her correspondence with Cockerell reveals her thrill at handling Brontë letters at the Fitzwilliam Museum. She sees Emily Brontë as the embodiment of passionate renunciation, as her gloss on Charlotte Brontë's remark, 'her nature stood alone' shows:

> Her nature stood alone. That was the awful fact—the tragedy of her life.
>
> Alone in its negation of all that other mortals hold most dear: alone in its unwavering pity for frailty and error—no touch of which could ever mar the righteousness and vigour of this one woman's heart; alone in suffering and achievement; in the dark uncompanioned vigils of its life and the triumphant conflict of its death. . . .

Some of Charlotte Mew's work was written against the background of the First World War and her ambivalent attitude to the concept of victory is one of her most striking *leitmotivs.* This concern takes various forms. In the early story 'The China Bowl', with Susannah's final 'revolt against the victories her soul had won so painfully, now to be wasted in a great defeat' and in 'Madeleine in Church', when the woman declares 'I do not envy Him His victories, His arms are full of broken things', it takes its most original form. It is no accident that 'Elinor', the story glorifying the renunciation of all love into itself a kind of passion, is structured around the concept of victory and develops the author's ambivalence towards it.

It was in her essay on Emily Brontë that she came closest to giving an account of what *she* meant by passion:

> It is said that her genius was masculine, but surely it was purely spiritual, strangely and exquisitely severed from embodiment and

> freed from any accident of sex. Never perhaps has passion been portrayed as she portrayed it—wayward and wild as storm, but pure as fire, as incorruptible as life's own essence—deathless in the face of death. And nature is presented to us by the same unerring hand. . . .

In the Emily/Elinor figure, Charlotte Mew merges her themes of renunciation and passion into a passion 'pure as fire'. (Fire is her characteristic image for passion, allied in turn with red in her colour imagery.) Alida Monro wrote that Charlotte 'was always conscious, she once admitted, of what seemed to her an earthly presence, a point of actual contact with the earth, "God of final peace in the heart of things" '. Charlotte Mew declared of Emily Brontë: 'Nature, the one subduing and consolatory power, she worshipped with all the intense and concentrated passion of her soul'. The theme of natural beauty is also present throughout the work. Alida Monro found her 'nostalgia for the country and her real, full enjoyment of life in London . . . again typical of the warring pair within her'—desire and negation, passion and renunciation.

These are some of the themes and subjects that run through Charlotte Mew's writing. Perhaps it is the very simplicity of her approach to timeless themes which explains in part the curious neglect the work has suffered. Her individuality, her passionate sincerity and the particular circumstances of her life do not permit her to be categorized with the writers and poets who were her contemporaries. Too experimental for Edward Marsh's taste, it was indeed a loss that her work was not included in *Georgian Poetry* whose phenomenal success would have kept it more in the public eye. The Poetry Bookshop published *The Rambling Sailor* posthumously in 1929. Though 'The Farmer's Bride' and to a lesser extent 'The Changeling' were frequently printed in anthologies including *Poems of Today,* widely used in schools, a revival of interest in her work was long overdue by 1953 when her *Collected Poems* was published by Duckworth, and Patric Dickinson broadcast a radio programme about her work. In Rose Macaulay's novel *The Towers of Trebizond,* first published in 1956, the Turkish students declare, ' "We study English Poetry . . . Dylan Thomas, Spender, MacNeice, Lewis, Eliot, Sitwell, Frost, Charlotte Mew" '. The listing after Frost, whose innovatory 'talk' poems developed out of dramatic monologue, is significant. Charlotte Mew's keynote is immediacy, derived from her distinctive use of the dramatic monologue. Frank Swinnerton, asked by Siegfried Sassoon to review her *Collected Poems* in *John o'London's Weekly* because he himself was too unwell to do so, extolled her poems in a way that needs only the number of years changing today: 'Since the poet's range is comparatively narrow I should have expected them, after thirty years, to seem a little old-fashioned. Instead, they come burning from the printed page as they always did.' As do her stories and essays. These she composed throughout her writing life, contributing to *Temple Bar, The Englishwoman* and other publications of the day. These writings are collected here for the first time, and to those already familiar with her poetry they will reveal new dimensions to her talent and provide new pleasures.

Though Charlotte Mew had intellect, talent and a reasonable financial position—at least a room of her own if not five hundred a year—she was damned by heredity. To a greater or lesser extent, all of us may be, but by the fear of hereditary insanity Charlotte Mew was so damned with a peculiar virulence. From her birth, she was forced to accept her own absence from lasting happiness. It is the mark of genius to transmute such suffering into art. Her work is a *cri de coeur* against the meaninglessness of life, if all it means is suffering. 'The Quiet House', which she considered 'perhaps the most subjective' of her poems, ends:

No one for me—
I think it is myself I go to meet:
I do not care; some day I *shall* not think; I shall not *be!*

In addition to the primary sources listed in the Bibliographical Note and documents in Somerset House, London, references are made to the following:

Alida Monro, 'Charlotte Mew—A Memoir', in *Collected Poems of Charlotte Mew* (London, 1953); Mary C. Davidow, 'The Charlotte Mew—May Sinclair Relationship: A Reply', *Bulletin of the New York Public Library,* LXXV, 3 (March 1971), pp. 295-300; Mary C. Davidow, 'Charlotte Mew: Biography and Criticism' (Brown University Ph.D. thesis, 1960); Katherine Lyon Mix, *A Study in Yellow* (Kansas and London, 1960); J. Lewis May, *John Lane and the Nineties* (London, 1936); Theophilus E. M. Boll, *Miss May Sinclair: Novelist* (New Jersey, 1973); T. E. M. Boll, 'The Mystery of Charlotte Mew and May Sinclair: An Inquiry', *Bulletin of the New York Public Library,* LXXIV, 3 (September 1970), pp. 445-53; Robert H. Ross, *The Georgian Revolt* (London, 1967); Christopher Hassall, *Edward Marsh, Patron of the Arts* (London, 1959); *Georgian Poetry I-IV*; Joy Grant, *Harold Monro and the Poetry Bookshop* (London, 1967); ed. Viola Meynell, *Friends of a Lifetime: Letters to S. C. Cockerell* (London, 1940); Wilfrid Blunt, *Cockerell* (London, 1964); the Benedictines of Stanbrook, *In a Great Tradition, Tribute to Dame Laurentia McLachlan Abbess of Stanbrook* (London, 1956); ed. Robert Gathorne-Hardy, *Ottoline: The Early Memoirs of Lady Ottoline Morrell* (London, 1958); ed. Nigel Nicolson, *The Question of Things Happening: The Letters of Virginia Woolf,* II (London, 1976); ed. Nigel Nicolson, *A Change of Perspective: The Letters of Virginia Woolf,* III (London, 1977); Vere H. Collins, *Talks with Thomas Hardy at Max Gate 1920-22* (London, 1928); Radclyffe Hall, *The Well of Loneliness* (first published 1928); E. M. Forster, *Maurice* (first published 1970); Rose Macaulay, *The Towers of Trebizond* (first published 1956); and local press reports of the inquest into Charlotte Mew's death, reviews of her books and obituaries.

The Introduction is an abridgment by the publisher of a fully annotated study by the editor based on these and other secondary sources and the primary sources listed under the Bibliographical Note.

Both Alida Monro's Memoir and Mary C. Davidow's 'Charlotte Mew' contain inaccuracies. ('Ascent into Nothingness: The Poetry of Charlotte Mew' by Jimmy Dean Bishop (Louisiana State University and Agricultural and Mechanical College Ph.D. thesis 1968) follows Davidow, op. cit., on Charlotte Mew's biography.) See also my 'Mary Magdalene and the Bride: The Work of Charlotte Mew' (*Poetry Nation,* 4 (1975), pp. 92-106), mainly about Mew's imagery and written without access to certain material, and the forthcoming special supplement on Charlotte Mew in *P.N. Review,* edited by me.

V.W.

BIBLIOGRAPHICAL NOTE

Charlotte Mew's first collection of poems, *The Farmer's Bride,* was published by the Poetry Bookshop, London, in 1916. This volume was reissued in 1921 with eleven additional poems, and published in America as *Saturday Market.* In 1929 the Poetry Bookshop published *The Rambling Sailor* posthumously. *Collected Poems* (Duckworth, 1953) reprints the contents of these volumes (but omits the last fifty-four lines of 'In Nunhead Cemetery') with a Memoir of Charlotte Mew by Alida Monro, formerly of the Poetry Bookshop.

The poems 'To a Little Child in Death' and 'Péri en mer' have not previously been collected. The apparently unpublished poems 'An Ending', 'A Question', 'Left Behind', 'A Farewell' and ' "There shall be no night there" ' are taken from 'Charlotte Mew: Biography and Criticism' by Mary Celine Davidow, unpublished Ph.D. thesis 1960, Brown University, to whom I express my indebtedness.

Charlotte Mew's stories and essays have not previously been collected. A reference is cited in Davidow, op. cit., proving Mew's authorship of 'The Governess in Fiction', printed under the initial 'M.' and apparently rewritten by the editor of *The Academy.* Typescripts of the apparently unpublished essay 'A Country Book' and the stories 'A Wedding Day', 'The Bridegroom's Friend', 'White World', 'Elinor' and 'Spine' are in the British Library (C.M. Mew Collection, BM MS 57754 (provisional classification)), and are printed here with grateful acknowledgement to the Board of Trustees of the British Library. 'The Minnow Fishers' is taken from Davidow, op. cit. The unfinished 'Aglaë' is taken from a manuscript in the Poetry Collection, Lockwood Memorial Library, State University of New York at Buffalo, with grateful acknowledgement to the Library.

The text of Charlotte Mew's play, *The China Bowl,* is taken from the script in the BBC Written Archives Centre at Caversham Park (some BBC stage directions removed by the editor), with grateful acknowledgement to the BBC.

The anonymous 'V. R. I.' sonnets, and 'A Reminiscence of Princess Mathilde Bonaparte', printed under the initials 'C.M.', were attributed to Charlotte Mew by Davidow, op. cit.

It has not been possible to trace the present whereabouts of the MSS of the poem 'Christmas 1880', written by Charlotte Mew as a child, or the story in Cornish dialect 'Thic Theer Kayser', which are therefore omitted from this volume.

The major collections of Mew papers, including letters, are in the British Library; the Poetry Collection, the Lockwood Memorial

Library, and the Berg Collection of the New York Public Library.

V.W.

Poems

THE FARMER'S BRIDE (1916)

TO ——

He asked life of thee, and thou gavest him a long life:
even for ever and ever..

THE FARMER'S BRIDE

Three Summers since I chose a maid,
Too young maybe—but more's to do
At harvest-time than bide and woo.
When us was wed she turned afraid
Of love and me and all things human;
Like the shut of a winter's day.
Her smile went out, and 'twasn't a woman—
More like a little frightened fay.
One night, in the Fall, she runned away.

"Out 'mong the sheep, her be," they said,
'Should properly have been abed;
But sure enough she wasn't there
Lying awake with her wide brown stare.
So over seven-acre field and up-along across the down
We chased her, flying like a hare
Before our lanterns. To Church-Town
All in a shiver and a scare
We caught her, fetched her home at last
And turned the key upon her, fast.

She does the work about the house
As well as most, but like a mouse:
Happy enough to chat and play
With birds and rabbits and such as they,
So long as men-folk keep away.
"Not near, not near!" her eyes beseech
When one of us comes within reach.
The women say that beasts in stall
Look round like children at her call.
I've hardly heard her speak at all.

Shy as a leveret, swift as he,
Straight and slight as a young larch tree,
Sweet as the first wild violets, she,
To her wild self. But what to me?

The short days shorten and the oaks are brown,
    The blue smoke rises to the low grey sky,
One leaf in the still air falls slowly down,
    A magpie's spotted feathers lie
On the black earth spread white with rime,
The berries redden up to Christmas-time.
    What's Christmas-time without there be
    Some other in the house than we!

    She sleeps up in the attic there
    Alone, poor maid. 'Tis but a stair
Betwixt us. Oh! my God! the down,
The soft young down of her, the brown,
The brown of her—her eyes, her hair, her hair!

FAME

Sometimes in the over-heated house, but not for long,
        Smirking and speaking rather loud,
    I see myself among the crowd,
Where no one fits the singer to his song,
Or sifts the unpainted from the painted faces
Of the people who are always on my stair;
They were not with me when I walked in heavenly places;
            But could I spare
In the blind Earth's great silences and spaces,
    The din, the scuffle, the long stare
    If I went back and it was not there?
Back to the old known things that are the new,
The folded glory of the gorse, the sweet-briar air,
To the larks that cannot praise us, knowing nothing of what we do
    And the divine, wise trees that do not care
Yet, to leave Fame, still with such eyes and that bright hair!
God! If I might! And before I go hence

Take in her stead
To our tossed bed,
One little dream, no matter how small, how wild.
Just now, I think I found it in a field, under a fence—
A frail, dead, new-born lamb, ghostly and pitiful and white,
A blot upon the night,
The moon's dropped child!

THE NARROW DOOR

The narrow door, the narrow door
On the three steps of which the café children play
Mostly at shop with pebbles from the shore,
It is always shut this narrow door
But open for a little while to-day.

And round it, each with pebbles in his hand,
A silenced crowd the café children stand
To see the long box jerking down the bend
Of twisted stair; then set on end,
Quite filling up the narrow door
Till it comes out and does not go in any more.

Along the quay you see it wind,
The slow black line. Someone pulls up the blind
Of the small window just above the narrow door—
"Tiens! que veux-tu acheter?" Renée cries,
"Mais, pour quat'sous, des oignons," Jean replies
And one pays down with pebbles from the shore.

THE FÊTE

To-night again the moon's white mat
Stretches across the dormitory floor
While outside, like an evil cat
The *pion* prowls down the dark corridor,
Planning, I know, to pounce on me, in spite

For getting leave to sleep in town last night.
But it was none of us who made that noise,
    Only the old brown owl that hoots and flies
Out of the ivy—he will say it was us boys—
    Seigneur mon Dieu! the *sacré* soul of spies!
    He would like to catch each dream that lies
        Hidden behind our sleepy eyes:
Their dream? But mine—it is the moon and the wood that sees;
All my long life how I shall hate the trees!

In the *Place d'Armes*, the dusty planes, all Summer through
Dozed with the market women in the sun and scarcely stirred
    To see the quiet things that crossed the Square—,
A tiny funeral, the flying shadow of a bird,
    The hump-backed barber Célestin Lemaire,
    Old madame Michel in her three-wheeled chair,
        And filing past to Vespers, two and two,
        The *demoiselles* of the *pensionnat*.
Towed like a ship through the harbour bar,
    Safe into port, where *le petit Jésus*
Perhaps makes nothing of the look they shot at you:
    Si, c'est défendu, mais que voulez-vous?
It was the sun. The sunshine weaves
A pattern on dull stones: the sunshine leaves
    The portraiture of dreams upon the eyes
        Before it dies:
    All Summer through
The dust hung white upon the drowsy planes
Till suddenly they woke with the Autumn rains.

        It is not only the little boys
        Who have hardly got away from toys,
But I, who am seventeen next year,
Some nights, in bed, have grown cold to hear
            That lonely passion of the rain
Which makes you think of being dead,
And of somewhere living to lay your head
            As if you were a child again,
Crying for one thing, known and near
Your empty heart, to still the hunger and the fear
    That pelts and beats with it against the pane.

But I remember smiling too
At all the sun's soft tricks and those Autumn dreads
In winter time, when the grey light broke slowly through
The frosted window-lace to drag us shivering from our beds.
And when at dusk the singing wind swung down
Straight from the stars to the dark country roads
Beyond the twinkling town,
Striking the leafless poplar boughs as he went by,
Like some poor, stray dog by the wayside lying dead,
We left behind us the old world of dread,
I and the wind as we strode whistling on under the Winter sky.

And then in Spring for three days came the Fair
Just as the planes were starting into bud
Above the caravans: you saw the dancing bear
Pass on his chain; and heard the jingle and the thud.
Only four days ago
They let you out of this dull show
To slither down the *montagne russe* and chaff the man *à la tête de veau*—
Hit, slick, the bull's eye at the *tir*,
Spin round and round till your head went queer
On the *porcs-roulants*. *Oh! là là! la fête!*
Va pour du vin, et le tête-à-tête
With the girl who sugars the *gaufres! Pauvrette*,
How thin she was; but she smiled, you bet,
As she took your tip—"One does not forget
The good days, Monsieur." Said with a grace,
But *sacrébleu!* what a ghost of a face!
And no fun too for the *demoiselles*
Of the *pensionnat*, who were hurried past,
With their *"Oh, que c'est beau—Ah, qu'elle est belle!"*
A lap-dog's life from first to last!
The good nights are not made for sleep, nor the good days for dreaming in,
And at the end in the big Circus tent we sat and shook and stewed like sin!

Some children there had got—but where?
Sent from the south, perhaps—a red bouquet
Of roses, sweetening the fetid air
With scent from gardens by some far away blue bay.
They threw one at the dancing bear;
The white clown caught it. From St Rémy's tower

The deep, slow bell tolled out the hour;
The black clown, with his dirty grin
Lay, sprawling in the dust, as She rode in.

She stood on a white horse—and suddenly you saw the bend
Of a far-off road at dawn, with knights riding by,
A field of spears—and then the gallant day
Go out in storm, with ragged clouds low down, sullen and grey
Against red heavens: wild and awful, such a sky
As witnesses against you at the end
Of a great battle; bugles blowing, blood and dust—
The old *Morte d'Arthur*, fight you must—.
It died in anger. But it was not death
That had you by the throat, stopping your breath.
She looked like Victory. She rode my way.

She laughed at the black clown and then she flew
A bird above us, on the wing
Of her white arms; and you saw through
A rent in the old tent, a patch of sky
With one dim star. She flew, but not so high—
And then she did not fly;
She stood in the bright moonlight at the door
Of a strange room, she threw her slippers to the floor—
Again, again
You heard the patter of the rain,
The starving rain—it was this Thing,
Summer was this, the gold mist in your eyes;—
Oh God! it dies,
But after death—,
To-night the splendour and the sting
Blows back and catches at your breath,
The smell of beasts, the smell of dust, the scent of all the roses in the world, the sea, the Spring,
The beat of drums, the pad of hoofs, music, the dream, the dream, the Enchanted Thing!

At first you scarcely saw her face,
You knew the maddening feet were there,
What called was that half-hidden, white unrest
To which now and then she pressed

Her finger tips; but as she slackened pace
And turned and looked at you it grew quite bare:
There was not anything you did not dare:—
Like trumpeters the hours passed until the last day of the Fair.

In the *Place d'Armes* all afternoon
The building birds had sung "Soon, soon,"
The shuttered streets slept sound that night,
It was full moon:
The path into the wood was almost white,
The trees were very still and seemed to stare:
Not far before your soul the Dream flits on,
But when you touch it, it is gone
And quite alone your soul stands there.

Mother of Christ, no one has seen your eyes: how can men pray
Even unto you?
There were only wolves' eyes in the wood—
My Mother is a woman too:
Nothing is true that is not good,
With that quick smile of hers, I have heard her say;—
I wish I had gone back home to-day;
I should have watched the light that so gently dies
From our high window, in the Paris skies,
The long, straight chain
Of lamps hung out along the Seine:
I would have turned to her and let the rain
Beat on her breast as it does against the pane;—
Nothing will be the same again;—
There is something strange in my little Mother's eyes,
There is something new in the old heavenly air of Spring—
The smell of beasts, the smell of dust—*The Enchanted Thing!*

All my life long I shall see moonlight on the fern
And the black trunks of trees. Only the hair
Of any woman can belong to God.
The stalks are cruelly broken where we trod,
There had been violets there,
I shall not care
As I used to do when I see the bracken burn.

BESIDE THE BED

Someone has shut the shining eyes, straightened and folded
The wandering hands quietly covering the unquiet breast:
So, smoothed and silenced you lie, like a child, not again to be questioned or scolded;
But, for you, not one of us believes that this is rest.

Not so to close the windows down can cloud and deaden
The blue beyond: or to screen the wavering flame subdue its breath:
Why, if I lay my cheek to your cheek, your grey lips, like dawn, would quiver and redden,
Breaking into the old, odd smile at this fraud of death.

Because all night you have not turned to us or spoken
It is time for you to wake; your dreams were never very deep:
I, for one, have seen the thin, bright, twisted threads of them dimmed suddenly and broken,
This is only a most piteous pretence of sleep!

IN NUNHEAD CEMETERY

It is the clay that makes the earth stick to his spade;
He fills in holes like this year after year;
The others have gone; they were tired, and half afraid
But I would rather be standing here;

There is nowhere else to go. I have seen this place
From the windows of the train that's going past
Against the sky. This is rain on my face–
It was raining here when I saw it last.

There is something horrible about a flower;
This, broken in my hand, is one of those
He threw in just now: it will not live another hour;
There are thousands more: you do not miss a rose.

One of the children hanging about
Pointed at the whole dreadful heap and smiled
This morning, after THAT was carried out;
There is something terrible about a child.

We were like children, last week, in the Strand;
That was the day you laughed at me
Because I tried to make you understand
The cheap, stale chap I used to be
Before I saw the things you made me see.

This is not a real place; perhaps by-and-by
I shall wake—I am getting drenched with all this rain:
To-morrow I will tell you about the eyes of the Crystal Palace train
Looking down on us, and you will laugh and I shall see what you see again.

Not here, not now. We said "Not yet
Across our low stone parapet
Will the quick shadows of the sparrows fall."

But still it was a lovely thing
Through the grey months to wait for Spring
With the birds that go a-gypsying
In the parks till the blue seas call.
And next to these, you used to care
For the lions in Trafalgar Square,
Who'll stand and speak for London when her bell of Judgment tolls—
And the gulls at Westminster that were
The old sea-captains' souls.
To-day again the brown tide splashes, step by step, the river stair,
And the gulls are there!

By a month we have missed our Day:
The children would have hung about
Round the carriage and over the way
As you and I came out.

We should have stood on the gulls' black cliffs and heard the sea
And seen the moon's white track,
I would have called, you would have come to me
And kissed me back.

You have never done that: I do not know
Why I stood staring at your bed
And heard you, though you spoke so low,

But could not reach your hands, your little head.
There was nothing we could not do, you said,
And you went, and I let you go!

Now I will burn you back, I will burn you through,
Though I am damned for it we two will lie
And burn, here where the starlings fly
To these white stones from the wet sky—;
Dear, you will say this is not I—
It would not be you, it would not be you!

If for only a little while
You will think of it you will understand,
If you will touch my sleeve and smile
As you did that morning in the Strand
I can wait quietly with you
Or go away if you want me to—
God! What is God? but your face has gone and your hand!
Let me stay here too.

When I was quite a little lad
At Christmas time we went half mad
For joy of all the toys we had,
And then we used to sing about the sheep
The shepherds watched by night;
We used to pray to Christ to keep
Our small souls safe till morning light—;
I am scared, I am staying with you to-night—
Put me to sleep.

I shall stay here: here you can see the sky;
The houses in the streets are much too high;
There is no one left to speak to there;
Here they are everywhere,
And just above them fields and fields of roses lie—
If he would dig it all up again they would not die.

THE PEDLAR

Lend me, a little while, the key
    That locks your heavy heart, and I'll give you back—
Rarer than books and ribbons and beads bright to see,
    This little Key of Dreams out of my pack.

The road, the road, beyond men's bolted doors,
    There shall I walk and you go free of me,
For yours lies North across the moors,
    And mine South. To what sea?

How if we stopped and let our solemn selves go by,
    While my gay ghost caught and kissed yours, as ghosts don't do,
And by the wayside this forgotten you and I
    Sat, and were twenty-two?

Give me the key that locks your tired eyes,
    And I will lend you this one from my pack,
Brighter than coloured beads and painted books that make men wise:
    Take it. No, give it back!

PÉCHERESSE

Down the long quay the slow boats glide,
    While here and there a house looms white
Against the gloom of the waterside,
    And some high window throws a light
    As they sail out into the night.

At dawn they will bring in again
    To women knitting on the quay
Who wait for him, their man of men;
    I stand with them, and watch the sea
    Which may have taken mine from me.

Just so the long days come and go.
    The nights, ma Doué! the nights are cold!
Our Lady's heart is as frozen snow,
    Since this one sin I have not told;
    And I shall die or perhaps grow old

Before he comes. The foreign ships
  Bring many a one of face and name
As strange as his, to buy your lips,
  A gold piece for a scarlet shame
  Like mine. But mine was not the same.

One night was ours, one short grey day
  Of sudden sin, unshrived, untold.
He found me, and I lost the way
  To Paradise for him. I sold
  My soul for love and not for gold.

He bought my soul, but even so,
  My face is all that he has seen,
His is the only face I know,
And in the dark church, like a screen,
  It shuts God out; it comes between;

While in some narrow foreign street
  Or loitering on the crowded quay,
Who knows what others he may meet
  To turn his eyes away from me?
  Many are fair to such as he!

There is but one for such as I
  To love, to hate, to hunger for;
I shall, perhaps, grow old and die,
  With one short day to spend and store,
  One night, in all my life, no more.

Just so the long days come and go,
  Yet this one sin I will not tell
Though Mary's heart is as frozen snow
And all nights are cold for one warmed too well.
  But, oh! ma Doué! *the nights of Hell!*

THE CHANGELING

Toll no bell for me, dear Father, dear Mother,
Waste no sighs;
There are my sisters, there is my little brother
Who plays in the place called Paradise,
Your children all, your children for ever;
But I, so wild,
Your disgrace, with the queer brown face, was never,
Never, I know, but half your child!

In the garden at play, all day, last summer,
Far and away I heard
The sweet "tweet-tweet" of a strange new-comer,
The dearest, clearest call of a bird.
It lived down there in the deep green hollow,
My own old home, and the fairies say
The word of a bird is a thing to follow,
So I was away a night and a day.

One evening, too, by the nursery fire,
We snuggled close and sat round so still,
When suddenly as the wind blew higher,
Something scratched on the window-sill.
A pinched brown face peered in—I shivered;
No one listened or seemed to see;
The arms of it waved and the wings of it quivered,
Whoo—I knew it had come for me;
Some are as bad as bad can be!
All night long they danced in the rain,
Round and round in a dripping chain,
Threw their caps at the window-pane,
Tried to make me scream and shout
And fling the bedclothes all about:
I meant to stay in bed that night,
And if only you had left a light
They would never have got me out.

Sometimes I wouldn't speak, you see,
Or answer when you spoke to me,
Because in the long, still dusks of Spring

You can hear the whole world whispering;
  The shy green grasses making love,
  The feathers grow on the dear, grey dove,
  The tiny heart of the redstart beat,
  The patter of the squirrel's feet,
The pebbles pushing in the silver streams,
The rushes talking in their dreams,
  The swish-swish of the bat's black wings,
  The wild-wood bluebell's sweet ting-tings,
    Humming and hammering at your ear,
    Everything there is to hear
In the heart of hidden things,
  But not in the midst of the nursery riot,
  That's why I wanted to be quiet,
    Couldn't do my sums, or sing,
    Or settle down to anything.
  And when, for that, I was sent upstairs
  I *did* kneel down to say my prayers;
But the King who sits on your high church steeple
Has nothing to do with us fairy people!

'Times I pleased you, dear Father, dear Mother,
  Learned all my lessons and liked to play,
And dearly I loved the little pale brother
  Whom some other bird must have called away.
Why did They bring me here to make me
  Not quite bad and not quite good,
Why, unless They're wicked, do They want, in spite, to take me
  Back to their wet, wild wood?
Now, every night I shall see the windows shining,
  The gold lamp's glow, and the fire's red gleam,
While the best of us are twining twigs and the rest of us are whining
    In the hollow by the stream.
Black and chill are Their nights on the wold;
  And They live so long and They feel no pain:
I shall grow up, but never grow old,
I shall always, always be very cold,
    I shall never come back again!

KEN

The town is old and very steep,
  A place of bells and cloisters and grey towers,
And black clad people walking in their sleep—
  A nun, a priest, a woman taking flowers
  To her new grave; and watched from end to end
  By the great Church above, through the still hours:
    But in the morning and the early dark
The children wake to dart from doors and call
Down the wide, crooked street, where, at the bend,
    Before it climbs up to the park,
Ken's is the gabled house facing the Castle wall.

When first I came upon him there
Suddenly, on the half-lit stair,
I think I hardly found a trace
Of likeness to a human face
  In his. And I said then
If in His image God made men,
Some other must have made poor Ken—
But for his eyes which looked at you
As two red, wounded stars might do.

He scarcely spoke, you scarcely heard,
    His voice broke off in little jars
To tears sometimes. An uncouth bird
  He seemed as he ploughed up the street,
Groping, with knarred, high-lifted feet
  And arms thrust out as if to beat
    Always against a threat of bars.

  And oftener than not there'd be
  A child just higher than his knee
Trotting beside him. Through his dim
  Long twilight this, at least, shone clear,
  That all the children and the deer,
    Whom every day he went to see
Out in the park, belonged to him.

  "God help the folk that next him sits
  He fidgets so, with his poor wits."

The neighbours said on Sunday nights
When he would go to Church to "see the lights!"
    Although for these he used to fix
    His eyes upon a crucifix
    In a dark corner, staring on
    Till everybody else had gone.
    And sometimes, in his evil fits,
You could not move him from his chair—
You did not look at him as he sat there,
    Biting his rosary to bits.
While pointing to the Christ he tried to say
        "Take it away."

        Nothing was dead:
He said "a bird" if he picked up a broken wing,
        A perished leaf or any such thing
        Was just "a rose"; and once when I had said
    He must not stand and knock there any more,
    He left a twig on the mat outside my door.

        Not long ago
The last thrush stiffened in the snow,
    While black against a sullen sky
        The sighing pines stood by.
But now the wind has left our rattled pane
To flutter the hedge-sparrow's wing,
The birches in the wood are red again
        And only yesterday
The larks went up a little way to sing
        What lovers say
    Who loiter in the lanes to-day;
    The buds begin to talk of May
    With learned rooks on city trees,
        And if God please
        With all of these
We too, shall see another Spring.

But in that red brick barn upon the hill
    I wonder—can one own the deer,
And does one walk with children still
        As one did here—

Do roses grow
Beneath those twenty windows in a row—
And if some night
When you have not seen any light
They cannot move you from your chair
What happens there?
I do not know.

So, when they took
Ken to that place, I did not look
After he called and turned on me
His eyes. These I shall see—

À QUOI BON DIRE

Seventeen years ago you said
Something that sounded like Good-bye;
And everybody thinks that you are dead,
But I.

So I, as I grow stiff and cold
To this and that say Good-bye too;
And everybody sees that I am old
But you.

And one fine morning in a sunny lane
Some boy and girl will meet and kiss and swear
That nobody can love their way again
While over there
You will have smiled, I shall have tossed your hair.

THE QUIET HOUSE

When we were children old Nurse used to say
The house was like an auction or a fair
Until the lot of us were safe in bed.
It has been quiet as the country-side

Since Ted and Janey and then Mother died
And Tom crossed Father and was sent away.
After the lawsuit he could not hold up his head,
Poor Father, and he does not care
For people here, or to go anywhere.

To get away to Aunt's for that week-end
Was hard enough; (since then, a year ago,
He scarcely lets me slip out of his sight—)
At first I did not like my cousin's friend,
I did not think I should remember him:
His voice has gone, his face is growing dim
And if I like him now I do not know.
He frightened me before he smiled—
He did not ask me if he might—
He said that he would come one Sunday night,
He spoke to me as if I were a child.

No year has been like this that has just gone by;
It may be that what Father says is true,
If things are so it does not matter why:
But everything has burned, and not quite through.
The colours of the world have turned
To flame, the blue, the gold has burned
In what used to be such a leaden sky.
When you are burned quite through you die.

Red is the strangest pain to bear;
In Spring the leaves on the budding trees;
In Summer the roses are worse than these,
More terrible than they are sweet:
A rose can stab you across the street
Deeper than any knife:
And the crimson haunts you everywhere—
Thin shafts of sunlight, like the ghosts of reddened swords have struck our stair
As if, coming down, you had spilt your life.

I think that my soul is red
Like the soul of a sword or a scarlet flower:
But when these are dead
They have had their hour.

I shall have had mine, too,
For from head to feet,
I am burned and stabbed half through,
And the pain is deadly sweet.

The things that kill us seem
Blind to the death they give:
It is only in our dream
The things that kill us live.

The room is shut where Mother died,
The other rooms are as they were,
The world goes on the same outside,
The sparrows fly across the Square,
The children play as we four did there,
The trees grow green and brown and bare,
The sun shines on the dead Church spire,
And nothing lives here but the fire,
While Father watches from his chair
Day follows day
The same, or now and then, a different grey,
Till, like his hair,
Which Mother said was wavy once and bright,
They will all turn white.

To-night I heard a bell again—
Outside it was the same mist of fine rain,
The lamps just lighted down the long, dim street,
No one for me—
I think it is myself I go to meet:
I do not care; some day I *shall* not think; I shall not *be*!

ON THE ASYLUM ROAD

Theirs is the house whose windows—every pane—
Are made of darkly stained or clouded glass:
Sometimes you come upon them in the lane,
The saddest crowd that you will ever pass.

But still we merry town or village folk
  Throw to their scattered stare a kindly grin,
And think no shame to stop and crack a joke
  With the incarnate wages of man's sin.

None but ourselves in our long gallery we meet,
  The moor-hen stepping from her reeds with dainty feet,
    The hare-bell bowing on its stem,
Dance not with us; their pulses beat
  To fainter music; nor do we to them
      Make their life sweet.

The gayest crowd that they will ever pass
  Are we to brother-shadows in the lane:
Our windows, too, are clouded glass
  To them, yes, every pane!

JOUR DES MORTES
(Cimetière Montparnasse.)

Sweetheart, is this the last of all our posies
  And little festivals, my flowers are they
But white and wistful ghosts of gayer roses
  Shut with you in this grim garden? Not to-day,
Ah! no! come out with me before the grey gate closes
  It is your fête and here is your bouquet!

THE FOREST ROAD

The forest road,
The infinite straight road stretching away
World without end: the breathless road between the walls
Of the black listening trees: the hushed, grey road
Beyond the window that you shut to-night
Crying that you would look at it by day—
There is a shadow there that sings and calls
But not for you. Oh! hidden eyes that plead in sleep

Against the lonely dark, if I could touch the fear
And leave it kissed away on quiet lids—
If I could hush these hands that are half-awake,
Groping for me in sleep I could go free.
I wish that God would take them out of mine
And fold them like the wings of frightened birds
Shot cruelly down, but fluttering into quietness so soon.
Broken, forgotten things; there is no grief for them in the green Spring
When the new birds fly back to the old trees.
But it shall not be so with you. I will look back. I wish I knew that God
would stand
Smiling and looking down on you when morning comes,
To hold you, when you wake, closer than I,
So gently though: and not with famished lips or hungry arms:
He does not hurt the frailest, dearest things
As we do in the dark. See, dear, your hair—
I must unloose this hair that sleeps and dreams
About my face, and clings like the brown weed
To drowned, delivered things, tossed by the tired sea
Back to the beaches. Oh! your hair! If you had lain
A long time dead on the rough, glistening ledge
Of some black cliff, forgotten by the tide,
The raving winds would tear, the dripping brine would rust away
Fold after fold of all the loveliness
That wraps you round, and makes you, lying here,
The passionate fragrance that the roses are.
But death would spare the glory of your head
In the long sweetness of the hair that does not die:
The spray would leap to it in every storm,
The scent of the unsilenced sea would linger on
In these dark waves, and round the silence that was you—
Only the nesting gulls would hear—but there would still be whispers in
your hair;
Keep them for me; keep them for me. What *is* this singing on the road
That makes all other music like the music in a dream—
Dumb to the dancing and the marching feet; you know, in dreams, you see
Old pipers playing that you cannot hear,
And ghostly drums that only seem to beat. This seems to climb:
Is it the music of a larger place? It makes our room too small: it is like a stair,
A calling stair that climbs up to a smile you scarcely see,
Dim, but so waited for; and *you* know what a smile is, how it calls,

How if I smiled you always ran to me.
Now you must sleep forgetfully, as children do.
There is a Spirit sits by us in sleep
Nearer than those who walk with us in the bright day.
I think he has a tranquil, saving face: I think he came
Straight from the hills: he may have suffered there in time gone by,
And once, from those forsaken heights, looked down,
Lonely himself, on all the lonely sorrows of the earth.
It is his kingdom—Sleep. If I could leave you there—
If, without waking you, I could get up and reach the door—!
We used to go together.—Shut, scared eyes,
Poor, desolate, desperate hands, it is not I
Who thrust you off. No, take your hands away—
I cannot strike your lonely hands. Yes, I have struck your heart,
It did not come so near. Then lie you there
Dear and wild heart behind this quivering snow
With two red stains on it: and I will strike and tear
Mine out, and scatter it to yours. Oh! throbbing dust,
You that were life, our little wind-blown hearts!
The road! the road!
There is a shadow there: I see my soul,
I hear my soul, singing among the trees!

MADELEINE IN CHURCH

Here, in the darkness, where this plaster saint
Stands nearer than God stands to our distress,
And one small candle shines, but not so faint
As the far lights of everlastingness
I'd rather kneel than over there, in open day
Where Christ is hanging, rather pray
To something more like my own clay,
Not too divine;
For, once, perhaps my little saint
Before he got his niche and crown,
Had one short stroll about the town;
It brings him closer, just that taint
And anyone can wash the paint
Off our poor faces, his and mine!

Is that why I see Monty now? equal to any saint, poor boy, as good as gold,
But still, with just the proper trace
Of earthliness on his shining wedding face;
And then gone suddenly blank and old
The hateful day of the divorce:
Stuart got his, hands down, of course
Crowing like twenty cocks and grinning like a horse:
But Monty took it hard. All said and done I liked him best,—
He was the first, he stands out clearer than the rest.
It seems too funny all we other rips
Should have immortal souls; Monty and Redge quite damnably
Keep theirs afloat while we go down like scuttled ships.—
It's funny too, how easily we sink,
One might put up a monument, I think
To half the world and cut across it "Lost at Sea!"
I should drown Jim, poor little sparrow, if I netted him to-night—
No, it's no use this penny light—
Or my poor saint with his tin-pot crown—
The trees of Calvary are where they were,
When we are sure that we can spare
The tallest, let us go and strike it down
And leave the other two still standing there.
I, too, would ask him to remember me
If there were any Paradise beyond this earth that I could see.

Oh! quiet Christ who never knew
The poisonous fangs that bite us through
And make us do the things we do,
See how we suffer and fight and die,
How helpless and how low we lie,
God holds You, and You hang so high,
Though no one looking long at You,
Can think you do not suffer too,
But, up there, from your still, star-lighted tree
What can You know, what can You really see
Of this dark ditch, the soul of me!

We are what we are: when I was half a child I could not sit
Watching black shadows on green lawns and red carnations burning in the sun,
Without paying so heavily for it

That joy and pain, like any mother and her unborn child were almost one.
I could hardly bear
The dreams upon the eyes of white geraniums in the dusk,
The thick, close voice of musk,
The jessamine music on the thin night air,
Or, sometimes, my own hands about me anywhere—
The sight of my own face (for it was lovely then) even the scent of my own hair,
Oh! there was nothing, nothing that did not sweep to the high seat
Of laughing gods, and then blow down and beat
My soul into the highway dust, as hoofs do the dropped roses of the street.
I think my body was my soul,
And when we are made thus
Who shall control
Our hands, our eyes, the wandering passion of our feet,
Who shall teach us
To thrust the world out of our heart; to say, till perhaps in death,
When the race is run,
And it is forced from us with our last breath
"Thy will be done"?
If it is Your will that we should be content with the tame, bloodless things,
As pale as angels smirking by, with folded wings.
Oh! I know Virtue, and the peace it brings!
The temperate, well-worn smile
The one man gives you, when you are evermore his own:
And afterwards the child's, for a little while,
With its unknowing and all-seeing eyes
So soon to change, and make you feel how quick
The clock goes round. If one had learned the trick—
(How does one though?) quite early on,
Of long green pastures under placid skies,
One might be walking now with patient truth.
What did we ever care for it, who have asked for youth,
When, oh! my God! this is going or has gone?

There is a portrait of my mother, at nineteen,
With the black spaniel, standing by the garden seat,
The dainty head held high against the painted green
And throwing out the youngest smile, shy, but half haughty and half sweet.
Her picture then: but simply Youth, or simply Spring
To me to-day: a radiance on the wall,

So exquisite, so heart-breaking a thing
Beside the mask that I remember, shrunk and small,
Sapless and lined like a dead leaf,
All that was left of oh! the loveliest face, by time and grief!

And in the glass, last night, I saw a ghost behind my chair—
Yet why remember it, when one can still go moderately gay—?
Or could—with any one of the old crew,
But oh! these boys! the solemn way
They take you, and the things they say—
This "I have only as long as you"
When you remind them you are not precisely twenty-two—
Although at heart perhaps—God! if it were
Only the face, only the hair!
If Jim had written to me as he did to-day
A year ago—and now it leaves me cold—
I know what this means, old, old, *old!*
Et avec ça—mais on a vécu, tout se paie.

That is not always true: there was my Mother—(well at least the dead are free!)
Yoked to the man that Father was; yoked to the woman I am, Monty too;
The little portress at the Convent School, stewing in hell so patiently;
The poor, fair boy who shot himself at Aix. And what of me—and what of me?
But I, I paid for what I had, and they for nothing. No, one cannot see
How it shall be made up to them in some serene eternity.
If there were fifty heavens God could not give us back the child who went
or never came;
Here, on our little patch of this great earth, the sun of any darkened day,
Not one of all the starry buds hung on the hawthorn trees of last year's May,
No shadow from the sloping fields of yesterday;
For every hour they slant across the hedge a different way,
The shadows are never the same.

"Find rest in Him" One knows the parsons' tags—
Back to the fold, across the evening fields, like any flock of baa-ing
sheep:
Yes, it may be, when He has shorn, led us to slaughter, torn the bleating
soul in us to rags,
For so He giveth His belovèd sleep.
Oh! He will take us stripped and done,
Driven into His heart. So we are won:

Then safe, safe are we? in the shelter of His everlasting wings—
I do not envy Him his victories. His arms are full of broken things.

But I shall not be in them. Let Him take
The finer ones, the easier to break.
And they are not gone, yet, for me, the lights, the colours, the perfumes,
Though now they speak rather in sumptuous rooms,
In silks and in gem-like wines;
Here, even, in this corner where my little candle shines
And overhead the lancet-window glows
With golds and crimsons you could almost drink
To know how jewels taste, just as I used to think
There was the scent in every red and yellow rose
Of all the sunsets. But this place is grey,
And much too quiet. No one here,
Why, this is awful, this is fear!
Nothing to see, no face,
Nothing to hear except your heart beating in space
As if the world was ended. Dead at last!
Dead soul, dead body, tied together fast.
These to go on with and alone, to the slow end:
No one to sit with, really, or to speak to, friend to friend:
Out of the long procession, black or white or red
Not one left now to say "Still I am here, then see you, dear, lay here your head."
Only the doll's house looking on the Park
To-night, all nights, I know, when the man puts the lights out, very dark.
With, upstairs, in the blue and gold box of a room, just the maids' footsteps overhead,
Then utter silence and the empty world—the room—the bed—
The corpse! No, not quite dead, while this cries out in me,
But nearly: very soon to be
A handful of forgotten dust—
There must be someone. Christ! there must,
Tell me there *will* be some one. Who?
If there were no one else, could it be You?

How old was Mary out of whom you cast
So many devils? Was she young or perhaps for years
She had sat staring, with dry eyes, at this and that man going past
Till suddenly she saw You on the steps of Simon's house

And stood and looked at you through tears.
I think she must have known by those
The thing, for what it was that had come to her.
For some of us there is a passion, I suppose
So far from earthly cares and earthly fears
That in its stillness you can hardly stir
Or in its nearness, lift your hand,
So great that you have simply got to stand
Looking at it through tears, through tears.
Then straight from these there broke the kiss,
I think You must have known by this
The thing for what it was, that had come to You:
She did not love You like the rest,
It was in her own way, but at the worst, the best,
She gave you something altogether new.
And through it all, from her, no word,
She scarcely saw You, scarcely heard:
Surely You knew when she so touched You with her hair,
Or by the wet cheek lying there,
And while her perfume clung to You from head to feet all through the day
That You can change the things for which we care,
But even You, unless You kill us, not the way.

This, then was peace for her, but passion too.
I wonder was it like a kiss that once I knew,
The only one that I would care to take
Into the grave with me, to which if there were afterwards, to wake.
Almost as happy as the carven dead
In some dim chancel lying head by head
We slept with it, but face to face, the whole night through—
One breath, one throbbing quietness, as if the thing behind our lips was endless life,
Lost, as I woke, to hear in the strange earthly dawn, his "Are you there?"
And lie still, listening to the wind outside, among the firs.

So Mary chose the dream of Him for what was left to her of night and day,
It is the only truth: it is the dream in us that neither life nor death nor any other thing can take away:
But if she had not touched Him in the doorway of the dream could she have cared so much?
She was a sinner, we are what we are: the spirit afterwards, but first, the touch.

And He has never shared with me my haunted house beneath the trees
Of Eden and Calvary, with its ghosts that have not any eyes for tears,
And the happier guests who would not see, or if they did, remember these,
Though they lived there a thousand years.
Outside, too gravely looking at me, He seems to stand,
And looking at Him, if my forgotten spirit came
Unwillingly back, what could it claim
Of those calm eyes, that quiet speech,
Breaking like a slow tide upon the beach,
The scarred, not quite human hand?—
Unwillingly back to the burden of old imaginings
When it has learned so long not to think, not to be,
Again, again it would speak as it has spoken to me of things
That I shall not see!

I cannot bear to look at this divinely bent and gracious head:
When I was small I never quite believed that He was dead:
And at the Convent school I used to lie awake in bed
Thinking about His hands. It did not matter what they said,
He was alive to me, so hurt, so hurt! And most of all in Holy Week
When there was no one else to see
I used to think it would not hurt me too, so terribly,
If He had ever seemed to notice me
Or, if, for once, He would only speak.

EXSPECTO RESURRECTIONEM

Oh! King who hast the key
Of that dark room,
The last which prisons us but held not Thee,
Thou know'st its gloom.
Dost Thou a little love this one
Shut in to-night,
Young and so piteously alone,
Cold—out of sight?
Thou know'st how hard and bare
The pillow of that new-made narrow bed,
Then leave not there
So dear a head!

Additional poems included in The Farmer's Bride, *1921 edition*

ON THE ROAD TO THE SEA

We passed each other, turned and stopped for half an hour, then went our way,
I who make other women smile did not make you—
But no man can move mountains in a day.
So this hard thing is yet to do.

But first I want your life:—before I die I want to see
The world that lies behind the strangeness of your eyes,
There is nothing gay or green there for my gathering, it may be,
Yet on brown fields there lies
A haunting purple bloom: is there not something in grey skies
And in grey sea?
I want what world there is behind your eyes,
I want your life and you will not give it me.

Now, if I look, I see you walking down the years,
Young, and through August fields—a face, a thought, a swinging dream perched on a stile—;
I would have liked (so vile we are!) to have taught you tears
But most to have made you smile.

To-day is not enough or yesterday: God sees it all—
Your length on sunny lawns, the wakeful rainy nights—; tell me—; (how vain to ask), but it is not a question—just a call—;
Show me then, only your notched inches climbing up the garden wall,
I like you best when you are small.

Is this a stupid thing to say
Not having spent with you one day?
No matter; I shall never touch your hair
Or hear the little tick behind your breast,
Still it is there,
And as a flying bird
Brushes the branches where it may not rest
I have brushed your hand and heard
The child in you: I like that best

So small, so dark, so sweet; and were you also then too grave and wise?
Always I think. Then put your far off little hand in mine;—Oh! let it rest;
I will not stare into the early world beyond the opening eyes,
Or vex or scare what I love best.
But I want your life before mine bleeds away—
Here—not in heavenly hereafters—soon,—
I want your smile this very afternoon,
(The last of all my vices, pleasant people used to say,
I wanted and I sometimes got—the Moon!)

You know, at dusk, the last bird's cry,
And round the house the flap of the bat's low flight,
Trees that go black against the sky
And then—how soon the night!

No shadow of you on any bright road again,
And at the darkening end of this—what voice? whose kiss? As if you'd say!
It is not I who have walked with you, it will not be I who take away
Peace, peace, my little handful of the gleaner's grain
From your reaped fields at the shut of day.

Peace! Would you not rather die
Reeling,—with all the cannons at your ear?
So, at least, would I,
And I may not be here
To-night, to-morrow morning or next year.
Still I will let you keep your life a little while,
See dear?
I have made you smile.

THE SUNLIT HOUSE

White through the gate it gleamed and slept
In shuttered sunshine: the parched garden flowers
Their fallen petals from the beds unswept,
Like children unloved and ill-kept
Dreamed through the hours.
Two blue hydrangeas by the blistered door, burned brown,
Watched there and no one in the town

Cared to go past, it night or day,
Though why this was they wouldn't say.
But, I the stranger, knew that I must stay,
Pace up the weed-grown paths and down,
Till one afternoon—there is just a doubt—
But I fancy I heard a tiny shout—
From an upper window a bird flew out—
And I went my way.

THE SHADE-CATCHERS

I think they were about as high
As haycocks are. They went running by
Catching bits of shade in the sunny street:
"I've got one," cried sister to brother,
"I've got two." "Now I've got another."
But scudding away on their little bare feet,
They left the shade in the sunny street.

LE SACRÉ-CŒUR

(Montmartre)

It is dark up here on the heights,
Between the dome and the stars it is quiet too,
While down there under the crowded lights
Flares the importunate face of you,
Dear Paris of the hot white hands, the scarlet lips, the scented hair,
Une jolie fille à vendre, très cher;
A thing of gaiety, a thing of sorrow,
Bought to-night, possessed, and tossed
Back to the mart again to-morrow,
Worth and over, what you cost;
While half your charm is that you are
Withal, like some unpurchasable star,
So old, so young and infinite and lost.

It is dark on the dome-capped hill,
Serenely dark, divinely still,
Yet here is the Man who bought you first
Dying of his immortal smart,
Your Lover, the King with the broken heart,
Who while you, feasting, drink your fill,
Pass round the cup
Not looking up,
Calls down to you, "I thirst."

"A king with a broken heart! *Mon Dieu!*
One breaks so many, *cela peut se croire*,
To remember all *c'est la mer à boire*,
And the first, *mais comme c'est vieux*.
Perhaps there is still some keepsake—or
One has possibly sold it for a song:
On ne peut pas toujours pleurer les morts,
And this One—He has been dead so long!"

SONG

Love, Love to-day, my dear,
Love is not always here;
Wise maids know how soon grows sere
The greenest leaf of Spring;
But no man knoweth
Whither it goeth
When the wind bloweth
So frail a thing.

Love, Love, my dear, to-day,
If the ship's in the bay,
If the bird has come your way
That sings on summer trees;
When his song faileth
And the ship saileth
No voice availeth
To call back these.

SATURDAY MARKET

Bury your heart in some deep green hollow
    Or hide it up in a kind old tree
Better still, give it the swallow
    When she goes over the sea.

In Saturday Market there's eggs a 'plenty
    And dead-alive ducks with their legs tied down,
Grey old gaffers and boys of twenty—
    Girls and the women of the town—
Pitchers and sugar-sticks, ribbons and laces,
    Posies and whips and dicky-birds' seed,
Silver pieces and smiling faces,
    In Saturday Market they've all they need.

What were you showing in Saturday Market
    That set it grinning from end to end
Girls and gaffers and boys of twenty—?
    Cover it close with your shawl, my friend—
Hasten you home with the laugh behind you,
    Over the down—, out of sight,
Fasten your door, though no one will find you
    No one will look on a Market night.

See, you, the shawl is wet, take out from under
    The red dead thing—. In the white of the moon
On the flags does it stir again? Well, and no wonder!
    Best make an end of it; bury it soon.
If there is blood on the hearth who'll know it?
    Or blood on the stairs,
When a murder is over and done why show it?
    In Saturday Market nobody cares.

Then lie you straight on your bed for a short, short weeping
    And still, for a long, long rest,
There's never a one in the town so sure of sleeping
    As you, in the house on the down with a hole in your breast.

Think no more of the swallow,
    Forget, you, the sea,
Never again remember the deep green hollow
    Or the top of the kind old tree!

ARRACOMBE WOOD

Some said, because he wud'n spaik
Any words to women but Yes and No,
Nor put out his hand for Parson to shake
He mun be bird-witted. But I do go
By the lie of the barley that he did sow,
And I wish no better thing than to hold a rake
Like Dave, in his time, or to see him mow.

Put up in churchyard a month ago,
"A bitter old soul," they said, but it wadn't so.
His heart were in Arracombe Wood where he'd used to go
To sit and talk wi' his shadder till sun went low,
Though what it was all about us'll never know.
And there baint no mem'ry in the place
Of th' old man's footmark, nor his face;
Arracombe Wood do think more of a crow—
'Will be violets there in the Spring: in Summer time the spider's lace;
And come the Fall, the whizzle and race
Of the dry, dead leaves when the wind gies chase;
And on the Eve of Christmas, fallin' snow.

SEA LOVE

Tide be runnin' the great world over:
T'was only last June month I mind that we
Was thinkin' the toss and the call in the breast of the lover
So everlastin' as the sea.

Heer's the same little fishes that sputter and swim,
Wi' the moon's old glim on the grey, wet sand;
An' him no more to me nor me to him
Than the wind goin' over my hand.

THE ROAD TO KÉRITY

Do you remember the two old people we passed on the road to Kérity,
Resting their sack on the stones, by the drenched wayside,
Looking at us with their lightless eyes through the driving rain, and then out again
To the rocks, and the long white line of the tide:
Frozen ghosts that were children once, husband and wife, father, and mother,
Looking at us with those frozen eyes; have you ever seen anything quite so chilled or so old?
But we—with our arms about each other,
We did not feel the cold!

I HAVE BEEN THROUGH THE GATES

His heart, to me, was a place of palaces and pinnacles and shining towers;
I saw it then as we see things in dreams,—I do not remember how long I slept;
I remember the trees, and the high, white walls, and how the sun was always on the towers;
The walls are standing to-day, and the gates: I have been through the gates, I have groped, I have crept
Back, back. There is dust in the streets, and blood; they are empty; darkness is over them;
His heart is a place with the lights gone out, forsaken by great winds and the heavenly rain, unclean and unswept,
Like the heart of the holy city, old, blind, beautiful Jerusalem,
Over which Christ wept.

THE CENOTAPH

Not yet will those measureless fields be green again
Where only yesterday the wild, sweet, blood of wonderful youth was shed;
There is a grave whose earth must hold too long, too deep a stain,
Though for ever over it we may speak as proudly as we may tread.
But here, where the watchers by lonely hearths from the thrust of an inward sword have more slowly bled,

We shall build the Cenotaph: Victory, winged, with Peace, winged too, at
the column's head.
And over the stairway, at the foot—oh! here, leave desolate, passionate
hands to spread
Violets, roses, and laurel, with the small, sweet, twinkling country things
Speaking so wistfully of other Springs,
From the little gardens of little places where son or sweetheart was born
and bred.
In splendid sleep, with a thousand brothers
To lovers—to mothers
Here, too, lies he:
Under the purple, the green, the red,
It is all young life: it must break some women's hearts to see
Such a brave, gay coverlet to such a bed!
Only, when all is done and said,
God is not mocked and neither are the dead.

For this will stand in our Market-place—
Who'll sell, who'll buy
(Will you or I
Lie each to each with the better grace)?
While looking into every busy whore's and huckster's face
As they drive their bargains, is the Face
Of God: and some young, piteous, murdered face.

THE RAMBLING SAILOR (1929)

IN THE FIELDS

Lord, when I look at lovely things which pass,
Under old trees the shadows of young leaves
Dancing to please the wind along the grass,
Or the gold stillness of the August sun on the August sheaves;
Can I believe there is a heavenlier world than this?
And if there is
Will the strange heart of any everlasting thing
Bring me these dreams that take my breath away?
They come at evening with the home-flying rooks and the scent of hay,
Over the fields. They come in Spring.

FROM A WINDOW

Up here, with June, the sycamore throws
Across the window a whispering screen;
I shall miss the sycamore more, I suppose,
Than anything else on this earth that is out in green.
But I mean to go through the door without fear,
Not caring much what happens here
When I'm away:—
How green the screen is across the panes
Or who goes laughing along the lanes
With my old lover all the summer day.

NOT FOR THAT CITY

Not for that city of the level sun,
Its golden streets and glittering gates ablaze—
The shadeless, sleepless city of white days,
White nights, or nights and days that are as one—
We weary, when all is said, all thought, all done.
We strain our eyes beyond this dusk to see

What, from the threshold of eternity
We shall step into. No, I think we shun
The splendour of that everlasting glare,
The clamour of that never-ending song.
And if for anything we greatly long,
It is for some remote and quiet stair
Which winds to silence and a space of sleep
Too sound for waking and for dreams too deep.

ROOMS

I remember rooms that have had their part
In the steady slowing down of the heart.
The room in Paris, the room at Geneva,
The little damp room with the seaweed smell,
And that ceaseless maddening sound of the tide—
Rooms where for good or for ill—things died.
But there is the room where we (two) lie dead,
Though every morning we seem to wake and might just as well seem to sleep again
As we shall somewhere in the other quieter, dustier bed
Out there in the sun—in the rain.

MONSIEUR QUI PASSE
(Quai Voltaire)

A purple blot against the dead white door
In my friend's rooms, bathed in their vile pink light,
I had not noticed her before
She snatched my eyes and threw them back to me:
She did not speak till we came out into the night,
Paused at this bench beside the kiosk on the quay.

God knows precisely what she said—
I left to her the twisted skein,
Though here and there I caught a thread,—
Something, at first, about "the lamps along the Seine,

JUNE, 1915

Who thinks of June's first rose to-day?
Only some child, perhaps, with shining eyes and rough bright hair will reach it down
In a green sunny lane, to us almost as far away
As are the fearless stars from these veiled lamps of town.
What's little June to a great broken world with eyes gone dim
From too much looking on the face of grief, the face of dread?
Or what's the broken world to June and him
Of the small eager hand, the shining eyes, the rough bright head?

NE ME TANGITO

"This man . . . would have known who and what manner of woman this is: for she is a sinner."—S. Luke *vii. 39.*

Odd, *You* should fear the touch,
The first that I was ever ready to let go,
I, that have not cared much
For any toy I could not break and throw
To the four winds when I had done with it. You need not fear the touch,
Blindest of all the things that I have cared for very much
In the whole gay, unbearable, amazing show.

True—for a moment—no, dull heart, you were too small,
Thinking to hide the ugly doubt behind that hurried puzzled little smile:
Only the shade, was it, you saw? but still the shade of something vile:
Oddest of all!
So I will tell you this. Last night, in sleep,
Walking through April fields I heard the far-off bleat of sheep
And from the trees about the farm, not very high,
A flight of pigeons fluttered up into an early evening mackerel sky;
Someone stood by and it was you:
About us both a great wind blew.
My breast was bared
But sheltered by my hair
I found you, suddenly, lying there,
Tugging with tiny fingers at my heart, no more afraid:

The weakest thing, the most divine
That ever yet was mine,
Something that I had strangely made,
So then it seemed—
The child for which I had not looked or ever cared,
Of whom, before, I had never dreamed.

OLD SHEPHERD'S PRAYER

Up to the bed by the window, where I be lyin',
Comes bells and bleat of the flock wi' they two children's clack.
Over, from under the eaves there's the starlings flyin',
And down in yard, fit to burst his chain, yapping out at Sue I do hear young Mac.

Turning around like a falled-over sack
I can see team ploughin' in Whithy-bush field and meal carts startin' up road to Church-Town;
Saturday arternoon the men goin' back
And the women from market, trapin' home over the down.

Heavenly Master, I wud like to wake to they same green places
Where I be know'd for breakin' dogs and follerin' sheep.
And if I may not walk in th' old ways and look on th' old faces
I wud sooner sleep.

MY HEART IS LAME

My heart is lame with running after yours so fast
Such a long way,
Shall we walk slowly home, looking at all the things we passed
Perhaps to-day?

Home down the quiet evening roads under the quiet skies,
Not saying much,
You for a moment giving me your eyes
When you could bear my touch.

But not to-morrow. This has taken all my breath;
Then, though you look the same,
There may be something lovelier in Love's face in death
As your heart sees it, running back the way we came;
My heart is lame.

ON YOUTH STRUCK DOWN

(From an unfinished elegy)

Oh! Death what have you to say?
"Like a bride–like a bride-groom they ride away:
You shall go back to make up the fire,
To learn patience–to learn grief,
To learn sleep when the light has quite gone out of your earthly skies,
But they have the light in their eyes
To the end of their day."

THE RAMBLING SAILOR

In the old back streets o' Pimlico,
On the docks at Monte Video,
At the Ring o' Bells on Plymouth Hoe
He'm arter me now wheerever I go.
An' dirty nights when the wind do blow
I can hear him sing-songin' up from sea:
Oh! no man nor woman's bin friend to me
An' to-day I'm feared wheer to-morrow I'll be,
Sin' the night the moon lay whist and white
On the road goin' down to the Lizard Light
When I heard him hummin' behind me.

"Oh! look, boy, look in your sweetheart's eyes
So deep as sea an' so blue as skies;
An' 'tis better to kiss than to chide her.
If they tell 'ee no tales, they'll tell 'ee no lies
Of the little brown mouse
That creeps into the house
To lie sleepin' so quiet beside her.

"Oh! hold 'ee long, but hold 'ee light
Your true man's hand when you find him,
He'll help 'ee home on a darksome night
Wi' a somethin' bright
That he'm holdin' tight
In the hand that he keeps behind him.

"Oh! sit 'ee down to your whack o' pies,
So hot's the stew and the brew likewise,
But whiles you'm scrapin' the plates and dishes,
A'gapin' down in the shiversome sea
For the delicate mossels inside o' we
Theer's a passel o' hungry fishes."

At the *Halte des Marins* at *Saint Nazaire*
I cussed him, sittin' astride his chair;
An' Christmas Eve on the Mary Clare
I pitched him a'down the hatch-way stair.
But "Shoutin' and cloutin's nothing to me,
Nor the hop nor the skip nor the jump," says he,
"For I be walkin' on every quay–"

"So look, boy, look in the dear maid's eyes
And take the true man's hand
And eat your fill o' your whack o' pies
Till you'm starin' up wheer the sea-crow flies
Wi' your head lyin' soft in the sand."

THE CALL

From our low seat beside the fire
Where we have dozed and dreamed and watched the glow
Or raked the ashes, stopping so
We scarcely saw the sun or rain
Above, or looked much higher
Than this same quiet red or burned-out fire.
To-night we heard a call,
A rattle on the window-pane,
A voice on the sharp air,

And felt a breath stirring our hair,
A flame within us: Something swift and tall
Swept in and out and that was all.
Was it a bright or a dark angel? Who can know?
It left no mark upon the snow,
But suddenly it snapped the chain
Unbarred, flung wide the door
Which will not shut again;
And so we cannot sit here any more.
We must arise and go:
The world is cold without
And dark and hedged about
With mystery and enmity and doubt,
But we must go
Though yet we do not know
Who called, or what marks we shall leave upon the snow.

ABSENCE

Sometimes I know the way
You walk, up over the bay;
It is a wind from that far sea
That blows the fragrance of your hair to me.

Or in this garden when the breeze
Touches my trees
To stir their dreaming shadows on the grass
I see you pass.

In sheltered beds, the heart of every rose
Serenely sleeps to-night. As shut as those
Your guarded heart; as safe as they from the beat, beat
Of hooves that tread dropped roses in the street.

Turn never again
On these eyes blind with a wild rain
Your eyes; they were stars to me.—
There are things stars may not see.

But call, call, and though Christ stands
    Still with scarred hands
Over my mouth, I must answer. So
I will come—He shall let me go!

THE TREES ARE DOWN

—and he cried with a loud voice:
Hurt not the earth, neither the sea, nor the trees—
(Revelation.)

They are cutting down the great plane-trees at the end of the gardens.
For days there has been the grate of the saw, the swish of the branches as they fall,
The crash of the trunks, the rustle of trodden leaves,
With the "Whoops" and the "Whoas," the loud common talk, the loud common laughs of the men, above it all.

I remember one evening of a long past Spring
Turning in at a gate, getting out of a cart, and finding a large dead rat in the mud of the drive.
I remember thinking: alive or dead, a rat was a god-forsaken thing,
But at least, in May, that even a rat should be alive.

The week's work here is as good as done. There is just one bough
    On the roped bole, in the fine grey rain,
        Green and high
        And lonely against the sky.
            (Down now!—)
        And but for that,
        If an old dead rat
Did once, for a moment, unmake the Spring, I might never have thought of him again.

It is not for a moment the Spring is unmade to-day;
These were great trees, it was in them from root to stem:
When the men with the "Whoops" and the "Whoas" have carted the whole of the whispering loveliness away
Half the Spring, for me, will have gone with them.

It is going now, and my heart has been struck with the hearts of the planes;
Half my life it has beat with these, in the sun, in the rains,
In the March wind, the May breeze,
In the great gales that came over to them across the roofs from the great seas.
There was only a quiet rain when they were dying;
They must have heard the sparrows flying,
And the small creeping creatures in the earth where they were lying—
But I, all day, I heard an angel crying:
"Hurt not the trees."

SMILE, DEATH

Smile, Death, see I smile as I come to you
Straight from the road and the moor that I leave behind,
Nothing on earth to me was like this wind-blown space,
Nothing was like the road, but at the end there was a vision or a face
And the eyes were not always kind.

Smile, Death, as you fasten the blades to my feet for me,
On, on let us skate past the sleeping willows dusted with snow;
Fast, fast down the frozen stream, with the moor and the road and the vision behind,
(Show me your face, why the eyes are kind!)
And we will not speak of life or believe in it or remember it as we go.

TO A CHILD IN DEATH

You would have scoffed if we had told you yesterday
Love made us feel, or so it was with me, like some great bird
Trying to hold and shelter you in its strong wing;—
A gay little shadowy smile would have tossed us back such a solemn word,
And it was not for that you were listening
When so quietly you slipped away
With half the music of the world unheard.
What shall we do with this strange summer, meant for you,—
Dear, if we see the winter through
What shall be done with spring?

This, this is the victory of the Grave; here is death's sting,
That it is not strong enough, our strongest wing.

But what of His who like a Father pitieth?
His Son was also, once, a little thing,
The wistfullest child that ever drew breath,
Chased by a sword from Bethlehem and in the busy house at Nazareth
Playing with little rows of nails, watching the carpenter's hammer swing,
Long years before His hands and feet were tied
And by a hammer and the three great nails He died,
        Of youth, of Spring,
Of sorrow, of loneliness, of victory the King,
        Under the shadow of that wing.

MOORLAND NIGHT

My face is against the grass—the moorland grass is wet—
    My eyes are shut against the grass, against my lips there are the little blades,
        Over my head the curlews call,
    And now there is the night wind in my hair;
My heart is against the grass and the sweet earth;—it has gone still, at last.
            It does not want to beat any more,
                And why should it beat?
            This is the end of the journey;
                The Thing is found.

            This is the end of all the roads—
        Over the grass there is the night-dew
And the wind that drives up from the sea along the moorland road;
        I hear a curlew start out from the heath
        And fly off, calling through the dusk,
            The wild, long, rippling call.
        The Thing is found and I am quiet with the earth.
Perhaps the earth will hold it, or the wind, or that bird's cry,
But it is not for long in any life I know. This cannot stay,
Not now, not yet, not in a dying world, with me, for very long.
                I leave it here:
            And one day the wet grass may give it back—

One day the quiet earth may give it back—
The calling birds may give it back as they go by—
To someone walking on the moor who starves for love and will not know
Who gave it to all these to give away;
Or, if I come and ask for it again,
Oh! then, to me.

Early poems printed at the end of The Rambling Sailor

AT THE CONVENT GATE

"Why do you shrink away, and start and stare?
Life frowns to see you leaning at death's gate—
Not back, but on. Ah! sweet, it is too late:
You cannot cast these kisses from your hair.
Will God's cold breath blow kindly anywhere
Upon such burning gold? Oh! lips worn white
With waiting! Love will blossom in a night
And you shall wake to find the roses there!"

"Oh hush! He seems to stir, He lifts His Head.
He smiles. Look where He hangs against the sky.
He never smiled nor stirred, that God of pain
With tired eyes and limbs above my bed—
But loose me, this is death, I will not die—
Not while He smiles. Oh! Christ, Thine own again!"

REQUIESCAT

Your birds that call from tree to tree
Just overhead, and whirl and dart,
Your breeze fresh-blowing from the sea,
And your sea singing on, Sweetheart.

Your salt scent on the thin sharp air
Of this grey dawn's first drowsy hours,
While on the grass shines everywhere
The yellow starlight of your flowers.

At the road's end your strip of blue
Beyond that line of naked trees—
Strange that we should remember you
As if you would remember these!

As if your spirit, swaying yet
To the old passions, were not free
Of Spring's wild magic, and the fret
Of the wilder wooing of the sea!

What threat of old imaginings,
Half-haunted joy, enchanted pain,
Or dread of unfamiliar things
Should ever trouble you again?

Yet you would wake and want, you said
The little whirr of wings, the clear
Gay notes, the wind, the golden bed
Of the daffodil: and they are here!

Just overhead, they whirl and dart
Your birds that call from tree to tree,
Your sea is singing on—Sweetheart,
Your breeze is flowing from the sea.

Beyond the line of naked trees
At the road's end, your stretch of blue—
Strange if you should remember these
As we, ah! God! remember you!

THE LITTLE PORTRESS
(St. Gilda de Rhuys)

The stillness of the sunshine lies
Upon her spirit: silence seems
To look out from its place of dreams
When suddenly she lifts her eyes
To waken, for a little space,
The smile asleep upon her face.

A thousand years of sun and shower,
The melting of unnumbered snows
Go to the making of the rose
Which blushes out its little hour.
So old is Beauty: in its heart
The ages seem to meet and part.

Like Beauty's self, she holds a clear
Deep memory of hidden things—
The music of forgotten springs—
So far she travels back, so near
She seems to stand to patient truth
As old as Age, as young as Youth.

That is her window, by the gate.
Now and again her figure flits
Across the wall. Long hours she sits
Within: on all who come to wait.
Her Saviour too is hanging there
A foot or so above her chair.

"Sœur Marie de l'enfant Jésus,"
You wrote it in my little book—
Your shadow-name. Your shadow-look
Is dimmer and diviner too,
But not to keep: it slips so far
Beyond us to that golden bar

Where angels, watching from their stair,
Half-envy you your tranquil days
Of prayer as exquisite as praise,—
Grey twilights softer than their glare
Of glory: all sweet human things
Which vanish with the whirr of wings.

Yet will you, when you wing your way
To whiter worlds, more whitely shine
Or shed a radiance more divine
Than here you shed from day to day—
High in His heaven a quiet star,
Be nearer God than now you are?

AFTERNOON TEA

Please you, excuse me, good five-o'clock people,
  I've lost my last hatful of words,
And my heart's in the wood up above the church steeple,
  I'd rather have tea with the birds.

Gay Kate's stolen kisses, poor Barnaby's scars,
  John's losses and Mary's gains,
Oh! what do they matter, my dears, to the stars
  Or the glow-worms in the lanes!

I'd rather lie under the tall elm-trees,
  With old rooks talking loud overhead,
To watch a red squirrel run over my knees,
  Very still on my brackeny bed.

And wonder what feathers the wrens will be taking
  For lining their nests next Spring;
Or why the tossed shadow of boughs in a great wind shaking
  Is such a lovely thing.

SHE WAS A SINNER

Love was my flower, and before He came—
  "Master, there was a garden where it grew
Rank, with the colour of a crimson flame,
  Thy flower too, but knowing not its name
Nor yet that it was Thine, I did not spare
But tore and trampled it and stained my hair,
My hands, my lips, with the red petals; see,
  Drenched with the blood of Thy poor murdered flower
I stood, when suddenly the hour
      Struck for me,
And straight I came and wound about Thy Feet
      The strands of shame
Twined with those broken buds: till lo, more sweet,
    More red, yet still the same,
Bright burning blossoms sprang around Thy brow

Beneath the thorns (I saw, I knew not how,
The crown which Thou wast afterward to wear
On that immortal Tree)
And I went out and found my garden very bare,
But swept and watered it, then followed Thee.

There was another garden where to seek
Thee, first, I came in those grey hours
Of the Great Dawn, and knew Thee not till Thou didst speak
My name, that 'Mary' like a flash of light
Shot from Thy lips. Thou wast 'the gardener' too,
And then I knew
That evermore our flowers,
Thine, Lord, and mine, shall be a burning white."

SONG

Oh! Sorrow, Sorrow, scarce I knew
Your name when, shaking down the may
In sport, a little child, I grew
Afraid to find you at my play.
I heard it ere I looked at you;
You sang it softly as you came
Bringing your little boughs of yew
To fling across my gayest game.

Oh! Sorrow, Sorrow, was I fair
That when I decked me for a bride,
You met me stepping down the stair
And led me from my lover's side?
Was I so dear you could not spare
The maid to love, the child to play,
But coming always unaware,
Must bid and beckon me away?

Oh! Sorrow, Sorrow, is my bed
So wide and warm that you must lie
Upon it; toss your weary head
And stir my slumber with your sigh?

I left my love at your behest,
   I waved your little boughs of yew,
But, Sorrow, Sorrow, let me rest,
   For oh! I cannot sleep with you!

UNPUBLISHED AND UNCOLLECTED POEMS

AN ENDING

You know that road beside the sea,
   Walled by the wavin' wheat,
Which winds down to the little town,
   Wind-blown and gray and up the crooked street?
         We'd used to meet
Just at the top, and when the grass was trodden down
         'Twas by our feet.
         We'd used to stand
And watch the clouds like a great fleet
   Sail over sea and over land,
         And the gulls dart
Above our heads: and by the gate
   At the road's end, when et was late
And all the ships was showing lights on quiet nights,
         We'd used to part.

So, Sir, you think I've missed my way,
   There's nothing but the Judgment Seat—
But ef I pray perhaps I may—what's that you say—
         A golden street?
   Give me the yellow wheat!
   Et edn't *there* we'm goin' to meet!
No, I'm not mazed, I make no doubt
   That ef we don't my soul goes out
'Most like a candle in the everlasting dark.
   And what's the odds? 'Twas just a spark
         Alight for her.
         I tell you, Sir,

That God He made et brave and plain,
Sin' He knows better than yon Book
What's in a look
You'd go to Hell to get again.

Another hour? An hour to wait—!
I sim I'll meet her at the gate—
You know that road beside the sea—
The crooked street—the wavin' wheat—?
(What's that? A lamp! Et made me start—)
That's where our feet—we'd used to meet—on quiet nights—
My God! the ships es showing lights!—
We'd used—to part.

A QUESTION

If Christ was crucified—Ah! God, are we
Not scourged, tormented, mocked and called to pay
The sin of ages in our little day—
Has man no crown of thorns, no Calvary,
Though Christ has tasted of his agony?
We knew no Eden and the poisoned fruit
We did not pluck, yet from the bitter root
We sprang, maimed branches of iniquity.

Have we who share the heritage accurst
Wrought nothing? Tainted to the end of time,
The last frail souls still suffer for the first
Blind victims of an everlasting crime.
Ask of the Crucified, Who hangs enthroned,
If man—oh! God, man too has not atoned.

LEFT BEHIND

Wilt thou have pity? intercede for me.
So near, at last thou standest to the throne,
Thou mayest call for mercy on thine own,

As here thine own for mercy calls on thee.
Fling then my soul, thy soul, upon its knee;
  Bestir these lips of mine for me to pray;
  Release this spirit from its tortured clay,
Remembering that thine, its mate, is free.

I wait thy summons on a swaying floor,
  Within a room half darkness and half glare.
  I cannot stir—I cannot find the stair—
    Thrust hands upon my heart—; it clogs my feet,
    As drop by drop it drains. I stand and beat—
I stand and beat my heart against the door.

A FAREWELL

Remember me and smile, as smiling too,
  I have remembered things that went their way—
  The dolls with which I grew too wise to play—
Or over-wise—and kissed, as children do,
And so dismissed them; yes, even as you
  Have done with this poor piece of painted clay—
  Not wantonly, but wisely, shall we say?
As one who, haply, tunes his heart anew.

Only I wish her eyes may not be blue,
  The eyes of the new angel. Ah! she may
Miss something that I found,—perhaps the clue
To those long silences of yours, which grew
  Into one word. And should she not be gay,
  Poor lady! Well, she too must have her day.

"THERE SHALL BE NO NIGHT THERE"

(In the Fields)

Across these wind-blown meadows I can see
  The far off glimmer of the little town,
  And feel the darkness slowly shutting down

To lock from day's long glare my soul and me.
    Then through my blood the coming mystery
Of night steals to my heart and turns my feet
Toward that chamber in the lamp-lit street.
    Where waits the pillow of thy breast and thee.

"There shall be no night there"—no curtained pane
    To shroud love's speechlessness and loose thy hair
For kisses swift and sweet as falling rain.
    No soft release of life—no evening prayer.
    Nor shall we waking greet the dawn, aware
That with the darkness we may sleep again.

V. R. I.

I. January 22nd, 1901
'A Nation's Sorrow.' No. In that strange hour
    We did but note the flagging pulse of day,
    The sudden pause of Time, and turn away
Incredulous of grief; beyond the power
Of question or of tears. Thy people's pain
    Was their perplexity: Thou could'st not be
God's and not England's. Let Thy spirit reign,
    For England is not England without Thee.
Still Thine, Immortal Dead, she still shall stake
    Thy fame against the world, and hold supreme
Thy unsuspended sway. Then lay not down
    Thy sceptre, lest her Empire prove a dream
Of Thine, great, gentle Sleeper, who shalt wake
    When God doth please, to claim another crown.

II. February 2nd, 1901
When, wrapped in the calm majesty of sleep,
    She passes through her people to her rest,
    Has she no smile in slumber? Is her breast,
Even to their sorrow, pulseless? Shall they weep
And She not with them? Nothing is so strange
    As this, that England's passion, be it pain,
    Or joy, or triumph, never shall again
Find voice in her. No change is like this change.

For all this mute indifference of death,
More dear She is than She has ever been.
The dark crowd gathers: not 'The Queen! The Queen!'
Upon its lips to-day. A quickened breath—
She passes—through the hush, the straining gaze,
The vast, sweet silence of its love and praise.

TO A LITTLE CHILD IN DEATH

Dear, if little feet make little journeys,
Thine should not be far;
Though beyond the faintest star,
Past earth's last bar,
Where angels are,
Thou hast to travel—
Cross the far blue spaces of the sea,
Climb above the tallest tree,
Higher up than many mountains be;
Sure there is some shorter way for thee,
Since little feet make little journeys.

Then, if smallest limbs are soonest weary,
Thou should'st soon be there;
Stumbling up the golden stair,
Where the angels' shining hair
Brushes dust from baby faces.
Very, very gently cling
To a silver-edged wing,
And peep from under.
Then thou'lt see the King,
Then will many voices sing,
And thou wilt wonder.
Wait a little while
For Him to smile,
Who calleth thee.
He who calleth all,
Both great and small,
From over mountain, star and sea,
Doth call the smallest soonest to His knee,
Since smallest limbs are soonest weary.

PÉRI EN MER
(Cameret)

One day the friends who stand about my bed
  Will slowly turn from it to speak of me
Indulgently, as of the newly dead,
  Not knowing how I perished by the sea,
That night in summer when the gulls topped white
  The crowded masts cut black against a sky
Of fading rose—where suddenly the light
  Of Youth went out, and I, no longer I,
Climbed home, the homeless ghost I was to be.
  Yet as I passed, they sped me up the heights—
Old seamen round the door of the Abri
  De la Tempête. Even on quiet nights
  So may some ship go down with all her lights
Beyond the sight of watchers on the quay!

Stories

PASSED

'Like souls that meeting pass,
And passing never meet again.'

LET those who have missed a romantic view of London in its poorest quarters—and there will romance be found—wait for a sunset in early winter. They may turn North or South, towards Islington or Westminster, and encounter some fine pictures and more than one aspect of unique beauty. This hour of pink twilight has its monopoly of effects. Some of them may never be reached again.

On such an evening in mid-December, I put down my sewing and left tame glories of fire-light (discoverers of false charm) to welcome, as youth may, the contrast of keen air outdoors to the glow within.

My aim was the perfection of a latent appetite, for I had no mind to content myself with an apology for hunger, consequent on a warmly passive afternoon.

The splendid cold of fierce frost set my spirit dancing. The road rung hard underfoot, and through the lonely squares woke sharp echoes from behind. This stinging air assailed my cheeks with vigorous severity. It stirred my blood grandly, and brought thought back to me from the warm embers just forsaken, with an immeasurable sense of gain.

But after the first delirium of enchanting motion, destination became a question. The dim trees behind the dingy enclosures were beginning to be succeeded by rows of flaring gas jets, displaying shops of new aspect and evil smell. Then the heavy walls of a partially demolished prison reared themselves darkly against the pale sky.

By this landmark I recalled—alas that it should be possible—a church in the district, newly built by an infallible architect, which I had been directed to seek at leisure. I did so now. A row of cramped houses, with the unpardonable bow window, projecting squalor into prominence, came into view. Robbing these even of light, the portentous walls stood a silent curse before them. I think they were blasting the hopes of the sad dwellers beneath them—if hope they had—to despair. Through spattered panes faces of diseased and dirty children leered into the street. One room, as I passed, seemed full of them. The window was open; their wails and maddening requirements sent out the mother's cry. It was thrown back to her, mingled with her children's screams, from the pitiless prison walls.

These shelters struck my thought as travesties—perhaps they were not—of the grand place called home.

Leaving them I sought the essential of which they were bereft. What withheld from them, as poverty and sin could not, a title to the sacred name?

An answer came, but interpretation was delayed. Theirs was not the desolation of something lost, but of something that had never been. I thrust off speculation gladly here, and fronted Nature free.

Suddenly I emerged from the intolerable shadow of the brickwork, breathing easily once more. Before me lay a roomy space, nearly square, bounded by three-storey dwellings, and transformed, as if by quick mechanism, with colours of sunset. Red and golden spots wavered in the panes of the low scattered houses round the bewildering expanse. Overhead a faint crimson sky was hung with violet clouds, obscured by the smoke and nearing dusk.

In the centre, but towards the left, stood an old stone pump, and some few feet above it irregular lamps looked down. They were planted on a square of paving railed in by broken iron fences, whose paint, now discoloured, had once been white. Narrow streets cut in five directions from the open roadway. Their lines of light sank dimly into distance, mocking the stars' entrance into the fading sky. Everything was transfigured in the illuminated twilight. As I stood, the dying sun caught the rough edges of a girl's uncovered hair, and hung a faint nimbus round her poor desecrated face. The soft circle, as she glanced toward me, lent it the semblance of one of those mystically pictured faces of some medieval saint.

A stillness stole on, and about the square dim figures hurried along, leaving me stationary in existence (I was thinking fancifully), when my medieval saint demanded 'who I was a-shoving of?' and dismissed me, not unkindly, on my way. Hawkers in a neighbouring alley were calling, and the monotonous ting-ting of the muffin-bell made an audible background to the picture. I left it, and then the glamour was already passing. In a little while darkness possessing it, the place would reassume its aspect of sordid gloom.

There is a street not far from there, bearing a name that quickens life within one, by the vision it summons of a most peaceful country, where the broad roads are but pathways through green meadows, and your footstep keeps the time to a gentle music of pure streams. There the scent of roses, and the first pushing buds of spring, mark the seasons, and the birds call out faithfully the time and manner of the day. Here Easter is heralded by the advent in some squalid mart of air-balls on Good Friday; early summer and late may be known by observation of that unromantic yet authentic calendar in which alley-tors, tip-cat, whip- and peg-tops, hoops and suckers, in their courses mark the flight of time.

Perhaps attracted by the incongruity, I took this way. In such a thoroughfare it is remarkable that satisfied as are its public with transient substitutes for literature, they require permanent types (the term is so far misused it may hardly be further outraged) of Art. Pictures, so-called, are the sole departure from necessity and popular finery which the prominent wares display. The window exhibiting these aspirations was scarcely more inviting than the fishmonger's next door, but less odoriferous, and I stopped to see what the ill-reflecting lights would show. There was a typical selection. Prominently, a large chromo of a girl at prayer. Her eyes turned upwards, presumably to heaven, left the gazer in no state to dwell on the elaborately bared breasts below. These might rival, does wax-work attempt such beauties, any similar attraction of Marylebone's extensive show. This personification of pseudo-purity was sensually diverting, and consequently marketable.

My mind seized the ideal of such a picture, and turned from this prostitution of it sickly away. Hurriedly I proceeded, and did not stop again until I had passed the low gateway of the place I sought.

Its forbidding exterior was hidden in the deep twilight and invited no consideration. I entered and swung back the inner door. It was papered with memorial cards, recommending to mercy the unprotesting spirits of the dead. My prayers were requested for the 'repose of the soul of the Architect of that church, who passed away in the True Faith—December—1887'. Accepting the assertion, I counted him beyond them, and mentally entrusted mine to the priest for those who were still groping for it in the gloom.

Within the building, darkness again forbade examination. A few lamps hanging before the altar struggled with obscurity.

I tried to identify some ugly details with the great man's complacent eccentricity, and failing, turned toward the street again. Nearly an hour's walk lay between me and my home. This fact and the atmosphere of stuffy sanctity about the place, set me longing for space again, and woke a fine scorn for aught but air and sky. My appetite, too, was now an hour ahead of opportunity. I sent back a final glance into the darkness as my hand prepared to strike the door. There was no motion at the moment, and it was silent; but the magnetism of human presence reached me where I stood. I hesitated, and in a few moments found what sought me on a chair in the far corner, flung face downwards across the seat. The attitude arrested me. I went forward. The lines of the figure spoke unquestionable despair.

Does speech convey intensity of anguish? Its supreme expression is in form. Here was human agony set forth in meagre lines, voiceless, but articulate to the soul. At first the forcible portrayal of it assailed me with the importunate strength of beauty. Then the Thing stretched there in the obdurate darkness grew personal and banished delight. Neither sympathy nor its vulgar substitute, curiosity, induced my action as I drew near. I was eager indeed to be gone. I wanted to ignore the almost indistinguishable being. My will cried: Forsake it!—but I found myself powerless to obey. Perhaps it would have conquered had not the girl swiftly raised herself in quest of me. I stood still. Her eyes met mine. A wildly tossed spirit looked from those ill-lighted windows, beckoning me on. Mine pressed towards it, but whether my limbs actually moved I do not know, for the imperious summons robbed me of any consciousness save that of necessity to comply.

Did she reach me, or was our advance mutual? It cannot be told. I suppose we neither know. But we met, and her hand, grasping mine, imperatively dragged me into the cold and noisy street.

We went rapidly in and out of the flaring booths, hustling little staggering children in our unpitying speed, I listening dreamily to the concert of hoarse yells and haggling whines which struck against the silence of our flight. On and on she took me, breathless and without explanation. We said nothing. I had no care or impulse to ask our goal. The fierce pressure of my hand was not relaxed a breathing space; it would have borne me against resistance could I have offered any, but I was capable of none. The streets seemed to rush past us, peopled with despair.

Weirdly lighted faces sent blank negations to a spirit of question which finally began to stir in me. Here, I thought once vaguely, was the everlasting No!

We must have journeyed thus for more than half an hour and walked far. I did not detect it. In the eternity of supreme moments time is not. Thought, too, fears to be obtrusive and stands aside.

We gained a door at last, down some blind alley out of the deafening thoroughfare. She threw herself against it and pulled me up the unlighted stairs. They shook now and then with the violence of our ascent; with my free hand I tried to help myself up by the broad and greasy balustrade. There was little sound in the house. A light shone under the first door we passed, but all was quietness within.

At the very top, from the dense blackness of the passage, my guide thrust me suddenly into a dazzling room. My eyes rejected its array of brilliant light. On a small chest of drawers three candles were guttering, two more stood flaring in the high window ledge, and a lamp upon a table by the bed rendered these minor illuminations unnecessary by its diffusive glare. There were even some small Christmas candles dropping coloured grease down the wooden mantelpiece, and I noticed a fire had been made, built entirely of wood. There were bits of an inlaid work-box or desk, and a chair-rung, lying half burnt in the grate. Some peremptory demand for light had been, these signs denoted, unscrupulously met. A woman lay upon the bed, half clothed, asleep. As the door slammed behind me the flames wavered and my companion released my hand. She stood beside me, shuddering violently, but without utterance.

I looked around. Everywhere proofs of recent energy were visible. The bright panes reflecting back the low burnt candles, the wretched but shining furniture, and some odd bits of painted china, set before the sputtering lights upon the drawers, bore witness to a provincial intolerance of grime. The boards were bare, and marks of extreme poverty distinguished the whole room. The destitution of her surroundings accorded ill with the girl's spotless person and well-tended hands, which were hanging tremulously down.

Subsequently I realized that these deserted beings must have first fronted the world from a sumptuous stage. The details in proof of it I need not cite. It must have been so.

My previous apathy gave place to an exaggerated observation. Even some pieces of a torn letter, dropped off the quilt, I noticed, were of fine texture, and inscribed by a man's hand. One fragment bore an elaborate device in colours. It may have been a club crest or coat-of-arms. I was trying to decide which, when the girl at length gave a cry of exhaustion or relief, at the same time falling into a similar attitude to that she had taken in the dim church. Her entire frame became shaken with tearless agony or terror. It was sickening to watch. She began partly to call or moan, begging me, since I was beside her, wildly, and then with heartbreaking weariness, 'to stop, to stay'. She half rose and claimed me with distracted grace. All her movements were noticeably fine.

I pass no judgement on her features; suffering for the time assumed them, and they made no insistence of individual claim.

I tried to raise her, and kneeling, pulled her reluctantly towards me. The proximity was distasteful. An alien presence has ever repelled me. I should have pitied the girl keenly perhaps a few more feet away. She clung to me with ebbing force. Her heart throbbed painfully close to mine, and when I meet now in the dark streets others who have been robbed, as she has been, of their great possession, I have to remember that.

The magnetism of our meeting was already passing; and, reason asserting itself, I reviewed the incident dispassionately, as she lay like a broken piece of mechanism in my arms. Her dark hair had come unfastened and fell about my shoulder. A faint white streak of it stole through the brown. A gleam of moonlight strays thus through a dusky room. I remember noticing, as it was swept with her involuntary motions across my face, a faint fragrance which kept recurring like a subtle and seductive sprite, hiding itself with fairy cunning in the tangled maze.

The poor girl's mind was clearly travelling a devious way. Broken and incoherent exclamations told of a recently wrung promise, made to whom, or of what nature, it was not my business to conjecture or inquire.

I record the passage of a few minutes. At the first opportunity I sought the slumberer on the bed. She slept well: hers was a long rest; there might be no awakening from it, for she was dead. Schooled in one short hour to all surprises, the knowledge made me simply richer by a fact. Nothing about the sternly set face invited horror. It had been, and was yet, a strong and, if beauty be not confined to youth and colour, a beautiful face.

Perhaps this quiet sharer of the convulsively broken silence was thirty years old. Death had set a firmness about the finely controlled features that might have shown her younger. The actual years are of little matter; existence, as we reckon time, must have lasted long. It was not death, but life that had planted the look of disillusion there. And romance being over, all goodbyes to youth are said. By the bedside, on a roughly constructed table, was a dearly bought bunch of violets. They were set in a blue bordered tea-cup, and hung over in wistful challenge of their own diviner hue. They were foreign, and their scent probably unnatural, but it stole very sweetly round the room. A book lay face downwards beside them—alas for parochial energies, not of a religious type—and the torn fragments of the destroyed letter had fallen on the black binding.

A passionate movement of the girl's breast against mine directed my glance elsewhere. She was shivering, and her arms about my neck were stiffly cold. The possibility that she was starving missed my mind. It would have found my heart. I wondered if she slept, and dared not stir, though I was by this time cramped and chilled. The vehemence of her agitation ended, she breathed gently, and slipped finally to the floor.

I began to face the need of action and recalled the chances of the night. When and how I might get home was a necessary question, and I listened vainly for a friendly step outside. None since we left it had climbed the last flight of stairs. I could hear a momentary vibration of men's voices in the room below. Was it possible to leave these suddenly discovered children of peace and tumult? Was it possible to stay?

This was Saturday, and two days later I was bound for Scotland; a practical recollection of empty trunks was not lost in my survey of the situation. Then how, if I decided not to forsake the poor child, now certainly sleeping in my arms, were my anxious friends to learn my whereabouts, and understand the eccentricity of the scheme? Indisputably, I determined, something must be done for the half-frantic wanderer who was pressing a tiring weight against me. And there should be some kind hand to cover the cold limbs and close the wide eyes of the breathless sleeper, waiting a comrade's sanction to fitting rest.

Conclusion was hastening to impatient thought, when my eyes let fall a fatal glance upon the dead girl's face. I do not think it had changed its first aspect of dignified repose, and yet now it woke in me a sensation of cold dread. The dark eyes unwillingly open reached mine in an insistent stare. One hand lying out upon the coverlid, I could never again mistake for that of temporarily suspended life. My watch ticked loudly, but I dared not examine it, nor could I wrench my sight from the figure on the bed. For the first time the empty shell of being assailed my senses. I watched feverishly, knowing well the madness of the action, for a hint of breathing, almost stopping my own.

Today, as memory summons it, I cannot dwell without reluctance on this hour of my realization of the thing called Death.

A hundred fancies, clothed in mad intolerable terrors, possessed me, and had not my lips refused it outlet, I should have set free a cry, as the spent child beside me had doubtless longed to do, and failed, ere, desperate, she fled.

My gaze was chained; it could not get free. As the shapes of monsters of ever varying and increasing dreadfulness flit through one's dreams, the images of those I loved crept round me, with stark yet well-known features, their limbs borrowing death's rigid outline, as they mocked my recognition of them with soundless semblances of mirth. They began to wind their arms about me in fierce embraces of burning and supernatural life. Gradually the contact froze. They bound me in an icy prison. Their hold relaxed. These creatures of my heart were restless. The horribly familiar company began to dance at intervals in and out a ring of white gigantic bedsteads, set on end like tombstones, each of which framed a huge and fearful travesty of the sad set face that was all the while seeking vainly a pitiless stranger's care. They vanished. My heart went home. The dear place was desolate. No echo of its many voices on the threshold or stair. My footsteps made no sound as I went rapidly up to a well-known room. Here I besought the mirror for the reassurance of my own reflection. It denied me human portraiture and threw back cold glare. As I opened mechanically a treasured book, I noticed the leaves were blank, not even blurred by spot or line; and then I shivered—it was deadly cold. The fire that but an hour or two ago it seemed I had forsaken for the winter twilight, glowed with slow derision at my efforts to rekindle heat. My hands plunged savagely into its red embers, but I drew them out quickly, unscathed and clean. The things by which I had touched life were nothing. Here, as I called the dearest names, their echoes came back again with the sound of an unlearned language. I did not recognize, and yet I framed them. What was had never been!

My spirit summoned the being who claimed mine. He came, stretching out arms of deathless welcome. As he reached me my heart took flight. I called aloud to it, but my cries were lost in awful laughter that broke to my bewildered fancy from the hideously familiar shapes which had returned and now encircled the grand form of him I loved. But I had never known him. I beat my breast to wake there the wonted pain of tingling joy. I called past experience with unavailing importunity to bear witness the man was wildly dear to me. He was not. He left me with bent head a stranger, whom I would not if I could recall.

For one brief second, reason found me. I struggled to shake off the phantoms of despair. I tried to grasp while it yet lingered the teaching of this never-to-be-forgotten front of death. The homeless house with its indefensible bow window stood out from beneath the prison walls again. What had this to do with it? I questioned. And the answer it had evoked replied, 'Not the desolation of something lost, but of something that had never been.'

The half-clad girl of the wretched picture-shop came into view with waxen hands and senseless symbolism. I had grown calmer, but her doll-like lips hissed out the same half-meaningless but pregnant words. Then the nights of a short life when I could pray, years back in magical childhood, sought me. They found me past them—without the power.

Truly the body had been for me the manifestation of the thing called soul. Here was my embodiment bereft. My face was stiff with drying tears. Sickly I longed to beg of an unknown God a miracle. Would He but touch the passive body and breathe into it the breath even of transitory life.

I craved but a fleeting proof of its ever possible existence. For to me it was not, would never be, and had never been.

The partially relinquished horror was renewing dominance. Speech of any incoherence or futility would have brought mental power of resistance. My mind was fast losing landmarks amid the continued quiet of the living and the awful stillness of the dead. There was no sound, even of savage guidance, I should not then have welcomed with glad response.

'The realm of Silence', says one of the world's great teachers, 'is large enough beyond the grave.'

I seemed to have passed life's portal, and my soul's small strength was beating back the noiseless gate. In my extremity, I cried, 'O God! for man's most bloody warshout, or Thy whisper!' It was useless. Not one dweller in the crowded tenements broke his slumber or relaxed his labour in answer to the involuntary prayer.

And may the 'Day of Account of Words' take note of this! Then, says the old fable, shall the soul of the departed be weighed against an image of Truth. I tried to construct in imagaination the form of the dumb deity who should bear down the balances for me. Soundlessness was turning fear to madness. I could neither quit nor longer bear company the grim Presence in that room. But the supreme moment was very near.

Long since, the four low candles had burned out, and now the lamp was struggling fitfully to keep alight. The flame could last but a few moments. I saw it, and did not face the possibility of darkness. The sleeping girl, I concluded rapidly, had used all available weapons of defiant light.

As yet, since my entrance, I had hardly stirred, steadily supporting the burden on my breast. Now, without remembrance of it, I started up to escape. The violent suddenness of the action woke my companion. She staggered blindly to her feet and confronted me as I gained the door.

Scarcely able to stand, and dashing the dimness from her eyes, she clutched a corner of the drawers behind her for support. Her head thrown back, and her dark hair hanging round it, crowned a grandly tragic form. This was no poor pleader, and I was unarmed for fight. She seized my throbbing arm and cried in a whisper, low and hoarse, but strongly audible: 'For God's sake, stay here with me.'

My lips moved vainly. I shook my head.

'For God in heaven's sake'—she repeated, swaying, and turning her burning, reddened eyes on mine—'don't leave me now.'

I stood irresolute, half stunned. Stepping back, she stooped and began piecing together the dismembered letter on the bed. A mute protest arrested her from a cold sister's face. She swept the action from her, crying, 'No!' and bending forward suddenly, gripped me with fierce force.

'Here! Here!' she prayed, dragging me passionately back into the room.

The piteous need and wild entreaty—no, the vision of dire anguish—was breaking my purpose of flight. A fragrance that was to haunt me stole between us. The poor little violets put in their plea. I moved to stay. Then a smile—the splendour of it may never be reached again—touched her pale lips and broke through them, transforming, with divine radiance, her young and blurred and never-to-be-forgotten face. It wavered, or was it the last uncertain flicker of the lamp that made me fancy it? The exquisite moment was barely over when darkness came. Then light indeed forsook me. Almost ignorant of my own intention, I resisted the now trembling figure, indistinguishable in the gloom, but it still clung. I thrust it off me with unnatural vigour.

She fell heavily to the ground. Without a pause of thought I stumbled down the horrible unlighted stairs. A few steps before I reached the bottom my foot struck a splint off the thin edge of one of the rotten treads. I slipped, and heard a door above open and then shut. No other sound. At length I was at the door. It was ajar. I opened it and looked out. Since I passed through it first the place had become quite deserted. The inhabitants were, I suppose, all occupied elsewhere at such an hour on their holiday night. The lamps, if there were any, had not been lit. The outlook was dense blackness. Here too the hideous dark pursued me and silence held its sway. Even the children were screaming in more enticing haunts of gaudy squalor. Some, whose good angels perhaps had not forgotten them, had put themselves to sleep. Not many hours ago their shrieks were deafening. Were these too in conspiracy against me? I remembered vaguely hustling some of them with unmeant harshness in my hurried progress from the Church. Dumb the whole place seemed; and it was, but for the dim stars aloft quite dark. I dared not venture across the threshold, bound by pitiable cowardice to the spot. Alas for the unconscious girl upstairs. A murmur from within the house might have sent me back to her. Certainly it would have sent me, rather than forth into the empty street. The faintest indication of humanity had recalled me. I waited the summons of a sound. It came.

But from the deserted, yet not so shamefully deserted, street. A man staggering home by aid of friendly railings, set up a drunken song. At the first note I rushed towards him, pushing past him in wild departure, and on till I reached the noisome and flaring thoroughfare, a haven where sweet safety smiled. Here I breathed joy, and sped away without memory of the two lifeless beings lying alone in that shrouded chamber of desolation, and with no instinct to return.

My sole impulse was flight; and the way, unmarked in the earlier evening, was unknown. It took me some minutes to find a cab; but the incongruous vehicle, rudely dispersing the haggling traders in the roadway, came at last, and carried me from the distorted crowd of faces and the claims of pity to peace.

I lay back shivering, and the wind crept through the rattling glass in front of me. I did not note the incalculable turnings that took me home.

My account of the night's adventure was abridged and unsensational. I was pressed neither for detail nor comment, but accorded a somewhat humorous welcome which bade me say farewell to dying horror, and even let me mount boldly to the once death-haunted room.

Upon its threshold I stood and looked in, half believing possible the greeting pictured there under the dead girl's influence, and I could not enter. Again I fled, this time to kindly light, and heard my brothers laughing noisily with a friend in the bright hall.

A waltz struck up in the room above as I reached them. I joined the impromptu dance, and whirled the remainder of that evening gladly away.

Physically wearied, I slept. My slumber had no break in it. I woke only to the exquisite joys of morning, and lay watching the early shadows creep into the room. Presently the sun rose. His first smile greeted me from the glass before my bed. I sprang up disdainful of that majestic reflection, and flung the window wide to meet him face to face. His splendour fell too on one who had trusted me, but I forgot it. Not many days later the same sunlight that turned my life to laughter shone on the saddest scene of mortal ending, and, for one I had forsaken, lit the ways of death. I never dreamed it might. For the next morning the tragedy of the past night was a distant one, no longer intolerable.

At twelve o'clock, conscience suggested a search. I acquiesced, but did not move. At half-past, it insisted on one, and I obeyed. I set forth with a determination of success and no clue to promise it. At four o'clock, I admitted the task hopeless and abandoned it. Duty could ask no more of me, I decided, not wholly dissatisfied that failure forbade more difficult demands. As I passed it on my way home, some dramatic instinct impelled me to re-enter the unsightly church.

I must almost have expected to see the same prostrate figure, for my eyes instantly sought the corner it had occupied. The winter twilight showed it empty. A service was about to begin. One little lad in violet skirt and goffered linen was struggling to light the benediction tapers, and a troop of school children pushed past me as I stood facing the altar and blocking their way. A grey-clad sister of mercy was arresting each tiny figure, bidding it pause beside me, and with two firm hands on either shoulder, compelling a ludicrous curtsey, and at the same time whispering the injunction to each hurried little personage,—'always make a reverence to the altar.' 'Ada, come back!' and behold another unwilling bob! Perhaps the good woman saw her Master's face behind the tinsel trappings and flaring lights. But she forgot His words. The saying to these little ones that has rung through centuries commanded liberty and not allegiance. I stood aside till they had shuffled into seats, and finally kneeling stayed till the brief spectacle of the afternoon was over.

Towards its close I looked away from the mumbling priest, whose attention, divided between inconvenient millinery and the holiest mysteries, was distracting mine.

Two girls holding each other's hands came in and stood in deep shadow behind the farthest rows of high-backed chairs by the door. The younger rolled her head from side to side; her shifting eyes and ceaseless imbecile grimaces chilled my blood. The other, who stood praying, turned suddenly (the place but for the flaring altar lights was dark) and kissed the dreadful creature by her side. I shuddered, and yet her face wore no look of loathing nor of pity. The expression was a divine one of habitual love.

She wiped the idiot's lips and stroked the shaking hand in hers, to quiet the sad hysterical caresses she would not check. It was a page of gospel which the old man with his back to it might never read. A sublime and ghastly scene.

Up in the little gallery the grey-habited nuns were singing a long Latin hymn of many verses, with the refrain 'Oh! Sacred Heart!' I buried my face till the last vibrating chord of the accompaniment was struck. The organist ventured a plagal cadence. It evoked no 'amen'. I whispered one, and an accidentally touched note shrieked disapproval. I repeated it. Then I spit upon the bloodless cheek of duty, and renewed my quest. This time it was for the satisfaction of my own tingling soul.

I retook my unknown way. The streets were almost empty and thinly strewn with snow. It was still falling. I shrank from marring the spotless page that seemed outspread to challenge and exhibit the defiling print of man. The quiet of the muffled streets soothed me. The neighbourhood seemed lulled into unwonted rest.

Black little figures lurched out of the white alleys in twos and threes. But their childish utterances sounded less shrill than usual, and sooner died away.

Now in desperate earnest I spared neither myself nor the incredulous and dishevelled people whose aid I sought.

Fate deals honestly with all. She will not compromise though she may delay. Hunger and weariness at length sent me home, with an assortment of embellished negatives ringing in my failing ears.

I had almost forgotten my strange experience, when, some months afterwards, in late spring, the wraith of that winter meeting appeared to me. It was past six o'clock, and I had reached, ignorant of the ill-chosen hour, a notorious thoroughfare in the western part of this glorious and guilty city. The place presented to my unfamiliar eyes a remarkable sight. Brilliantly lit windows, exhibiting dazzling wares, threw into prominence the human mart.

This was thronged. I pressed into the crowd. Its steady and opposite progress neither repelled nor sanctioned my admittance. However, I had determined on a purchase, and was not to be baulked by the unforeseen. I made it, and stood for a moment at the shop-door preparing to break again through the rapidly thickening throng.

Up and down, decked in frigid allurement, paced the insatiate daughters of an everlasting king. What fair messengers, with streaming eyes and impotently craving arms, did they send afar off ere they thus 'increased their perfumes and debased themselves even unto hell'? This was my question. I asked not who forsook them, speaking in farewell the 'hideous English of their fate'.

I watched coldly, yet not inapprehensive of a certain grandeur in the scene. It was Virtue's very splendid Dance of Death.

A sickening confusion of odours assailed my senses; each essence a vile enticement, outraging Nature by a perversion of her own pure spell.

A timidly protesting fragrance stole strangely by. I started at its approach. It summoned a stinging memory. I stepped forward to escape it, but stopped, confronted by the being who had shared, by the flickering lamp-light and in the presence of that silent witness, the poor little violet's prayer.

The man beside her was decorated with a bunch of sister flowers to those which had taken part against him, months ago, in vain. He could have borne no better badge of victory. He was looking at some extravagant trifle in the window next the entry I had just crossed. They spoke, comparing it with a silver case he turned over in his hand. In the centre I noticed a tiny enamelled shield. The detail seemed familiar, but beyond identity. They entered the shop. I stood motionless, challenging memory, till it produced from some dim corner of my brain a hoarded 'No'.

The device now headed a poor strip of paper on a dead girl's bed. I saw a figure set by death, facing starvation, and with ruin in torn fragments in her hand. But what place in the scene had I? A brief discussion next me made swift answer.

They were once more beside me. The man was speaking: his companion raised her face; I recognized its outline,—its true aspect I shall not know. Four months since it wore the mask of sorrow; it was now but one of the pages of man's immortal book. I was conscious of the matchless motions which in the dim church had first attracted me.

She was clothed, save for a large scarf of vehemently brilliant crimson, entirely in dull vermilion. The two shades might serve as symbols of divine and earthly passion. Yet does one ask the martyr's colour, you name it 'Red' (and briefly thus her garment): no distinctive hue. The murderer and the prelate too may wear such robes of office. Both are empowered to bless and ban.

My mood was reckless. I held my hands out, craving mercy. It was my bitter lot to beg. My warring nature became unanimously suppliant, heedless of the debt this soul might owe me—of the throes to which I left it, and of the discreditable marks of mine it bore. Failure to exact regard I did not entertain. I waited, with exhaustless fortitude, the response to my appeal. Whence it came I know not. The man and woman met my gaze with a void incorporate stare. The two faces were merged into one avenging visage—so it seemed. I was excited. As they turned towards the carriage waiting them, I heard a laugh, mounting to a cry. It rang me to an outraged Temple. Sabbath bells peal sweeter calls, as once this might have done.

I knew my part then in the despoiled body, with its soul's tapers long blown out.

Wheels hastened to assail that sound, but it clanged on. Did it proceed from some defeated angel? or the woman's mouth? or mine? God knows!

THE CHINA BOWL

Chapter I Mother and Son

RACHEL PARRIS was an old woman now, close upon eighty years; and David, the son of her maturity, who came, when all the rest had gone, to reawaken the warmth of motherhood in her chilled breast, was going to take unto himself another woman, and become but half her child.

Of all her children, he, the last, had been the comeliest and most dear.

Three had died in infancy, bearing the freshness of their mother's youth into the land of mist, and two were taken by the sea.

One—the only girl who lived to maidenhood—was lost in other waters, wrecked on the darker waves of a dread city, which never washed, as kindlier seas might do, her poor tossed body into the arms of watchers by the shore.

Long they watched for Jenefer—at first, when David was a quiet boy just stepping into manhood, and Rachel still a strong but ageing woman, worn with many vigils, and too much looking on the face of death—sitting together in the white-roofed cottage with its four wide windows looking out to sea, and listening for unreturning feet, and to the heavy moaning of the surf without.

'You'm not the lad to judge her, Davy?' she used to ask, when the presentiment of the girl's return pressed close upon her. And David—never a man of words—would answer briefly, 'Nay.'

A long watching and a long waiting, for Jenefer met judgement at another bar.

For nearly forty years his mother had cleaved to David as rocks cleave to the sea, praying he might not be required of her, painfully apprehensive of the glances cast upon him by brighter, if less deeply jealous, eyes.

And scarcely straying since he left her breast, David had clung to her.

In his earlier manhood, once or twice he had turned aside—almost perforce—to note the welcome playing around younger lips for him; but his heart, then only touched, returned to chase her terrors, and win again to tenderness that pitiably anxious gaze.

'Davy'll be lookin' for a maid', the women at their doors would call to her when he was but a boy.

'Tes time', she would reply serenely—a younger woman then—and go back into the cottage, there to smooth out his rough shirts with a steady hand, and making believe she bent to it, would murmur:

'Tes the Lord's plan that every woman's son'll come to be another woman's care.'

Such nights she never tasted sleep, but lay stiffly quiet upon her bed, pressing her palms together—half in agony and half in prayer.

Rising early, with the heavy stifling hours still hanging round her in the keen morning air, she would adventure bravely:

'Tes a clibby mornin', but you'm lookin' brave and handsome, Davy; the maids'll soon be chasin' 'ee.'

To which he would reply slowly, and with a comprehending smile: 'May so well go home, mother; I'm not for they.'

'Reckon they'll have 'ee though; tes the maids' way.'

'Gie en leave to try,' was his conclusive consolation; and then, noting the still stern closure of her lips, would smile again with jesting reassurance. 'You'm not lookin' for another man?'

'Nay, I can make a shift to do wi' 'ee.'

'You may.'

And so, for a time, the darkness lifted, and the shadow of separation glided by.

The years went on, and David weathered several storms of unengulphing love.

He was a tall, fair, placid fisherman, gentle and generous of nature, rarely stirred to spontaneous speech or speculative thought.

The friend and playfellow of children, for whom he had a clumsy tenderness, himself a child, as they with subtle intuition knew.

The vigour and the freshness of the sea were his. His eyes reflected its most luminous and peaceful blue; their steady—almost dreamy—gaze seemed fixed upon some certain tide, the ceaseless ebb and flow of things mysterious yet sure—a look which well befitted one of Nature's children whose lot it was to hear her greatest voice, and watch the grandest motion of her breast. His massive limbs washed—like the rocks—by many-tempered waves, seemed, like them, hewn in some fashion by the mighty waters to welcome and rebut their force.

For generations the Parrises had been fishermen, living within the shelter of the vast cliffs that overhung the haven, upon the base of which the huge Atlantic waves beat with a wild futility, rearing from their white crests, when the wind rose, drab clots of whirling foam. For fisher-people they were well-to-do; the old woman 'a little nearie', it was whispered in Tregarveth, where to be 'nearie' with a little was but natural, and with more but seemly, yet noticeable all the same.

A bad season sifted David from his fellows as one on whom bad seasons but lightly fell. There was enough and to spare for that unencumbered householder and his ageing mother, and still to spare. Something, too, always to spare from David's pockets or David's board for the broad-faced, solemn-eyed children who hung about his door.

Rachel suffered them in silence, hiding within her heart the bitterness they nurtured—a haunting fear lest he might learn, even thus late, from their companionship, to hunger for playmates of his own.

'Reckon you'm weary o' the children', he had said more than once, spelling out roughly from her face the pages of her soul.

'Maybe', she would admit sometimes. 'They'm teasy for an old woman that's a' done with children, but if you've tuk a consait for en I wud'n chase en away.'

'Tes pretty work to watch en', he said simply. 'Tho' simmee tes may-games to 'ee.'

'It lights they eyes o' your'n, so let em bide; but mine be dim.'

Yet there were times when kindlier, more natural emotions stirred her breast—times when she brought herself to picture children with his voice and smile waking old echoes in the childless house. Till, like a sudden cloud, the vague form of the woman who must bear them came athwart it, blurring the vision—clogging, as of old, the fresh springs of her heart.

The image of hands that would be 'fain to do for Davy', of a face that must thrust itself between her own and his—setting her definitely in the background of his life—was one she could not school herself to view.

The last of all her children, and the best—so ran the old refrain—surely the Lord would spare him for the few years left to her.

If Jenefer had wandered home, or one of the lads so swiftly taken been delivered from the grudging deep, the jealous prayer might never have ascended up to God. At first a fitful hope, it grew to be the burden of her thought, hushing itself at length into the murmur of a dying fear.

Suddenly, sharply, it sprang forth again to the old tune of terror—now not vague, but piteous in its weakness, as only the cry of age can be. It died away. In the long roll of barren prayers it took its place, and found its record in the register of death.

David—the time had come at last—was going to take unto himself another woman, and while he waited, troubled, despondent, for his marriage-bells, lest they might never ring, his mother heard them clanging high above all voices, clashing discordant music above the ceaseless sighing of the sea.

For him there had been no choice from the beginning. The first glint from Susannah's daring, half-savage eyes had vanquished him. She came upon him like a storm. Stunned for the moment he retreated, but the moment passed, and he was at her feet.

As yet the word had not been spoken, but he knew, and Susannah knew, and Rachel knew, that it must be.

Mother and son sat facing each other in the low-raftered room, where prints of stiff, unlifelike ships, breasting unnatural billows, were dotted about the walls. Jenefer's childish sampler, framed, hung by the fire. The careful, brilliant stitches, fitfully lit, set forth between the little stunted trees and comic birds—'JENEFER PARRIS—aged 13'. An assortment of figures up to ten, and then a row of solemn flowers headed the closing legend, chosen by whom? Not surely by the child? One cannot say. 'All things that are of the earth shall turn to the earth again, and that which is of the waters doth return unto the sea. But Thy Providence, O Father, governeth it, for Thou hast made a way in the sea, and a safe path in the waves.' Two Noah's ark figures flanked it on either side, and the date—March 16th, 1844, in gold, the only faded colour—was traced below. On a shelf beside it rested the huge Bible, wherein the names of Rachel's dead husband and the children who had followed him were written in her laboured hand. And last came David's name, added in darker ink, such as had chronicled his father's end in the same month and year. Upon the unwieldy book rested the china bowl, brought from the East in their first year of mariage, and used to christen their first child.

This side the hearth was her accustomed seat, and she sat upright in the broad arm-chair—a frail, stiff figure, the bands of thin grey hair strained tightly across her lined but curiously clear brow. Pale, searching eyes peered from its shadow, set in deep hollows, still hoarding sparks of their first fire.

David sat opposite, his great frame stooping forward, his hands travelling slowly up and down each knee. The firelight cast his unrestful shadow upon the floor, the window, showing still a square of vanishing twilight, framed the vague outline of his bent head and shoulders in the darkening room.

Rachel, between the flashing needles in her fingers, saw the dark silhouette, and caught the moving shadow his restless motions cast upon the floor. She waited for him to break the heavy silence, although aware that he would sit on thus indefinitely, seeking vainly the words which would not overtake his slowly-travelling thought.

But wearied out at length she spoke: 'Be any boats gone out tonight?'

' 'Bout half a score.'

'You'm lazy, lad.'

'I be long to be. I bain't thinkin' o' fish tonight.'

'The woman, I suppose?'

'Sure 'nuff.' He stirred uneasily and shifted back the chair.

'Maids be so slippery as fish—so they do say—and yet the men be slocked by en.'

'Clain off,' he admitted, staring intently at the fire.

'When be going to ask Susannah?'

'May so well tonight.'

'Thee'rt finely hurried; have 'ee tuk time to look roun' the maid thee'rt so mazed to wed?'

'Her'll take some lookin' roun',' he said, 'but that'll bide. Tes like this heer,' he went on ponderously; 'a man may look at en a score o' times and they be norry times the same. Now tes ice and nex' tes fire, and then tes up and off like a gale to sea. I mind the time when et dedn't sim fitty work to chatty to things like they. A tried to get me, but I wud'n'—he paused—'Susannah Basset have a' got me, and that es all about et now.'

'Dost think 'ee have got she?' his mother questioned.

'I be main loth to doubt et.'

'Should 'ee be scat ef her said "No"?'

' 'Most like a boat wi' a split keel, tossin' out yonder i' the dark; t'would be th' end o' daylight, simmin' to me.'

Rachel let fall the needles and pressed her palms together upon her knee. She watched his face with pitiful intentness, now lit by the flame in sudden flashes, now ploughed into deeper furrows by the flickering glare. It was—as she beheld it—changed, clouded, yet glowing with an inward light; terribly strange, yet terribly familiar; near, but very far away. His latest words, the end of daylight, found their echo in her troubled soul.

'Tes bad work when et do come to that', she said, beginning to rescue the dropped stitches.

'Tes bad work, sure, when a man be past en's prime and the maid i' flower and a pair o' prinked up lads clamourin' to en, "Will 'ee ha' me?" and me wi' all my mouth-speech gone.'

'Thee never had too much to lose.'

'I never wanted et afore.'

'You'm terribly set 'pon Susannah.'

'A man 'most es terrible set 'pon hes life when he es nigh to lose et.'

'You'm roadling, man; her'll have 'ee at first say.'

'Dost think et?'

Rachel answered him with the grim certainty of despair: 'I be sure. What o'clock es et?'

He turned to the brass dial by the door; her failing eyes were hardly keen enough to read it.

'Half arter seven.'

'Eden't et no mor'n that?' she questioned wearily. The hour had gone slowly. Then with a tremulous, impatient gesture, 'Rig thysel' out,' she said, 'and master thicky business afore croust. Thee'lt be so good as wed by then. I promise 'ee. Look slippy, bring en home ef thee'st a mind, and don't 'ee sit glazing theer like a mazed boy.'

The speech escaped her dry lips quickly, it rang curiously hard and clear, but David did not notice the new accent. There was no room for it in his absorbed and troubled thought. Two presentations were beyond his range of vision. To see things clearly he must see them singly, and for the present Susannah blotted out the woman at his side. For Rachel had risen and stood behind him, to shut the working of her face from view. She rested a shrunken hand upon his shoulder, but withdrew it quickly, remembering what its unsteadiness might betray.

'Begone and wish 'ee well', she ended.

He got up, following almost mechanically the childish habit of obedience, and strode towards the door.

'You'm never goin' i' thicky coat', she called out after him. He stopped on the threshold, filling the narrow doorway and blocking out the slit of sky.

'Iss, as I be.'

'The maids 'll sneat and chitter to be'old 'ee courtin' sich a fashion. Do 'ee come back and trim thysel' a bit.'

The hardly conscious ruse to keep him there, to hold her own for a few minutes longer, failed.

'Let a' be, mother,' he cried almost harshly. 'Ef I be goin' I must go.'

It sounded the first note of conflict, and she shrank from it, as from a looming blow, back into the empty room. Its loneliness appalled her; that space soon to be filled with the dreaded presence, that silence soon to be broken by the more dreaded voice, smote her with boding like a knife drawing its gnawing edge across her soul.

She looked towards the window. There the night had not quite left the fading pane. It loitered with the embers of the fire. Between was darkness. She made a movement to kindle the accustomed light and then remembering, stopped—

For whom?

To lighten—what?

She dropped the match, and before it had flickered out, with no definite purpose, stumbled to the door.

'Davy', she called. He did not hear. He had gone but a few steps down the steep unwinding road; his figure cut the faint line of sea below it, and stood out darkly against the patch of sky. 'Davy', she cried again.

And a little shrill voice out of the twilight street took up the cry.

He did not hear.

His pace quickened; faster and faster he seemed to swing down the straight road between the dim white houses, growing a dwindling speck, and then a blurr, like some receding memory to the watcher at her door.

Chapter II The Other Woman

SUSANNAH stood by the window where the sunlight, a strong glare outside, managed to struggle in. It touched to softer gold the heavy masses of red hair which seemed almost to overweight her startling face; her white skin, with the faint flush upon it, clothed too tenderly the powerful features, glimmering palely round the widely open eyes, dark with dull fire. Her full, decisive lips were closed; they cut across the white superbly, with a line of crimson deeper than that which splashes most fair faces, giving to this one such a vividness as few fair faces wear. She stood where the light centred, drawn to her great height, a figure of striking symmetry and vigour, seeming to absorb all the vitality and colour, and to dwarf the small dimensions of the room. A singular contrast to the man who had chosen her, at first stormed by her beauty and then bewildered by her love; a love primitive, startling and half savage like herself, which fascinated while it puzzled him and sometimes hurt him while it clung.

At arm's length she held a picture, in a highly ornamented gilt frame, on which she looked with evident approval, shifting its position now and then for a more favourable view.

An upright mirror on the mantelpiece, with its oval medallion of the inevitable full-rigged ship, set in the centre of a speckled silver frieze, threw back her image; so that the chamber held, at the moment, three presentments of the woman whose forcible presence filled it. The picture in her hand was a fantastic rendering of the flesh—a rough but subtle analysis of the soul; the image in the glass—a blameless likeness—robbed the living figure of some brilliancy and gave the grand lines hints of a softness they did not possess.

And Susannah herself, the actual creature, the breathing, brilliant thing of life, who might never behold the beauty she so prized except through some imperfect, material or human medium—stood dividing glances between glass and canvas with a contented smile.

A shadow crossed the doorway and David lumbered in. He looked older, more careworn, but his eyes enshrined a happier light.

'What do 'ee think of et?' she asked, handing him the object of her lengthy contemplation.

'Tes what they do call "a study"; Miss Maxwell done it for a pictur' her calls "Judith", tho' her do say there never were yet a Judith painted wi' thicky sken an' hair.'

'Tes 'ee an' tesn't 'ee', he said, taking it from her to regard it carefully. 'The face es your'n, but the look behind it be mighty strange. I s'pose 'twouldn't be properly a pictur' ef 'twas too similar to life.'

'Simmin' to me, *tes* similar to life,' she said, 'an' I be goin' to fix et heer.'

She crossed the room and took down hastily the sampler from its nail, disclosing a lighter patch of paper on the wall where it had hung so long. She saw a look of dissatisfaction cross David's face.

'Gie et to me', she proceeded with a determination born of doubt.

'May so well find another place', observed her husband mildly.

'I'm thinkin' to put et heer', she answered. 'Tes the place I've settled for et. Miss Maxwell did say as 'twere the only light to show en 'oop, and heer I main for et to go.'

'I'm not wishful to cross 'ee, Susannah,' he continued, 'but thicky piece o' work's been theer a matter o' nigh 'pon fifty year, an' us'd miss et ef 'twas shifted; et must bide.' He spoke with unwonted readiness and new authority, and his wife met the unusual accent with surprise and obvious resentment and quick response.

'Tes a pretty thing to be so set on', she broke out, her eyes flashing, her breast beginning to heave with ominous unrest. 'Shu'd ha' thought 'ee wanted nothin' to mind 'ee of her that done et. Tell 'ee straight, I never cu'd 'bide et 'bout the place. Be so set 'pon callin' everyone to mind thy sister an' en' shame?'

'Was but a child when t'were adone,' he answered gently, 'an' ef God do please, her's but a child agen. So us do think of en.'

'Thee was brought up a good Methody, Davy', she reminded him with a touch of scorn. 'Ded a teach 'ee to make so light o' sin?'

'A teached me to make somethin' o' forgiveness', he replied still gently.

'Mayst leave that to th' Almighty', she said rebelliously.

'Not ef th' Almighty have a left et to me.'

She was not occupied with the theological consideration, but with the more practical dispute in hand.

'Gie et to me', she demanded, reaching forward for the precious portrait.

'You'm not to hang et theer.'

David confronted her, real protest in his attitude, real displeasure in his eye.

'An' why?'

'Because mother'll look to see et where t' have always been.'

She turned upon him suddenly, her eyes ablaze, her face aflame to the white brow. Taller than he by less than an inch, she yet seemed to tower above him, challenging him with her great beauty, with her tried supremacy, and fine defiance to an unequal fight.

'Be this my house or her'n?'

It was not the first time the question had presented itself; but it was the first time she had given it utterance, and David winced before it; sooner or later he had vaguely felt that it must come.

He passed a hand clumsily across his eyes, as if to shut out the distracting vision, and prepare himself for an unbiassed answer.

'Et be mine', he said at last, firmly, but flinching before her stormlit gaze. 'An' I be master in et.'

'Who be mistress?' she pursued, raising her voice to a high pitch of penetration as she became aware of a halting step upon the stair.

He put out a hand to check her; but it was too late. The door swung back and Rachel entered.

The situation was immediately clear to her. The empty space upon the wall, Susannah's angry voice and David's gesture of expostulation plainly told the tale. She made as if to speak, but finally kept silence, and going towards the chair where Susannah had placed the sampler, took it in her hand. As she did so, she looked neither at David nor Susannah, but fixed her aged eyes upon the childish stitches, and moved towards the door.

'Mother', her son began, but an imperative glance from Susannah stopped him.

'You can bring et back', she interposed. If a concession must be made, it should be she, not he, that made it.

'I wu'd sooner take it away', Rachel replied in tones slightly tremulous, but determinate. And closing the door behind her she carried it, without further comment, to the room above. She had but a room now in David's house and but a room, though that a warm one, in David's heart.

Susannah turned to her husband with a glance prepared for final conquest, but he did not meet the wonderful eyes.

He was not to be won, she saw, by argument or anger. There remains to women always another way. She took it, putting a touch upon his arm.

'Why ded 'ee wed me, David, ef 'ee meant to make me only half a wife? There was lads, an' many, that would ha' had me, an' turned their kin to doors for me.'

'I do knaw et', he said, probed by the touch—the softened accents, and looking reluctantly into the dangerous face, more fateful in its tenderness than in its wrath.

The close, warm presence, the tightening fingers, the breath upon his cheek, the lips so near his own, were weakening him. He felt resistance ebbing and drew back; but she accepted no repulse, feeling her power.

'Will 'ee gie me the place that's mine?' she pleaded, 'or will ee set another woman in et?'

'I never done that', he said distressedly, wandering in a maze of tangled thought.

'Think o' this hour agone,' she urged; 'an which ded 'ee put first?'

He was too slow of mind, too poor of words, to parry this treacherous thrust. He vaguely felt the sophistry of the question, but was powerless to expose it.

'What do 'ee want? To fix the picture?' he asked bewilderedly, groping, seeing no further.

'Ef I've a mind to, an' to do whatever else I ha' a mind to in the home you've brought me to.'

It was a lover's plea and uttered in a lover's fashion, urged ultimately with a kiss.

'Do what 'ee please,' he said at length; 'but don't 'ee please, ef thee can help it, to hurt mother as thee've hurted en today.' He detached himself from the clinging arms and ventured smiling, 'Tes late for we to be sweetheartin' thicky way, mor'n four months wed.'

She drew him back again.

'Ef I can put oop wi' et——' She paused and smiled, and smiling, thrust him off, and pushed him toward the inner door.

'Go an' cleanse thysel'; tes brave an' late, I be going to set the cloam.'

The clatter of the crockery was audible in the room above, where Rachel sat, her hands crossed idly upon her knee. The preparation of David's meals, the knitting of David's socks, were lawful duties which his bride had been swift enough to claim. And Rachel saw her old place—certainly in his daily life, possibly in the recesses of his heart—filled by another woman. She had yielded up each little office in unprotesting silence, and with wan smiles which cost her dear. She sat now often in the little bed chamber, which had become a refuge, with no companionship but languid memory, no occupation but present pain. The hum of voices reached her there—Susannah's always dominant and sometimes shrill. It inspired her, like Susannah's presence, with a kind of fear. A woman of gentler spirit, of softer aspect, might have won her love, but love, save in the common guise of passion, was alien to Susannah's heart. Farther and farther out of sight, to Rachel sank the buried years; only the tired weight of present hours hung round her in a gathering twilight of dying vision and dying sound.

'Mother', called David's voice from the room below, and as he spoke, Susannah's broke in with some loud question.

Rachel went down, feeling her way by the rail and wall of the steep short stair.

The meal passed quietly, and when it was over David went out to fetch the big fishing boots and the reels, which hung outside the door. Susannah followed him and they stood talking till he started for the bay.

When he was gone, she stepped back into the room, a smile lurking about the corners of her mouth.

'To look at Davy,' she said, beginning to clear the table noisily, 'you'd think he was different fro' other men. But at the root they be all the same.'

'I always thought en different,' his mother said from her seat beside the fire, where now, in place of the little square of canvas, the new portrait of Susannah stared down at her, a face of unlifelike flesh with strange relentless eyes; adding, 'why did 'ee choose en when 'ee might have had a younger lad, ef all do seem the same to 'ee?'

'I s'pose in a score o' pilchers some be bigger and better than the rest.'

'Sure 'nuff he es a better man, he were a better lad. None o' the other lads was like en.'

The memory of him as a child was sweet; she liked to linger over it, and would have lingered now, but Susannah cut her short.

'He might so well be a saint in a painted windey to hear 'ee talk,' she interrupted sharply; 'but he be jest a man, an' men at th' root, as I telled 'ee afore, be much 'bout the same.'

Rachel said nothing more; the last word must, of necessity, be Susannah's, and she had got into a habit now of dreading that last word. Things were not going well between the two; Rachel was conscious of the younger woman's enmity, and Susannah resented Rachel's presence, which seemed to wrest a rightful supremacy from her in her new kingdom. And more even than her actual presence, she resented the subtler presence of Rachel's passion for her son; that grand, immutable love of motherhood, which has no transitions and no transparencies; whose first aspect is as its last; which begins with birth and does not end with death. Vaguely she felt its greater depth, its wider range; she knew no pity for it, made no way. It robbed her of complete possession of David's life. Strong in the vigour of her youth, the power of her beauty, she meant to vanquish her strange enemy, that frail old woman, with almost visibly shrinking cheeks and empty hands, stooping over the fire. The purpose was truly but half defined, not wholly conscious; yet instinctively she worked towards it.

Love may sometimes be 'strong as death', but surely jealousy is ever 'cruel as the grave.'

Chapter III The China Bowl

'FROM the first moment I entered the room—and what a charming room it is!' remarked Miss Maxwell in a high, rather drawling, distinguished voice, accustomed to make itself individually heard above the general conversation in crowded drawing-rooms, sounding somewhat out of place in the simple chamber—'I said to myself, "I positively *must* have that delicious bowl." I shall be really broken-hearted if I have to go away without it. I shall, indeed!'

She was a slim, studiously-dressed personage of about thirty, looking five or six years younger. She flung off the superfluous years with a peremptory hardihood, as she would have flung off any appendage that did not suit her complexion, or fit her scheme of work, or choice of pleasure; a person used to excite attention, and compel admiration, and to achieve, moreover, any aim which she had in view.

'Of course,' she proceeded, 'you were just going to say it's a family treasure, or something dreadful of that kind, and that you can't possibly part with it, and I shall be wretched. Oh!' she broke off, apparently just perceiving the portrait by the mantelpiece, 'so you've hung it there; that's the very place for it; how nice of you to put my poor little sketch in the place of honour! Did I suggest it? Oh! then it was because I thought you *ought* to have the place of honour. Really it looks very well. You know I'm coming down in the autumn with the picture, on purpose for you to sit; it's going to be a regular success, you know; everyone asks me who "Judith" is. But I keep it a secret, or Tregarveth would be besieged by people in knickerbockers bringing down canvases to take you away on, and then what would your husband say?'

She had adroitly turned the subject, to give Susannah time for reflection, but she intended, if flattery, persuasion, or money could win it, to carry off the coveted bowl. It was, in fact, mainly for that purpose that she had come. Susannah *was* reflecting; she knew the disposal of it presented difficulties, but she did not wish to offend Miss Maxwell, and even a short acquaintance had taught her that to cross that lady in a pet project meant offence. She did not care for the thing itself; it had always seemed cumbrous and useless; she had more than once meditated its removal, and now apparently it was convertible into gold.

Susannah was a person of two passions; one was power and the other wealth; she saw a close analogy between the two. If she sold the piece of china, David would probably be angry, and Rachel certainly dismayed, but David—had not experience proved it?—was easily enough appeased. She stole a glance at her reflection in the old upright mirror as a warrior may feel the edge of a trusted weapon, and felt secure.

Rachel—deep, dark, dark in its shadows is the human heart—Rachel might finally rebel. It was not a design, it was only a sudden unbidden thought, springing from a subconscious purpose. Rachel might lose her self-control; that would mean open warfare, and open warfare, for the weaker, means defeat. Subjection, flight—the possibilities flitted through her mind in rapid sequence; cruel they were, truly, and for a second she recoiled from self, but only the next moment to embrace it. After all, the deed was lawful, pardonable, not a crime.

'How much wu'd 'ee say 'twas worth?' she asked, totally ignorant of its value.

'I would gladly give two pounds for it', the lady said evasively. 'I daresay it's not really valuable, only I've taken such a fancy to it, you know, and it does, doesn't it rather, just a little bit lumber up the shelf?'

'I wud'n an' David wud'n, I be sure, part wi' it under five.'

She named this large sum at a venture.

'That's a good deal', said the maker of many artistic bargains, suavely, with a glance at Susannah's countenance, now somewhat disturbed. It gave, however, no promise of abatement. 'Very well', she agreed, drawing out a bulky, monogrammed purse, and laying the gold pieces upon the table. 'My man is outside with the pony-cart. I suppose, if you didn't mind, of course, he could take it now.'

Susannah lifted it from the big Bible without comment, and laid it beside the money, dubiously satisfied. The sum was paid too readily; she might have asked for more, having herself undoubtedly some price to pay.

She looked up to encounter the figure of Rachel, her spare shoulders covered with an old shawl, her grey hair partially hidden under an antiquated bonnet, standing at the door.

'What be doin' wi' that bowl?' she demanded, addressing Susannah and ignoring the intruder, who had risen and was preparing to welcome the newcomer with one of those special smiles of hers, reserved exclusively for the interesting poor. Confident of her capacity to carry elegantly through any delicate business, and not altogether disliking the exercise of what she considered a unique accomplishment, she quickly divined the position, and before Susannah could speak she replied: 'Susannah has parted with it to me; I admired it so much, perhaps I was a little importunate; but I hope'—with one of her most successful gestures—'you are not displeased.'

'What's the meanin' o't?' pursued Rachel, still ignoring the speaker and addressing Susannah.

'You ded hear,' said Susannah sullenly, 'I've parted wi' it, an' that's true.'

The two women faced each other; the younger obdurate, prepared to make no concession, give no recall; Rachel amazed—a sense of terrible helplessness stealing over her, which she dismissed with a strong effort, trying to straighten her bent frame. Slowly and distinctly she began: 'It wadn't your'n to part wi'—put et back.'

Susannah laughed. The mirthless sound, low though it was, filled the small chamber like some soulless creature's cry.

Rachel gave one long frightened look at the lips from which it came; then she turned trembling from it to the composed spectator of the scene.

'The bowl be mine,' she said; 'an' my dead husband brought et back to me fro' hes first voyage the year that us was wed. 'Twere used to christen my first child, et have a' stood theer 'pon the Book 'bout sixty year an' more; I wu'd so soon part wi' my right hand. What have 'ee got to say?'

'Tes I, not she, as have a' got the sayin',' broke in Susannah roughly, 'an' I say I've sold et, an' the price of et lies theer.'

'Wadn't et enough,' Rachel burst forth, loosing for the first time her long-pent anguish—'wadn't et enough for 'ee to steal my son but you must make away wi' a bit o' a keepsake, like this heer, that were mine afore ever 'ee was born!'

'This is very distressing', said the lady, beginning to stammer over her diplomatic part. 'I'm afraid'—glancing uneasily at the sovereigns on the table—'a bargain is a bargain; and if it takes two to make one, it must take two to break it. But if Susannah releases me——'

'I don't', she answered doggedly; and then to Rachel, 'I have David's word for't', she said, twisting her mind to think this was the truth. 'He gie'd me leave to do whatever I'd a mind to in the home that's hes an' mine. Call yon man,' she said, pointing imperiously to the door, 'and tell en to take et out.'

'If that is so', began the unfortunate purchaser, and then obeying another peremptory gesture from Susannah, 'Withers', she called going toward the door. The man jumped down. 'You can take that to the carriage; I shall walk to the post-office; the pony can wait there.'

He took the great piece of china in his arms and stolidly bore it away.

'Forgive me', she ventured, turning to Rachel, and again broke off. She might have been speaking to a battered image—a pidce of speechless clay.

'Tesn't over pleasant for 'ee heer', Susannah remarked, and without holding out her hand, 'Wish 'ee good-day.'

And Helena Maxwell, the accomplished disciple of Delsarte, the famous organizer of artistic poses, hurried to obey, pushing with almost vulgar haste upon the threshold against the man about to enter.

He drew back to let her pass. It was, and on looking back she marked it as, the first ungraceful exit in her career.

Chapter IV The Sequel

DAVID had seen the familiar piece of china resting on the seat of the pony-trap, for which he had stood aside to make way, as it clattered down the narrow street. He had not understood its presence there. He could not reach conclusions quickly, but as he walked up home a sinister presentiment crossed his puzzled brain.

When he entered the room, his mother's whitening cheeks and the defiant bearing of Susannah, as she met his questioning gaze, slowly enlightened him. His glance fell on the money spread out upon the table, and his brow darkened.

'What's the meanin' o't?' he asked, repeating his mother's question; and again Susannah laughed, but this time the harsh notes were weighted with an element of fear.

The sound, for a second, chilled him and then suddenly seemed to set his blood on fire.

'Take that damned money', he said in heavy, laboured tones, 'to her that it belongs to, and fetch back to mother the thing that's her'n.'

His head began to swim, he felt overwhelmed by the passion rapidly surging up within him, foreign to his placid nature, threatening to govern in the place of thought.

Susannah did not move.

'Take et, I say,' he repeated, his voice rising, his blue eyes burning ominously.

She did not move.

He advanced a step towards her.

Rachel's eyes were fixed upon his set lips and clouding face. She came forward and put a shaking hand upon his arm. He removed it gently and Susannah noticed the tenderness of that repulse.

'Let your mother take et', she said savagely; 'tes her work to make trouble i' this house, and set 'ee agen me. Let her take et or let et bide, *I* say.'

'Do's I bid 'ee', he broke forth, losing possession of himself and raising a threatening arm.

Once again she laughed, flinging from lips and eyes derision and defiance into his now distorted face.

He stepped forward, and dashed the coins from the table; they fell jingling and scattering along the floor. He faced Susannah.

'Will 'ee do's I bid 'ee?' he cried once more.

'No!' she said, with blazing cheeks.

Rachel had almost flung herself between them, uttering a moaning, repressive cry. She was too late. Before she reached them, he had struck out blindly and dealt Susannah a heavy stunning blow.

It was the first and the last violence of his gentle life.

She staggered back and steadied herself against the wall. He watched her as through a mist, heard her first words as in a horrible, disordered dream. He turned to go.

'Stay theer', she said; 'you'd best take notis' of 'em, for they'm the las' words I've agot to spaik to 'ee. You've choosed the wrong woman, David Parris, to sarve as 'ee've a'sarved me this same minnit. Hark'e,' she went on, lifting her voice above its first vibrating whisper, 'never will I mend, or clain, or do for 'ee agen. Never will I hold spaich with 'ee, or take that hand o' your'n, or lie beside 'ee, so long as us do live. An' never mark'ee, David Parris, never shall the child that's to be born, so long as I can kape'n from et, hear hes father's name. I cast 'ee off. You'm patient, but I'll outlast 'ee. God judge atween us, David Parris, I've adone with 'ee.'

She ended in a shrill crescendo, which mingled with the contentious trebles of childish voices outside the door.

The three actors in this short drama stood apart. Rachel, her shawl dropped off, her bonnet fallen back, was leaning against the mantelpiece, one hand shaking as if with palsy, resting upon it, a shrunken form of fear, a face of ashes, beneath the thin dishevelled hair. Susannah stood erect, magnificent, breathless, her features overspread with sudden pallor, with eyes like those of some unconquered animal, and lips like those of a vengeful god.

David remained by the doorway, from which Susannah's first words had recalled him, motionless, with bowed head, before the two women whose love had wrought his woe. He heard, as if from a great distance, the chorus of piping voices outside the door.

'So be et, Susannah', he said brokenly, at last. 'So let et be.'

Chapter V Banned

IN a little square-built hut, pitched upon a ledge of rock which overhung the bay, with grey railed steps leading upward to the high roadway, flanked on one side by the sea, and on the other by the desolate tract of downs stretching away beyond the haven, Rachel had taken refuge. The two small windows looked down directly on the sea, let in its ceaseless sighing and intermittent roar. At night, far out across the pitiless black water, the red spark shone and disappeared and shone again, reminding her of those who, but for man's warning and God's mercy, must 'return unto the sea'.

Here, for a time, she dwelt alone—doubly alone in the strange room with its poor and unfamiliar furniture; until one day, driven from his home by silent and persistent enmity, David joined her, to find there, in a bitterer sense, his refuge too.

Susannah had kept her vow.

He had been patient and she had outlasted him. The food choked him which he had had to take from his own table like a thief; his very clothes, unwashed, untended, irked him. The vengeful silence made him hunger for a word, even of fierce upbraiding; the desolation of her dead presence filled him with a dull longing for some companionship resembling life.

Through it all—knowing the while how vainly—he had striven to hide his shame. He would not go to any other woman, even to his mother, for assistance in the common necessities of life. The maintenance of the two households was bringing his resources low. He had aged in a few months; the change was visible in his altered face and bearing; sorrow left untouched only his fair, boyishly-curling hair.

When they met, Rachel noted these signs but did not speak of them; his trouble was never spoken of between them. There was something awful about this reticence, but it was characteristic of the two.

At last, worn out by silence and neglect and his own impotence, he fled to her. So again they sat together, but not as in other days; an invisible presence parted them. David was haunted by an indefinite sense of remorse, which lent to his manner an added gentleness; but she had grown to regard him—and he was dimly conscious of it—with a kind of diffidence akin to fear.

The shadow of separation had fallen between them long ago, and now it would not pass away.

One evening they were together in the tiny living-room, where a bed had been put up for David; Rachel was seated upon it. He was standing at the door. Above the murmur of lapping water rose the shouts and screams of the children, playing among the boats upon the beach below.

'Thee was never a riotous lad,' she began, peering back through the years at the little ones who were gone, 'not like the others; a passel o' times they was very plaguen'. Father liked to hear en racket; he ded say that "rackettin' lads 'ud make the bravest men". But I mind thee, Davy, when 'ee was a lad, brave and quiet an' different fro' the rest.'

' 'Twould be fine and peaceful,' he said, looking round at her with a smile that could not veil its wistfulness, 'to be a lad agen.'

It was the first allusion to his trouble, and she was afraid to notice it.

'They'm properly noisy,' she said timidly, after a while, getting up and looking down upon the little scurrying specks upon the shingle. 'Have 'ee forgot the children, Davy? You used to look for'n; they was always blinchin' round the door.'

'I've a lost my way wi' en', he said wearily. 'Simmee altogether I've lost my way.'

Yet it was upon childhood that his thoughts were set; upon his own child, just about to be born.

For Susannah was near her time.

Only that morning he had passed his home and seen the strange woman at the door.

He turned from looking down upon the bay, where the men were standing in scattered groups around the boats in the deepening twilight. Beyond them were the crowded lights, the huddled houses of the little town. He came and stood by Rachel at the window, and for a moment they watched together the faint red star rise fitfully across the dim white breakers of the shadowed sea.

' 'Tes likely 'twill be born tonight', he said, slowly and painfully. 'Would 'ee be so good as to go up land an' ask Susannah ef so be as she's wantin' to see her man?'

She met his anxious glance with one of scared entreaty. Her long life had been one of many apprehensions, and now in these latter days they crowded in upon her still.

'I dare not go mysel',' he said, 'or I wud'n ask 'ee. Will 'ee go, mother? Thee was always brave and good to me.'

For answer, she laid her thin wrinkled hand upon his great brown fingers and passed it caressingly up and down, saying at length: 'An' thee've a been always brave and good to me, Davy.'

'I doubt et,' he said sadly; 'no, I doubt et, mother.'

But she shook her head with a new and happier smile.

'I'll go,' she said, at last, 'but reckon 'twould be better if thee'd go thysel'.'

'I cudn' ', he answered. 'Do 'ee go, mother, do 'ee go.'

She lit the lamp and set the table, going feebly about the simple tasks, and then put on the old bonnet and well-worn shawl. He watched her toil slowly up the steps and a little way along the high sloping road, till a tooth of jutting rock suddenly shut her figure from his view. Then he came back into the room and sat by the spread-out table, his arms resting upon it, his head fallen across them—waiting. Once he looked up for the brass dial of the clock, to find it was not there.

'I miss the tick', he muttered to himself, reminded of its absence. 'I miss the tick; 'twas company.' And thus recalled to the visible common things of life, he could shut them out no more.

He got up, but there was no space for restlessness in the small encumbered chamber, and he sat down again to watch with dull, unreal interest the insignificant objects facing him—his own coat and yellow sou'wester hanging by the door; his mother's apron flung across the opposite chair; the little row of books set along a shelf hard by. He began to spell out the titles, which seemed unfamiliar, though he had known them all his days. *The Wesleyan Pulpit, The Christian Gentlewoman's Magazine, John Salt's Temptation,* bound in bright blue, profusely gilt—his one prize, of which his mother had been so proud. He wanted to move about; the idea occurred to him to go and meet her, but he shunned the sympathy, the possible comments, of those whom he might also meet. His suspense was not poignant; there was nothing poignant in his nature, but it was none the less almost unbearable.

He suffered in a blind fashion, groping through the mystery of pain.

He felt in a way that he was suffering justly; it was nothing to him that other men repeatedly committed the same fault and slept at ease; he was, as his mother had told him, different from the rest.

At last he heard the expected footsteps, and Rachel entered. She unfastened her things deliberately, and he waited patiently for her to speak.

'Eat thy supper, lad', she began, looking at the untasted food, and trying to evade his look of dumb anxiety.

'I cudn' touch a scred of et', he said simply. 'What ded a say?'

'Must I tell 'ee?' she pleaded pitifully. 'Tes fine and whist to hear.'

He nodded, and left the table, taking a seat beside the fire.

'I did ask what 'ee telled me, Davy, an' "What be talkin' 'bout?" she says, wi' a face so white as death, an' then were quiet so's ef her were slaipen. "Davy sent me to ask 'ee ef so be as you'm wanting to see your man", I says agen, an' she sat up. "I have no man", her said, and wudn' open lips agen. I waited Davy, but her turned away.'

'Her turned away,' he repeated heavily, 'so th' Almighty have a'done this day.'

Rachel could find no answer. She took a chair and sat down opposite him, as she had done on the evening of his betrothal, to watch the strange yet familiar face with the same feeling of its being very far away. She longed to reach his sorrow as she had never longed to reach his joy; if he had spoken, she might have put a finger on it, but he did not speak.

For long they remained thus, with silence set between them, but it grew late and she got up at length to go to bed. As he did not move to bid her the customary 'Wish 'ee goodnight', she made as if to go without it, but came back, and pausing behind him, laid her fingers lightly upon the fair curling hair of his bowed head. He put up a hand in clumsy recognition of the touch, and then she left him, sitting before the fire, staring at it, and as on the night when they had first spoken together of Susannah, passing a hand mechanically up and down each knee.

In the morning he was gone. His boat was missing from the beach, but no one knew how he had launched it; no one could tell in what direction it had started from the bay.

Chapter VI David Comes Home

'Thy Providence, O Father, governeth it: for Thou hast made a way in the sea and a safe path in the waves.'

IN the advancing twilight of her life—a dusk swiftly approaching night—Rachel's dim eyes were fixed upon these words, traced on the little sampler by small, unthinking fingers so many years ago. Her thought was bounded by the sea. Night and morning, and through the long pause of day, it sounded in her ears; she sat surrounded by the menace of the water, clasping the promise of that mercy which had failed before, but yet might save and send the last of her lost children back, to close her eyes and set her forth, in peace, upon that journey which seemed at times so near.

He had been gone two months and had sent no word. He might have reached some foreign port, or found a home somewhere along the coast within sight of Tregarveth: finally she let go profitless conjecture and waited, companioned by the last of all her terrors—he might have been taken by the sea.

Together they had watched for Jenefer, long and patiently and lovingly; listening vainly for unreturning feet, but still together. Now, for David, she watched alone, rarely stirring from her seat at the window looking upon the bay.

Not far off, at the top of the sloping road, in the white house with its four wide windows facing seaward, Susannah was watching too. David's child was at her breast, and with some mysterious power it had pleaded for him and wrung pardon from its mother's heart.

'God forgie me,' she said at night, laying her head beside his vacant pillow. 'God forgie me, I let 'ee go.'

Welcome was lodged in that rebellious breast, and tended by the tiny fingers which clung to it; a gentler light shone in the once avenging eyes, as they looked down with new-lit tenderness upon the burden in her arms, which was to give his father greeting when he came.

So the two women watched for the man's coming, which was to sweeten death and re-awaken life; both looked for the slow speech and quiet eyes, and heavy footsteps; and at last, with a great silence laid upon him, with arrested gaze, and feet that had touched land beyond the haven where they waited, David came.

It had been a night of sudden storm; the wind raving in hollow fury round the frowning cliffs, the waves breaking in thunderous beats upon the shore. No boats were out and so Tregarveth slept, only awakened now and then by gusts which swept up the steep streets in dreary violence from the defiant sea.

Rachel had early left her bed, and wrapt in a shawl, crept to the window, where she leant against the clattering frame. An awful loneliness had fallen upon her, shutting out every other fear. The desolate old woman shivered in the howling darkness, helplessly craving some near sign of human presence, some sense of comfort and living care. She would have turned in that forsaken moment even to Susannah, if Susannah had been near.

The younger woman slept, cradling the tiny creature that rested by her side.

The morning broke kindly with drifting clouds; the wind dropped as suddenly as it rose; only the waves, not quite appeased, ran high, and fell, licking the shore with grating tongues, and raking the shingle with white teeth of spray. At noon the clouds let through the sun, which cast their shadows in great sapphire bands far out across the emerald water, which shoreward rolled up sullen brown. Later, the sky, swept fully clear, hung high, a fading azure above the gold-flecked track of grey and purple sea.

Tregarveth was astir. The women were talking in the streets, the men in groups about the beach, where the boats tossed on the returning tide. It was on this returning tide that David Parris had come home, washed into shore a little way beyond the haven, off Pentarras Head, the next cove to the bay. Now they were bringing him along.

The news came to Susannah at her door. At the first hint of it, her hoarded gentleness took flight. He had come too late, and Too Late is a harder word for those who have to utter it, than Never-more. A wild, inhuman madness shook her spirit, a revolt against the victories her soul had won so painfully, now to be wasted in a great defeat. She had achieved a greeting never to be met, she had allowed her heart to hunger for his coming, and he came to mock that hunger with cold lips and loveless eyes. She had even stooped to pray, and the prayer was answered by this barren hour. There had been pardon for the living, there was no welcome for the dead.

'Tes no business o' mine's', she muttered hoarsely, when the messenger had told his tale. 'They can car' en home to hes mother's. That be the place for en. They oft to knaw et. They can car' en theer.' And going back into the house, she shut the door, and hushed the child, who had begun to cry for her, with hardening mouth; regarding its restless motions with a new unnatural stare.

Her soul was torn. For, in a strange fashion, she had loved him—with all the heart she had. A small heart, here and there, is Nature's whim: and love has many ways: hers—not altogether of her own choosing—had been a crooked way.

The men with their burden presently passed the window, and she watched them from it, with the babe upon her knee. A frenzy, gathering force, fed by her own last utterance, seized her. 'Home to his mother's.' That was the end and the beginning of it all. Rachel first and last: herself but a brief and minor interlude in David's life.

It was the strained conclusion of a distracted soul, a self-distorted mind. From it, suddenly, a distorted impulse sprang, and almost before it had taken shape in thought she put it into act. The child was sleeping now; she carried it upstairs and left it carefully covered up—a tiny bundle in the midst of the wide bed. Then hastening down, she crossed the threshold and stepped out, passing rapidly between the groups of chattering neighbours, down the steep, uneven street. They looked after her with curious glances and partially silenced tongues. She took small note of them, but hurried forward, never slackening pace, nor shifting her cruel steady gaze, fixed on the blackening patch of sea, until she reached the little hut perched on its ledge of rock above the bay.

Without pausing to knock for admittance, she thrust open the door, which stood ajar.

His great boots, split to the heel, cut from the drowned man's limbs, had been left standing just within it: she stumbled over them on entering.

Rachel was standing by the body of her son. Her face, marked by the night of watching and its awful morrow, was pinched and drawn and grey. She was not looking now on his terribly changed features: her eyes rested where her last touch had lain, upon the fair boyishly-curling hair. Some stray bits of wet seaweed still clung about it, and some which had been hanging to his clothing had slipped and lay strewn here and there, making damp trails across the floor.

At the sight of Susannah, she did not speak, but stretched out her arms in piteous supplication. He had come back, like those before him, cruelly defaced but not unkindly strange; was he at this last moment to be snatched away?

Mutely she cried for mercy, but Susannah's heart was obdurate to the living, even in the presence of the dead. It was possessed by the sole passion which is not shaken in the face of death: before those alienated features hate recoils, and vengeance hangs its head, and love falls weeping, and lust learns its shame; while jealousy alone, in its last impotence, burns on, feeding, even with that poor fuel of mortality, its hungry fire.

'No', she said with cruel distinctness, answering the appeal; 'I dedn't come for to look at a dead starin' man. I dedn't come to claim en, though he be mine not your'n. I comed to ha' a las' word with 'ee, Rachel Parris, an' to take a las' look at the woman who've a' killed her son.'

She advanced a step and at that approach Rachel shrank back taking, affrighted, refuge in the farthest corner of the room.

Susannah filled her place beside the bed.

'Be afear'd', she asked, pointing to the prone figure there, 'the dead'll rise to gie me another blow? There es none left to strike for 'ee or spaik for 'ee. You be alone wi' me. You'm be fo'ced to hear what I be goin' to tell 'ee. An' tes words to think 'pon. Mark'en, Rachel Parris. David do owe hes death to 'ee this day.' Her voice rose and rang out savagely shrill. ' 'Twas easy work to part we—that were soon done—an' easy work to 'tice en back to 'ee, but 'twere the finish of en. 'Twadn't sich easy work for he to bide with 'ee; he cudn't bide. You was the one that made a brute of en, jest for a piece o' painted cloam; that were the price o' wife an' child for David, an' tes to pay et he lies theer. Deds't think', she went on, stung by bitter memory, 'two months agone I wud ha' tuk en back for words o' your'n. You knawed I wudn'. Reckon you mastered et he shudn' come himsel'. 'Twas I that sent him to hes death, so I did hear em tellin' as I comed along. They'm wrong; the Lord be witness, that were left to thee.'

She paused for some sign of suffering from the stricken woman; some defensive answer. Rachel had none to give. Neither speech nor moan escaped that dumb, half-huddled object, barely visible in the dark corner, facing its accuser with blanched, shrivelled cheeks, and scared, unweeping eyes.

She saw Susannah indistinctly, through the thickening mists of sense and sight, stationed before her like a hideous revengeful spirit, voice and form almost impalpable, yet striking horror with unearthly power to the soul.

This mute acceptance of her utterance renewed the poison in Susannah's spirit, loaded her lips again.

'Come heer an' look at en!' she cried, making as if she would drag the shrinking figure forward, but quickly stepping back from the crouching, hated form. 'Tes time for that when I be gone. I stopped 'ee, but I wudn' stop 'ee now. Mayst take thy fill o' glazin' at the last o' all thy sons, but never think that he comed back to 'ee. He knawed so well as I what you'd adone for en. Most nights as he sat theer with 'ee he thought of et, an' ef he loved 'ee once, 'twas over then. 'Twas over when 'ee tuk the light fro' they blue starin' eyes o' hes. I were the only light of en; time an' agen he telled me so. I were the light and you the darkness of hes life. He minded et, I tell 'ee, night and day. Hes heart were gone from 'ee afore hes body. He leaved 'ee wi'out a word, an' he comed back to me. Body an' soul you had a' lost en, an' ef so be as the dead do rise agen, and theer be judgment, nuther i' this world nor the nex' will he ha' part nor lot wi' thee.'

She ended, and the last inhuman notes struck hard against the silence. She stood erect and panting from her breathless outburst, casting a final glance round the dark room. The quiet form, hardly discernible, stretched out beside her, was scarcely stiller than the living figure which she could not see. She thrust the door back, and stood a moment on the threshold, still looking backward into the black room. The motion of the waves outside arrested her.

'Tide's runnin'; hark'ee to et, hark'ee to et, Rachel Parris', she called out high above it. ' 'Twill help 'ee to remember me.'

The presence passed, but still the voice ran on. Rachel lifted herself up at last, and groped towards the door. The bolt was rusted with long disuse, but with barely conscious fingers she managed to draw it to.

There were to be no more footsteps, there was to be no more speech. There must, she felt blindly and dizzily, be no more separation now. She sank down on the floor beside the bed, and leant her head against the frame. Through the window—now an almost indistinguishable square—the faint red star appeared and disappeared, and started out again. And still she heard the tide. She had no power to shut that sound away. The night fell darkly; wrapped in its shadow, mother and son were left alone. For a short space it curtained them, and then the day broke to the same old burden of waves lapping against the shore.

Not now to tortured ears which heard in it all notes of anguish. For these a Hand had hushed that tide.

And they who slept within the silenced chamber slept secure from human severance and human woe.

No hand, nor voice, nor presence, nor dividing sea, had further power this side the last great barrier to separate those twain.

SOME WAYS OF LOVE

I

'Les âmes sont presque impénétrables les unes aux autres, et c'est ce qui vous montre le néant cruel de l'amour.'

'AND so you send me away unanswered?' said the young man, rising reluctantly, taking his gloves from the table and glancing meanwhile at the obdurate little lady on the sofa, who witnessed his distress with that quizzical kindness, which distracted him, in her clear, rather humorous blue eyes.

'I will give you an answer if you wish it.'

'I would rather hope,—you do give me a ray of hope?'

'Just a ray', she admitted, laughing, with the same disturbing air of indulgence. 'But don't magnify it—one has a habit, I know, of magnifying "rays"—and I don't want you to come back—if you do come back—with a whole blazing sun.'

'You are very frank, and a little cruel.'

'I am afraid I mean to be—both. It is so much better for you.' She was twisting the rings round her small fingers while she spoke, as if the interview were becoming slightly wearisome.

'You treat me like a boy', he broke out, with youthful bitterness.

'Ah! the cruellest treatment one can give to boys', she answered, looking up at him with her hovering brilliant, vexatious smile. But meeting his clouded glance she paused, and abandoned temporarily the lighter line of argument.

'Forgive me, Captain Henley——'

He scanned the treacherous face to see if the appellation so sedately uttered were not designedly malicious, but her next words reassured him.

'I will be more serious. See,—frankly, cruelly perhaps,—I do not know my heart.' She did not falter over the studied phrase. 'You are not the first', observing his troubled features ruefully, as she dealt the innocent blow. 'You may not be—the last.'

It left her lips a little labouredly, despite its apparent levity, but he was too much absorbed to notice fine shades of accent, and she went on,—'I am not so charming as you think me, but that's a foregone conclusion. Shall I say, not so charming as I seem? At eighteen I made—I will not suggest I was led into—a loveless marriage. It was a failure, of course. I do not want to make another. I shrink from helping, shall we say, you? to a similar mistake. You must pardon me if I admit I do look upon you as—young; for years, you know, are deceptive things,—even with women.'

His boyish face expressed annoyance.

'Ah! I meant you to smile, and you are frowning. I should not be outraged if any one offered me the indignity you resent so foolishly; but then I am not—fortunately or unfortunately—so young as you. Come, be reasonable', she urged, with a singular sweetness of persuasion: 'if I do not know my mind, is it so strange in me to suppose that yours may change? Again forgive me if I anticipate you. I have been glib enough with "nevers" and "for evers" in my day; but I shun them. I listen to them with more caution now. "Never", "for ever",' she repeated, and mused for a moment over the words. 'I sometimes imagine one is only safe in speaking them on the threshold of another life than this. It is a fancy of mine we should not use them now. Please humour it.'

'I am not so diffident, doubtful, nor possibly so cynical', he began; but she interposed with the wave of a little glittering hand.

'Precisely; therefore I warn you. Why,' she proceeded, with an unmistakable note of tenderness, which he did not catch, 'you are even younger than I thought. I am glad—heartily—that you are going to the front. Cut up as many rascals as you can,—a little fighting will bring you a lot of wisdom, and—oh yes! I know what a brute I am!—you want it badly. Come back in a year with your V.C. or without it: anyhow, with an ounce or two of experience in your pocket, and, if you do come back to me'—he winced at the repetition of the 'if' and the doubt implied by it—'I promise to treat you like a man.'

'And give me my answer?'

'Yes.' She pronounced it with sudden softness.

'Meanwhile?'

'Meanwhile, husband the "ray" if you like, but don't extend it; and remember it pledges us both to nothing. You'—she rapidly substituted 'we—are free.'

'You are free of course, Lady Hopedene', he agreed, with becoming solemnity. 'I shall always consider myself bound. I—I—should like you to know that I do not consider myself free.'

'As it please you', she yielded, with a flash of amusement shot at the melancholy countenance.

'It will be my only consolation', he returned, with ponderous sadness.

'So be it, then: I mustn't rob you of that. But remember, if the occasion calls, that I acquit you absolutely from reappearance at this bar.'

A slight break in her voice reminded her that the time had come for his dismissal, and she proceeded promptly: 'Now we must say Good-bye.'

'Only *au revoir*.'

'You are very literal; I like the old phrase best.' She rose and took his hand, holding it longer than usual; and he looked down at her perturbedly. 'Am I to have only a frown to keep?'

'Keep that', he cried, suddenly stooping to kiss the frail white fingers in his palm.

Then he turned away quickly, went out and closed the door, missing, behind it, that curious fragrance of her presence, fresh and keen like morning air in meadows, subtler and sweeter than the faint perfume that hung about her person.

She stood motionless, tasting his departure: the smile which she had given him leave to take had faded from her eyes, and they were staring blankly at the door.

'Have I done well—for him?' she asked herself. 'He may—he will—surely meet other women perhaps less scrupulous than I. And for myself?' She went towards a mirror set between the windows, and studied critically the reflexion that faced her there. It showed a diminutive, delicately-tinted face, beneath the childishly fair hair waved carefully above it, and for the moment, robbed of its insouciance, it looked wistful and a little wan. 'I can spare a year,' she decided, after a pause of close regard, 'and at any rate my conscience is delightfully clear. My heart—"I do not know my heart." ' She laughed unsteadily. 'He swallowed that absurdity; he might have read—bah', she cried, throwing her hands out with a gesture caught abroad, sometimes recurring with other un-English tricks of manner. 'He is too young to read anything without a stammer yet. A woman has no right to take advantage of such a boy's first fancy. Assuredly I have done well.'

She went back to the sofa and rested her head among the vivid cushions. When at length she raised it, the gay blue eyes were dim.

II

The *Nubia* was homeward bound, and her passengers were experiencing the inconveniences incidental to a passage through the Red Sea. Now and then the picturesque figure of a lascar darted across the semi-darkness. The stewards were throwing the mattresses upon the deck under a starlit sky. The captain and his first officer had just surprised a *tête-à-tête* taking place in a quiet corner of the ship, with diversified feelings of annoyance.

'Is Henley serious?' the former inquired irritably. 'Because it's a deuced awkward business. Miss Playfair is in my charge, and it isn't the first time I have had trouble over little affairs of the kind. Relatives are always unreasonable—even other people's relatives—but, by

Jove, I think the attractive objects of their solicitude are worse.'

'They met in India, so I suppose it's all right', returned the young man curtly, disinclined to discuss a situation which inspired him personally with a sensation of despair.

'I shall be glad to see Plymouth and the last of such an embarrassing cargo', returned the captain, turning on his heel.

'Moi aussi', muttered the young lieutenant sulkily.

But the subjects of this brief discourse did not apparently share these sentiments of relief at the prospect of gaining port.

'In spite of this awful heat, I wish it would never end', a deep voice proclaimed from the darkness. 'It's ideal! The sea and the sky, this glorious sense of solitude, and you and I the only people on earth, it seems, in the midst of it. Say'—in a lower key—'you wish it might never end.'

'What is the good of wishing, when you persist that it must end when we go ashore?'

'The gods may be merciful.'

'You mean Lady Hopedene may be—cold?'

'She is always cold; a lovely little piece of ice. She never cared a hang for me, Mildred, or don't you think she must have betrayed it then?'

'I suppose she wanted to see what stuff you were made of. Why did she give you the chance of going back?'

'It was only a manner (she has a charming manner) of saying "No". Women'—he pronounced it with an air of profundity—'don't try experiments on the men they love.'

'Then why go back at all? It is only inviting humiliation, if that's your view of it.' Her tone, usually languorous, took a brisker note.

'I must, dearest: I gave my word.'

'But you say she insisted upon not pledging you?'

'I pledged myself.'

'You are too quixotic. Suppose you find her consoled?'

'Let us suppose it,'—he seized her hands,—'the other possibility stuns me, let us forget it. Tonight, tomorrow, and still tomorrow are ours. Mildred—'

She released herself. 'How can we forget it? It poisons today, it blunts tomorrow. It makes a farce of—of everything.'

'I ought not to have spoken,' he said remorsefully, 'and, but for that other fellow, I should have waited till I was free. Do you forgive me?'

'I do not know.'

'Whatever happens, the world will never hold any woman for me but you.'

'You have possibly said that before?'

'I was a young fool—she told me so; and, good heavens! I know it now.'

'Tell me', she said; 'let us walk about. What is this other woman like?'

'Let us forget her', he pleaded.

'I want to know.'

'Very small and fair; remarkably fair and witty and—well, I hardly know how to put it, courageous: it was the kind of fine unfeminine courage she seemed to have, that—that trapped my fancy. It struck me as an uncommon trait; if she had been a man she would have been cut out for a soldier. You see it was not love, darling; it began with a sort of impersonal admiration, and that's what it has come back to now.'

'She will marry you', the girl assented conclusively. 'I think I understand her better than you.'

'And you will hate my memory?'

'Yes, for a time; and then—then I suppose I shall marry some one else.'

'If I were you, I would rather spend my life alone.'

'It is not so easy for women to talk or think of loneliness; but I love you, Alan', she ended passionately.

They bade each other a troubled and subdued good-night.

III

> '... tandis que, dans le lointain, le cloche de la paroisse—emplissait l'air de vibrations douces, protectrices, conseillères de bon sommeil à ceux qui ont encore des lendemains— —'

Lady Hopedene closed the book brusquely, with the little recurrent foreign gesture of impatience.

'I must avoid this man; he is deplorably enervating.' The china clock on the opposite wall struck four, and, summoned by its chime, the rejected phrase returned, to be rapidly dismissed again. *Ceux qui ont encore des lendemains.*

She passed a hand across her eyes, and pushed back the brilliant cushions against which her head rested uneasily. They framed the gold hair superbly, but seemed to have chased the delicate flush, once sweetly permanent, from the childish face. It looked out now from them nearly colourless and a little drawn.

The door opened, and a mechanical voice announced, 'Captain Henley'.

She did not rise, and he advanced towards her.

'Alan!' The name escaped her, poignant, even piteous in the suddenness and intensity of its utterance. A long succession of days, of weeks—a weight of waiting—seemed to be visibly thrust before him, painted on the wing of that swift cry.

And something more: behind it lurked a note of anguish, faint, but clashing audibly against its joy.

Insensibly he recoiled before the unfamiliar greeting. It was unlike her, unlike anything he had heard before. But in a moment the blue eyes, so strangely lit, resumed their old expression of half-bantering welcome; and she beckoned him forward, with the well-known wave of a small commanding hand.

'Come here, you wonderful apparition; I want to assure my senses, test my sanity. Is it actually *you?*'

'Unmistakably. I have come for my answer', he began briefly, hurriedly: aware that she had given it, before his question, in that startling and involuntary utterance of his name.

'You speak as if you were presenting a bill,' she responded, laughing, 'and the demand sounds somewhat peremptory, when I have been wondering if I should ever have to meet it. Oh, there are long arrears, I know', she added, taking his hand as he stood beside her. 'Sit here.' She made a place for him, and looked frankly, earnestly, at his slightly matured face.

'Why,' she said, drawing back in mock alarm, 'it *is* a man I have to deal with!' And then, with a quick and winning sweetness, 'shall I tell you a secret, Captain Henley? I am rather disappointed, for—for—as a fact I loved the boy.'

'Then why did you play with him?' he broke out, hardly able to control his bitterness, and returning her close gaze intently. 'Your whim'—he spoke the truth baldly, careless, for the moment, whether or not she caught his meaning—'your whim has cost me much an honest answer would have saved me.'

'You have a right, knowing so little, to reproach me. I will tell you', she returned gently. 'It was after all, I suppose, mere egotism, because I cared for you more than myself. Your happiness was, is, will always, so I fancy, be more to me than mine.'

An impulse came to him to put the truth before her, to tell his story plainly. For this woman whom he had loved inspired him strongly still with trust. Her mind, he knew, was sounder than the minds of other women he had met, and he could not fail to trust the heart that shone so clearly, straightly, through the blue eyes regarding him. He might have yielded to that momentary impulse, had she not broken in too hastily upon his wavering thought.

'I chose the most effectual lie that I could frame that day—do you remember?—when I told you that you were not the first, you might not be the last. You *are* the first'—her glance fell suddenly upon the yellow volume which had slipped, at his entrance, from the sofa to the floor—'you will be certainly the last. Lying always disgusts me. I pray you forgive my first and only lie.'

He offered no response, but rose and stood silently, awkwardly beside her, loth to return her honesty with artificial protestation, knowing that speech was required of him, painfully seeking words.

She laughed, remembering him sometimes dumb of old, and went on with a trace of hesitation in her tone.

'My openness surprises you; but look at this', and she spread out before him a denuded, shrunken hand.

'How bare it is!' he said, taking it quietly in his own. 'Where are the old adornments? Why have you forsaken them?'

She replied ruefully, 'They have forsaken me. Perhaps'—she pointed lightly to her cheeks—'you have remarked that other adornments have turned traitors too. Sooner or later I must tell you: why not now? My physicians'—she pronounced the words with a mock pomposity, and punctuated them with a slight grimace—'give me a year, or not so long perhaps, for the pomps and vanities of this delightfully wicked world. And so, you see, out of pure consideration, the pomps and vanities are withdrawing gradually in preparation for their final exit.'

She relinquished the accent of raillery, and began hurriedly and anxiously to caress his detaining hand. He seized her wrists and bent an incredulous glance upon her.

'It is some wretched jest. I do not believe you serious.'

'Just now I am as serious as I shall ever be.'

'You do not mean. . . .' He could not achieve the obvious question, and stood holding the small fingers closely—stammering—silenced.

'Yes, truly, I have got marching orders, with a respite. There is a year for speech, for folly, for wisdom—if it were not so dull—and a year, my dear, for love.'

'My G——!' he cried. 'You have stunned me, Ella. You are here; I can see and hear you; but I can't manage to understand. It is like a nightmare. It isn't *true?*'

She released and laid her hands upon his arm, and checking his outburst with the flicker of a smile, protested,—'You do not meet the enemy like a soldier.'

'I have not your nerve', he answered. 'Surely,' he ventured, 'some other man will give you hope or time.'

She shook her head, and quoted lightly,—' "If we die today, if we die tomorrow, there is little to choose. No man may speak when once the Fates have spoken." '

Her eyes were challenging his to courage. 'You loved your life far more than most of us', he said, immediately wishing the words back.

'I adored—I adore it. You link me with the past tense too readily. We will have no future nor subjunctive moods, only the present and imperative. *Je t'aime—aime-toi, par exemple.*'

'Ella,' he cried, 'for God's sake be serious. I don't know how long you have known what you have told me. Remember it is new to me.'

'It is passably new to me.' She flashed a swift rebuke towards him from the brave blue eyes. 'Do you wish me to play the coward?'

'You could not', he asserted brokenly. 'You are a good soldier spoiled.'

'The finest, if the clumsiest, compliment you have ever paid me.'

'It is not that', he said almost roughly. 'You shame me heart and soul; I feel like a deserter.'

'They are cut after another pattern', she observed, with sweet decision. 'We were neither of us made to turn our backs upon what lies before us or pull long faces at a foe. Through this long year—I will confess to a weary year—it never occurred to me as a reality that you would fail. I thought you might—I did not fear you *would;* but if you had, I should have faced it, and it would have been harder to face than death.'

'I will never fail you', he said determinately; and as the 'never' left his lips, he recalled her little speech upon the employment of that far-reaching term; only safely to be spoken, she had said, as now he spoke it, upon the threshold of the grave. And then it flashed across him how that interview had been a curious prototype of this. Then they had touched on death and laughter, and looked forth, too, upon the passage of a year. This was the ending to that unreal dream. But he was not to view its empty structure; she should not spend last hours picking up the petals of his fallen love.

'I will not fail you', he repeated passionately.

She listened with some wonder to the reiterated phrase.

'My dear, I do not doubt you.'

'I have not said what I came to say, Ella. Will you be my wife?'

He asked the question foreseeing its consequences, but impelled to it by something deeper and more grave than pity. For a moment, she did not reply. She had been standing by him, but now sat down and began to finger the embroidered cushion, while she framed her answer. It came at last, but slowly from so quick a speaker.

'Love,' she said, 'though we don't often think of it, has an extensive wardrobe. Everyone cannot wear his richest garment,—we cannot, you and I. Let us be glad he offers us any, for without his charity we must indeed go bare. We can be comrades, you and I, and only that, I think. It is the sanest, the best compact possible, since lovers end as we may not. You will keep watch with me, as if we were both good friends, good soldiers, till the enemy strikes, and he *will* strike, you know.'

'That is a cold night's watch', he forced himself to say, remembering her cry of greeting, and wondering how she kept such guard upon her heart.

'Warm enough', she said; 'much warmer than the dawn which is to end it. You will wait and keep this watch with me?'

'I will do anything you bid me.'

'Then I bid you cultivate a smile for all weathers, and not to shiver yet.' She took his hand again and led him to the window, where the lamps were being lit beside the railings of the park. 'It is spring outside; I noticed the trees in bud this morning. The Fates have not been too unkind. They have lent us all the seasons; summer, my favourite, is coming, and—you have come.'

He stooped and caught and kissed the little fingers loosely clasping his.

'Your last kiss has found a friend', she whispered; 'it has lain for a long while lonely there.'

'Give me your rings', he suggested; 'I will get them altered. I like to see you wearing them.'

'Yes', she agreed, 'it is stupid to give them up. I will send—no, I will fetch them myself, if you will excuse me.'

Loosing his hand, she crossed the darkening room and left him there alone, confronting the first great problem of his life.

IV

Mildred Playfair rose and left her seat by the window to stand beside the fire. She was renewing, without much display of friendliness, her acquaintance with an English spring. Henley was standing by the mantelpiece, and her movement brought them face to face. She lifted her dark eyes to his, and remarked, with the lingering intonation habitual to her, 'There seems to be nothing more to say; I almost wonder why you came.'

'Because you sent for me. I have put everything before you—the case as it stands, as it must stand for me. Perhaps it was better to come and tell you myself.'

'You need not have waited for my summons.'

'I meant to write. I thought it would be less painful for us both. It wasn't an easy matter, though. I was making a bungling attempt at an explanation on paper when your letter came.'

'The explanation that you were going to relinquish me for a poetic and almost feminine fancy?'

'I had no choice.'

'I did not know that men went in for this kind of thing. I imagined they were more—definite.'

'I did not know myself that I could have done it a month ago; but women—a good woman—can turn a man inside out sometimes, and show him what he can and cannot do.'

She had been holding her hands towards the fire, but now she turned and took from a table an Indian paper-knife and began slipping it in and out the uncut pages of a magazine.

'The fact is that you love this other woman still.'

He hesitated, experiencing an almost Puritan desire to speak the barest truth.

'Not in the way you mean. I have learned this week that there are many ways of love.'

'Is that original?' she asked, running a finger up and down the carved blade in her hand. "Are you sure you are not echoing a phrase of hers?'

'Perhaps. Mildred,' he cried, 'you make things even harder than they were. If you saw my heart, you would know I am not a traitor—at least to you.'

To that other, he did not feel that he was playing altogether an untreacherous part.

'Your intricacies elude me. I admit I do not understand your way—your "ways".'

'Not after I have told you everything: when I have begged you to wait for me, as perhaps I ought not, as I surely should not have done if I did not care for you so much, dread losing you so terribly?'

'You must have known I should not consent to see you implicitly the lover of another woman.'

'I am not her lover', he said briefly.

'Another fine distinction which I cannot grasp.'

'If you could see my heart—' he began again; but she broke in.

'I can see enough of it to know it is not wholly mine.'

'Do you want protestations?' he asked heavily, but without bitterness. 'How can I make them now, with your refusal—with the vanity of hope—before me, with nothing but good-bye to say?'

'If you cared, you would not say it!'

Again he repeated, 'I have no choice.'

'Because you have chosen.'

'In my heart, in my soul, I have chosen you.'

'And yet you are going back to some one else?'

'For a year, and possibly less than that. Cannot you look at it as I do? We have life before us, but there is death in her eyes—death already, as I saw it, upon her lips. There is the grave between us', he urged, and ended with a new note of sadness. "Isn't that space enough?'

'It is invisible,' she returned, 'so do not blame me if I cannot see it. I can see only that there is a woman, or her shadow, between you and me.'

'Is that your last word?' he asked, almost at that moment hoping it might be, aware that words had availed them little—brought no illumination and no relief.

'No', she broke forth suddenly, doffing the coldness and the calmness of her attitude petulantly, like an overweighted garment. 'My last word is that I love you, Alan, and that by your own admission you belong to me.' She crossed the room and threw herself upon him,—'I cannot and I will not let you go.'

He caught her with a short, familiar cry of welcome, and held her for a second; then releasing her, he rested a hand upon her dark and slightly ruffled hair.

'So you will wait?'

He spoke simply his first thought; but at its utterance she sprang away.

'No, not that—not that.'

'What, then?' he asked bewilderedly. 'You will not trust me?'

'*She* trusted you', the girl exclaimed, letting through her lips, in this last moment of distraction, the reminder which had hovered behind them once or twice before. '*She* let you go; and though she does not know it, you have failed her, or so you say; indeed, I do not know what to believe of you.'

'That is true', he said. 'God knows that I have failed her; *that* is true.'

'Give me a pledge that you will not fail *me*.'

'What pledge?' he asked; and added passionately; 'any, any I can give is yours.'

'Give me the only credible one,' she urged, 'and stay with me.'

He paused,—perplexed, dubious, stung; swaying upon a second choice. To which woman did he owe most? They seemed, as he stood there irresolute, both stationed before his vision, calling upon him that he should not fail. The one more distant, miniature and frail, a form of fading loveliness, in the posture of halting life; the other—she who stood beside him—vigorous, beautiful, distinct and dear, her feet strongly planted upon the stair of youth. The physical contrast struck him forcibly, and yet it was not that which brought conclusion to his contending thought. It was a sentence, spoken sweetly by a decisive voice proceeding from a chamber, which to his view was dimmer than the room wherein he stood—'We were neither of us made to turn our backs upon what lies before us or pull long faces at a foe.'

With that in his ears he faced the tacit foe before him urging mutely in counter-claim.

'You will not trust me?' he asked again, this time with a dull accent of humility that might not have missed an older heart.

'I cannot', she replied rebelliously.

He met the dark, unyielding eyes, to find they stated an unyielding fact.

The woman who compelled it could not hear his answer; she would have understood it.

'And I,' he said simply, with a regret that reached beyond the passion of the moment, 'I cannot stay.'

IN THE CURÉ'S GARDEN

I

I discovered it in summer. I do not know what it is like in spring; golden with daffodils, perhaps, and haunted by hidden violets, walled in by lilac trees, and sweetened with the scent of may.

I can imagine it to be the first meeting-place of budding things, a garden of the resurrection, where the birds re-assemble to recapture last year's song, and mate again, and build their nests anew.

Then, when the trees are leafless, or just starting into bud, one must see the convent on the hill more plainly, and hear less clearly above the birds' busy twitter, the bell tinkle across the fields. Then, in the skeleton poplar avenue, one may be able even to distinguish the figures of the good Sisters of our Lady of Compassion, as they pace slowly up and down. Today, one cannot catch a glimpse of them, but only now and then the outline of the distant walls, between green branches where they part.

In spring, Père Laurent says the garden has an air *plus béni, l'odeur plus fraîche, et plus consacré au repos.*

I can believe it; in these August days, the scents are heavy, insistent, almost over-sweet; the colours, fiercely brilliant, still more luminous at early twilight, in the narrow walks where among roses the carnations bloom. Was not their odour almost passionate? I asked him once, in one of our little discursive talks, and were they not *par excellence* the flowers of seduction and desire?

Par excellence, he agreed; adding that yet it was well they should be there, diffusing their distracting fragrance; they were reminders of the world, the flesh: *fleurs des sens, fantômes de la chair, toujours tentant et qui doivent toujours être crucifiées.*

This sultry afternoon, however, it was not Père Laurent whom I had come to see. I passed him in the village and he stopped me to say that I should assuredly find Anita, if I were bound that way; that she would 'make his amend' for absence, and if I were pleased to loiter, he would return later to smoke a pipe with me. I was content with the proposed 'amend'.

Though both could speak it (the Curé had taught Anita; where he himself had learned it I do not know), they 'loved not the English', and would sometimes slip suddenly for relief or emphasis into the more natural tongue.

'Ah', Anita would cry, vainly seeking expression for a too subtle phrase, 'here is one of the things you cannot say. It suffices only that you think it; but in your language,—truly a great one, but *lourd*, you pardon me? it is a thought *enterrée*; do you call it dumb?'

I thrust open the little gate through which the Curé's mutinous flowers were pushing, peeping into the white forsaken road to catch the gallant glances of some passer-by. There were so few to pass, the truants might peer safely as Anita, who cared so much less than they for passers-by. At most, they would only encounter some straggling figure, following half-a-dozen dreamy cows; a straying child, or a boy whistling, who would smite their flushed faces as he went past them with his swinging hand. And later, towards evening, Père Laurent himself, leisurely walking homeward—a sombre figure, the last gleams of sunlight catching the silver buckles of his shoes.

The low white house of the Curé hid itself in summer-time behind the garden, modestly leaving welcome to the flowers. As I strolled in, I could see, beyond lines of pink and crimson blossom, the ponderous figure of Henriette taking in the clothes, which dry so quickly in this summer sun. Her voice disturbed the slumbrous stillness of the sunshine; she was singing in her unmelodious alto, *O que j'aime les militaires!*

I sat down on the little bench under the chestnut tree, where Père Laurent was wont to bring his books and smoke peacefully, till the twilight dimmed their pages, with Anita sitting smiling over her *méditations* by his side. I did not mean to seek her this afternoon; she was probably in the kitchen, devising some simple surprise for the Curé's evening meal. By-and-by she would saunter along the scented path and find me, and I awaited the child's greeting, the accustomed: 'Ah! it is you, monsieur? a thousand welcomes', and the gracious wave of the little hand. How long was it, I began to wonder, since that little hand had held me here? Only a few weeks in fact, and yet it seemed for a sweet eternity that I had loitered in the Curé's garden, to learn how bare a place without Anita the wider world might be. I found, not indeed a thousand, but one generous welcome here; always the wish on Père Laurent's lips that I would remain so long as I was not weary, always a smile to second it from the happy, musing child.

A step stole softly up behind me, and the 'thousand welcomes' was in my ear.

'Where did you spring from?' I asked, springing up myself, as the girl before me rose and stood still as the sunshine under the green shade. 'I imagined you in the kitchen, helping or hindering Henriette, and you appear, like an angel, suddenly to disperse my earthly dreams.'

'Henriette is *méchante* today', she explained; 'it is the washing that discomposes her. I have taken myself away.'

'That is not pretty in you; you should have more sympathy.'

'But if it is, as you say, impossible, if you cannot love me?'

'Can it be otherwise,' she asked simply, 'when I have occupied myself with love?'

'Will you begin to think of it a little; begin to think of *me*?'

'I have always retained you in my thoughts; in my prayers also, though you are not of our faith; I shall remember you, yes always, but not *comme ça*.'

'You are decided?'

'It is decided for me.' She put out her hand and added with singular simplicity and sweetness, 'Will you also remember me, and that it is not I, *mon ami*, who decide?'

'Then I may not speak to Père Laurent? It was for that I came this afternoon. You forbid it?'

'It is not for me to forbid. But he would say precisely as I have said.'

'That it is not your destiny?'

'*C'est positif*. Yes, he will make that explanation. It may be well that you should address yourself to him. It is possible he will give you the reasons why it cannot be?'

Her rejection was so positive, so persistent, that for the moment I was disinclined to combat it. I got up to go.

She arrested me with quick reproach. 'You are going? I have gravely displeased you; you are wounded. Will you never return? You are not about to leave us with an aspect so *sévère*.'

'Why should I stay, when you dismiss me?'

'I do not do that. I implore you to remain. You have been so much our friend; is that forgotten? Then it is true what they say of it, *l'amour est la passion cruelle qui désole et qui trahit*.'

Her distress was unmistakable; it cast the first shadow which I had ever seen upon that exquisitely cloudless face. I yielded to it and said caressingly, 'Then I will stay.'

'To supper?' she demanded quickly.

'If you are so good.' This definite assent restored to her the familiar untroubled smile. 'And you will perhaps gather me some flowers to take back with me?'

The suggestion delighted, completely reassured her.

'*Voyons*. You shall make your choice immediately, and I will preserve them till the sad moment when we say "good-night". To commence, then—carnations, I divine rightly they are the favourites.' She bent over the crowded beds to make a critical selection. 'It must not be too small, the bouquet', she decided; 'that—I repeat your expression in the affair of Henriette—would not be "pretty" for us, and one too big, that will appear ridiculous for you. It is in fact the size.' She held it out for admiration and approval. 'I present it to you now, monsieur; I will render it up,' she paused in preparation for a triumphant idiom, 'by-and-by.'

'By-and-by is perfect,' I said, 'as perfect as the bouquet.' I took it from her. 'You and your flowers, Mademoiselle Anita, have some strange affinity. When I think of you, it is as if I thought of them, and when I think of them, it is as if I thought of you.'

'You think too much of them,' she admonished gravely, 'I have remarked it. You give to them imaginations, dispositions of your own; they are not what you make of them and they have no relationship with me. I see them as I see the sky, *de loin, mais nous ne nous touchons pas,* we scarcely smile, we do not speak, we are not *en rapport.*'

'I do not believe it; see,' I thrust towards her the scented nosegay, 'they are speaking now. I do not, but you ought to understand what they say.'

'It is not speech, this beautiful odour; it is solely their breath, their life. Truly, we are apart; we have the life immortal, and their existence is but during the spring, the summer—very short.'

'Is that one of your *"méditations"*?'

'Ah, no, they are more *sérieuses*. But look', she cried; she had caught sight of the Curé's upright figure at the top of the descending road. He was walking slowly down the hill. 'We will go to meet him.'

'Presently,' I suggested, 'the flowers will want some water.'

Throwing upon me a little glance of mockery, she suggested, 'if they are so *sensibles,* as you believe, they will have patience till our return. Give them to me; you devise fine phrases for them, and yet I have more faith in them than you.'

She led the way down the path, opened the little gate, stooping there to gather from the bush of roses another straggling bud.

'I perceive by his step', she said, 'that he is tired; he is too often tired, *le petit père*. He will sit for an hour, two hours, with his head upon his hand, thus, and say nothing at all; and when he observes me, it is as if to say, "Go then, Anita. I am too weary even for you." '

'I have never noticed it.'

'It is possible; with you he is gay, you make him smile; but I am less fortunate; why, I do not comprehend, but it is my unhappiness sometimes to make him sigh.'

'That must be a fancy, merely', I protested.

'No,' she insisted, 'for I have not *des fantaisies;* it is the cloud which alone obscures my sunshine. It is so.'

II

Anita had left the table, supper was over, and we had pushed our chairs back, when Henriette, with an air of exasperated forbearance, presented herself to clear away.

Did we wish another meal? Or were we seated in preparation for *déjeuner*? What in fact was the meaning, the explanation of our obstructive presence? she demanded vindictively, planting her massive person before the Curé and sweeping away his empty plate.

'A little more patience, Henriette, and you would be perfect', he responded mildly, and rising in reply to this expostulation.

Henriette retorted that if her patience were miraculous enough to meet the demands upon it, she would indeed be fit to die.

'Permit monsieur to think better of us; it is only five, or is it four minutes past the hour of dismissal, and we are going, Henriette, we go.'

It was the fiat of this exacting handmaid that the Curé should, after his evening meal, immediately retire and smoke elsewhere his pipe of peace. Tonight he had for the moment forgotten it, and was loitering in the forbidden room.

' "*Ite! missa est*",' he said, leading into the garden and making his way to the bench where Anita had found me in the afternoon. 'Women, alas! are either too sweet or too sour, there is no gradation with them; it is my experience, one doubtless that you have shared, Monsieur Vidal, one must make one's selection of the sugarplum or the pill, and these are both enemies of the constitution is it not so? One does well to avoid both, if one may.'

'You have found a sanctuary,' I suggested, 'which is not open to all of us, whence you can regard them undismayed.'

'Truly, but, from the distance, one beholds them even more clearly; no man may know them better—or shall I say more profoundly—than does the priest.'

He bade me seat myself and proceeded to light his pipe. His remarkable personality had from the first moment of our acquaintance attracted me, but it is not one easy to reproduce.

His tall, spare figure was erect and unmistakably commanding; his face, painfully thin, and black about the shaven, hollow cheeks and narrow chin, was youthful in outline, but in expression unnaturally mature, while the compressed unyielding lips—a common feature in the faces of the Roman priesthood—lent it a character impressive and severe. Not much over forty, a young man still, he wore a dignity, an authority, befitting a far greater age. Only about the eyes, between which two deep lines were cut, there lingered traces of repudiated youth. A fine incisiveness and an almost patriarchal gentleness were mingled in his speech, as in his nature there seemed to be at war two forces—a tenderness which God had given him and a severity which thought enjoined.

'Anita has flown', he said, taking a seat beside me; 'she is undoubtedly at this moment the recipient of the monstrous wrongs of Henriette.'

'She escaped from that martyred personage', I said, 'this afternoon, to fall into my clutches; I fear I startled her, I spoke to her of—love.'

He made a slight movement, knocked out the ashes, and relit his pipe.

'You made, in fact, a proposal? It was premature, Monsieur; you should have addressed yourself to me.'

'It is our English fashion to, as we put it, sound the lady first. It is a sort of principle with us, or I should have paid more deference to yours.'

'And having—what is the expression?—"sounded" Anita, how did she reply?'

'She referred me to you.'

'Naturally; but she received your proposition with favour, with disfavour, which? I am interested. I should like to hear.'

'She said that marriage was not her fate, or something of the sort; that you would tell me why.'

'She said no more?'

'No more than that, but that was uttered very positively; she held out no hope, she was painfully conclusive. I look to you for a less mysterious and discouraging reception.'

'She said truly', he replied, after a pause; 'she is promised'—and he pointed through the branches towards the walls of the convent on the hill—'to the good sisters over there.'

'It is monstrous, incredible', I broke forth, forgetting his restrictive presence.

'Nevertheless, I assure you, it is true.' His response was cold and judicial, uttered almost without inflection; but with one of the strange transitions peculiar to him, he went on, touching a softer note. *'Je ne peux la chasser toutefois. Je suis faible, pas assez fort; mais un jour, un jour proche, il le faut.'*

'Why, then,' I asked, 'did you constantly invite me here and allow me to misinterpret your unstinted hospitality? Of course I supposed that it implied approval of my attitude towards Anita. You cannot have mistaken that. It must have been obvious that mine was more than a stranger's interest, that I meant to make more than a stranger's claim.'

'I had complete confidence in Anita', he observed quietly. 'Yes, it was sufficiently evident, the admiration, agreeably sincere; but at your age one has many admirations, yours will recover itself, *mon ami*; it is not fatal, this little affair. The child has not many pleasures, but few diversions, and your charming society was a recreation, a relief from my own, which is not always enchanting, and from that of Henriette, which is rarely so.'

'It did not occur to you that I should not regard the matter so lightly; that to Anita herself it might not seem so trivial? You did not consider it probable that I was tremendously in earnest, or that she might possibly come to think of me not merely as a recreation or a relief?'

'I have a supreme confidence in Anita,' he repeated, 'and you perceive it has not been badly placed. For you, I repeat, there are many admirations. Confess this is not the first. There will follow—others.'

'I have never wished to marry any woman before.'

'Ah! then it appears to you very serious. I regret if I become responsible for a lacerated heart. But it will heal itself, my son, believe me, it will not draw the life-blood. Yet, in the future, I will take more care.'

'It is serious enough,' I returned, 'and we may leave the question of its subsequent fate to conjecture; but at present, I protest against the shutting up of that beautiful child. For life; but it is not for life, it is for death, the most dreary death to which one mortal can condemn another. It is the worst kind of sacrilege. If it were not Anita, but any girl as bright and lovely, I should say the same.'

'You are violent, monsieur, but this is a matter on which your countrymen think violently. It presents itself quite differently to us. There is, in the present case, no compulsion, no constraint, and what you represent as death is in reality a much higher life than that which is assigned to most women. It is a holy, a protected life.'

I reined in, remarking, 'I deserve your rebuke, Père Laurent, one should not let prejudice carry off one's courtesy; and, of course Anita consents, she is a little monument of piety; but this destiny to which she refers so solemnly, and considers so unalterable, what does it amount to? What, after all, does it mean?'

'You desire to know?'

'If it is not an impertinent desire.'

He devoted a second to reflection, and then announced simply, 'Anita has a history common enough, but nevertheless sad. *C'est une enfant abandonnée,* and there remains, there should remain, for such a one solely *la vie rêveuse,* the guardianship of angels, the victory of the soul. *La mère est morte,*' he continued, in the easier tongue, '*peut-être pénitente, peut-être pardonnée, et l'enfant peut expier sa faute par le suprême supplice de femme, la mortification de la chair.*'

'You knew the mother?' I inquired.

'I have seen her—yes.'

'I suppose she was beautiful? Was she like Anita? Do you remember her?'

'She was not of those', he replied meditatively, 'whom one can forget. No, she did not resemble Anita; hers was a beauty upon which the holy angels could not smile. *Une beauté de ravissement, de perdition, mais la beauté, ah! Dieu le sait.*'

The description suggested a minute and vivid recollection, but I remarked merely, 'Anita has avenged the angels. And the father?'

The pause was barely noticeable; it gave the Curé time, however to remove an insect which had crawled up and found a barren shelter on his knee; but momentary as it was, it oppressed me.

'Le père est inconnu', he answered quietly. *'Nous ne le cherchons plus.'*

Nor did I seek him. I was content to examine, with new interest, the immovable, emaciated face before me, and as I did so, the Curé smiled.

'I am the guardian', he proceeded. 'On one side at least—the mother's—her blood is noble; it is to that she owes the unique air of serenity, of distinction, which to her loveliness lends so fine a charm. But there is no money, only submission and a pure heart; the good sisters are willing to receive her, I have done as I have considered best.'

'She is to suffer for, to expiate, her mother's fault? Her father's also, I presume.'

'Both assuredly. *C'est assez juste.*'

'To sacrifice an innocent human victim for the atonement of a passably common sin? It is not pardonable,' I said again, 'it is monstrous. Of course you have reflected, but I beg you to reflect again.'

'It is fitting, sad, perhaps, as you regard it, but just enough.'

'It is, pardon me, almost pagan.' Then I put forth a studied and daring plea. 'Père Laurent,' I said, 'can you imagine yourself the father, put yourself in the father's place? Face to face with the child, whom you had created, a beautiful creature, capable of blessing and even of purifying others; a real and visible atonement for that forgiven sin; would you destroy in her, for your own propitiation, all the natural instincts and pleasures which are possible to her? To you, the priest, they naturally assume a forbidden aspect, cannot perhaps appeal, but in the person I ask you, for the moment, to represent, would you deny to her the life that no one had denied you, which you yourself had generously enjoyed? Could you contemplate the years which would gradually rob this being, for whose welfare you were responsible, of youth and vigour and beauty, leaving no human alleviation, except the barren consolations of the religious life? I am pleading for Anita, in her unknown father's name. Surely our own sins bring us suffering enough, entail their expiation soon or late, but beyond this, in God's name, we are entitled to some freedom, some choice at least. And it is not credible that, with this legend of expiation in her ears, with her "submission", her "pure heart", and her complete ignorance of life, Anita has been in the position to make that choice.'

He had listened attentively to this long speech, and said on its conclusion, 'This is an eloquence, Monsieur, hardly English; but it befits the lover.' I did not know whether to consider the comment ironical or polite, until he added less ambiguously, 'There is some reason, if too much passion, in what you say. You plead, in fact, that I should revoke the destiny?'

'That you should give Anita, at any rate, an alternative one.'

He seemed to be pondering, deliberating, and after an interval of apparently deep reflection, he got up. His features, as he regarded me, remained impassive.

'I am, as you know, wealthy,' I pursued, 'I would not interfere with her religion. She should have extensive opportunities for charity; she should spend what she would, or what you recommended, in masses or intercessions for her parents' exacting souls.'

'You are bitter,' he answered at length, 'and now perhaps you, yourself, are not scrupulously just. But I am inclined to be indulgent. I am almost persuaded to yield to your appeal. I do not expect that Anita will reverse her decision. But your plea is granted, Monsieur Vidal, I will accord to her the permission of choice. It is a great,' he paused, as if on the point of wavering, 'an almost terrible concession. I make it for the sake of Anita, who has grown very dear to me. It is a sacrifice, a tremendous one. I admit it. I make it for Anita's sake.'

Catching his solemn tone, I replied: 'Then in the name of her parents, in Anita's name, I thank you. It is a great concession. I am sensible of it, I am aware of that.'

'In the name', he rejoined, 'in which you have pleaded, I accept your acknowledgements, but I make one condition. The decision must be made in my presence, and I should prefer that it be made tonight.'

'The sooner the better', I agreed. 'May I fetch Anita now?'

'I will summon her myself', he said; adding, 'this is your idea of justice, what you call fair play. You notice, I make no effort to influence her; give myself no time; but you will allow me to make the proposition. Believe me, it is in your interest that I should.'

I nodded assent, and he turned down the path, walking slowly towards the house. In a few minutes they returned together, and as they reached me he took Anita's hand.

'I have summoned you, my child,' he began, 'to make a momentous decision. Consider it without haste, *avec sérénité*. Monsieur Vidal has asked me for your hand. I have recounted to him your history, but I desire that you tell him yourself, quite openly, *franchement,* what is your *destinée*.'

She cast upon him a glance of rapid question, and then recited simply, '*C'est ma destinée de me dédier au Dieu, de prier toute la vie pour ma mère pécheresse et mon pauvre père inconnu.*'

'*C'est bien,*' he said, 'but this evening, I place before you another picture. This gentleman is rich; he loves you, he does you the honour to choose you for his wife. If you desire to accept him for your husband, you have my sanction, my permission. He will not disturb your faith. He offers you opportunities,—great ones—of charity, of pleasure, of liberty. It is for you to decide if you will embrace them, or if you prefer to seek the protection of the Holy Church. *Tu peux faire le choix*', he concluded, in a tone of cold and colourless authority. '*Je te le permets.*'

For some seconds she did not speak, but stood looking mutely, anxiously towards the priest, who had turned from her and was toying with the frayed edges of his sleeve.

'*Veux-tu*', she cried at last, with a curiously clear but troubled intonation, '*que j'accepte un tel mari, moi, l'épouse promise de Dieu?*'

The Curé was silent.

'*Réponds, réponds*', she exclaimed, more rapidly, flinging out her arms in supplication.

'It is for you to respond', he said, without raising his eyes to hers. '*Décide-toi*', he commanded coldly. '*Fais ton choix.*'

Her eyes were fixed upon his averted face, her answer hung upon his silence. It was persistent, and at last she said: 'It is decided for me; but no; it is I myself who decide. I am already promised.' Taking her childish eyes from his motionless figure, she lifted them towards the darkening sky and seemed to be murmuring a prayer. Then for the first time turning to me, she added with a gesture so tranquil, so conclusive, that it afforded me no protest, no conceivable reply—'*Le petit père le veut, le grand Père le bénira, et moi, je les aime tous les deux, et je consens.*'

She put out a hand, and I noticed it tremble slightly as she laid it upon Père Laurent's arm. At the touch, he looked up and scrutinized her face.

It glimmered palely in the advancing dusk, but there was nothing tremulous, nothing uncertain, there. It was composed, luminous, almost radiant, and they stood together thus in the rapidly approaching twilight. Above, the stars were beginning reluctantly to dot the fading blue, and below, the lines of crimson were growing darker, blurred; here and there only, a rose bush taller than the rest was discernible, pencilled delicately against the failing light.

The colours were hushed, the outlines every instant becoming fainter, but the scents, as happens always towards night, were sweeter to the sense, more poignant, like speech in darkness, and the insistent odour of carnations was everywhere.

Of what use now to call it passionate, to find in it the mystical breath of love? I looked at the child and back again to the shrouded, unextinguished flowers. She had indeed no part with them; as she had said truly, '*Nous ne nous touchons pas.*'

I was in haste to leave them. Their fragrance had become too sad, too eloquent. I turned to go. But as I did so, she started forward with a detaining gesture, a murmur of recall.

'One moment, Monsieur'—I caught her hand, it was quite cold, and for a breathing space—it seemed no longer—she let it remain in mine. Suddenly a shadow crossed her face. Her lips parted, a smile replaced it, a strange, wavering, quivering little smile. 'One moment,' she repeated, pointing towards the house and slipping from me, 'you have forgotten—the bouquet.'

AN OPEN DOOR

I

LADY ARMITAGE settled herself upon the sofa, with a gesture too finished to be quite spontaneous, accompanied by an unpremeditated sigh.

The other occupant of the room was her daughter Stella, whose irremediable mediocrity had alienated early her mother's interest in her career.

Of the fact that her younger sister absorbed it Stella was vividly aware, it was a consciousness on which, for her, the sun rose every day.

She had been the recipient of her mother's hopes—ambitions—schemes, with regard to Laurence, and she was now the confidante of her despair.

'I wrote no details', said Lady Armitage, with an air of frank exhaustion. 'I was and am', she smoothed the wrinkles from a glove which she was coaxing up a plump, reluctant finger, 'too unnerved, too broken. If it were a death, one might resign oneself; but this is paralysing. What can one give out? One doesn't even know what line to take.'

'What line does Laurence take?'

'Suicidal immobility. To repulsive gossip—immobility, to natural affection—immobility. One might be droning through the Litany, and instead of the obvious Good Lord deliver us, she repeats the stupefying formula—"It's true enough but I have no choice." '

'Perhaps she has no choice. Aren't fanatics usually beyond it? and there are occasions'—Stella's thought was edged with something keener than a mere impersonal reflection—'when one may have a very small amount of choice.'

'No choice, no fiddlestick! And if you are going to bolster up your sister in this moonstruck business, I give in. Birchington won't marry now, unless he gets entangled with his nurse, which God forbid! I hear he's failing rapidly, and unless things take a very unexpected turn, Tony will be Lord Birchington before the year is out. Is that a chance to fling away to go and preach to pigtails—yes, the last barbaric touch is China!—and get decapitated with the next deserving batch of methodistical mischief-makers? But it's all too frightful and amazing when one remembers her advantages; the most ruinous school in Paris, the most thievish milliner in town.'

'Isn't it doubtful whether a suburban education and an inexpensive taste in hats would have averted the catastrophe? You know papa had crazes, supported women's suffrage and collected Huguenot wills—and——'

'Your poor father, Stella, never went beyond absurdity. If this were only silly—but it's low. It *sounds* so low, and—and—violent. One knows of two or three nice girls with disappointments or deformities who have very properly taken vows,—but—a missionary! As I said to Laurence when she brought it out, Why not a cassowary or a kangaroo! I was quite light-headed.'

'What is the process; I suppose there is a scheme?'

'Merciful Heaven, is there not a scheme! A course, a three years' course, a whirligig of physic and jargon in the company of over-educated riff-raff in some neighbourhood called Bloomsbury. I said at once she couldn't have the brougham, but it appears, and providentially, that piety contents itself with cabs. It's all sublimity and flighty twaddle. The duties and decencies of life, of course, are dross. I hear from Bennet, she is giving half her evening frocks away.'

'That suggests more than a passing whim.'

'She wrote last night to Tony giving him his *congé* as calmly as you leave an *entré,* and you talk of passing whims!'

'They must have quarrelled.'

'My dear good simpleton, you cannot quarrel with stained glass, a flat saint in a painted window is the present pose. The next stage will be seeing visions. *Après!* Well, I wish you joy of coming back to this volcano of a house and waiting for the next eruption.'

'That will probably not be in our direction. If I know Tony, he will do his share.'

For her part, Stella did not contemplate more than the mildest interference. Laurence had persistently, not consciously, indeed, but most effectually made her ineffective, and if fate, if folly, intervened so late on her behalf, by all the laws of compensation why not let them intervene? She took a book from a side table and began to turn the leaves.

But Lady Armitage proceeded buoyantly, 'Talk of religion! I consider it profane. If it were one of those poor Howard girls, one could see some sort of a divine provision in it, or Winifred du Port, an incarnation of morbid fads, hygienic underclothes, large candles and small clergy, there's your article ready-made. But Laurence is not even *passée*!'

'Or if it were I!' commented Stella, placidly, 'the element of tragedy would disappear, my opportunities being meagre, my distinction *nil,* my present and future, in fine, devoid of any possibilities which annihilation could affect. I admit, with compunction, it should certainly have been—I.'

'My dear Stella, don't, for goodness' sake, be so incorrigibly selfish. Is this a moment for a display of egotism when your sister's social and practical salvation is at stake?'

'Need one take the matter quite so seriously? The probation will prove too unpleasant. Time will mix his usual sedative and she will take it. I imagine Laurence——'

The supposition was not achieved; it was arrested by the entrance of the girl herself. She supported wonderfully a wonderful gown, but she wore beauty with a more positive and finished grace.

The apparel with which God clothes His creatures is, but for the rents man's fall may make in it, most fitting; hers was exquisitely fine. Fineness was its distinctive texture, fairness its prevailing hue. The white skin, delicately flushed, the features not severe in detail, but statuesque in purity of structure, the hazel eyes darting at times an almost yellow light, were crowned with hair, which, but for its pale brilliancy, looked like a covering of blanched and faded gold. Tonight, her neck and arms were bare, and the slight, upright figure asserted its youth and curious simplicity of outline in spite of an elaborate and costly gown.

Lady Armitage greeted this apparition with another aggressive sigh, while nodding approval of her daughter's toilette.

Stella looked up and said, without inflection, 'You look as usual like a truant angel; but mamma has just proved conclusively that you are merely a wayward, feverish and very stupid child.'

'I cannot refute mamma', the girl said, with a note of weariness.

Her intonation was slow and extremely clear, a high, sweet treble. Someone had called it a 'retarded voice', and it was certainly marked by an unstudious drawl.

'Do you know', her sister proceeded, 'what people will say if this ridiculous report of your broken engagement gets about?'

'Much that is absurd, probably. I cannot speculate.'

'They will say you have been jilted.'

'Fortunately, or unfortunately, that is exactly the reverse of fact.'

'So much the better for its plausibility. The world does not restrict itself to facts.'

'The "world", or our small section of it, may as well leave me out of its reckoning; I shall so soon be leaving it out of mine.'

'Miserable child; but *we* aren't leaving it!' her mother broke in with a gesture of acute exasperation. 'Stella and I remain to face the innuendos and grimaces, the revolting rumours upon which you turn your back.'

'And you will deal with them infinitely better than I ever could.'

'That is true enough,' said Stella, 'but irrelevant. The world—to use a phrase—mamma and I and Tony, may all be immensely inferior to the exigencies of your suddenly-discovered soul or mission, or whatever it may be, but you owe us more consideration, more response.'

'To remonstrance? What answer can I give? This new voice in my ear contends against old voices, insists that I relinquish near, dear things, for what is strange and far.'

'You can at least show us the consideration of delay', Stella pursued, urging the point most likely to win concession.

Laurence got up and with an unusually rapid motion pushed back her chair.

'Ah! no', she cried, seeming in one swift gesture to thrust off the vision of that angel who was spreading an unlawful world before her view. '*That* I cannot do. Delay is, for me, denial. What I do I must do quickly. Oh! mamma and I have talked so much of this, and words have availed so little. Will you not leave it for tonight?' With a lingering, halting sweetness of appeal, a plea on her own side for patience, she added, 'Things cannot seem so strange to anyone as they do just now to me.'

She crossed the room ostensibly to reach her cloak from a table by the window, where it had been flung upon her entrance; but her real movement was towards her sister—an appeal for recognition, comprehension. Stella connected her approach with a domestic grievance and rose to push a curtain back and glance into the twinkling street.

'We shall have to get rid of Dykes, sooner or later; he is making a dogma of unpunctuality', she announced, generally. Then turning to Laurence, who faced her, passive, undivined, unanswered, she observed, 'In spite of perplexities, you are looking very well tonight.'

The girl's aspect indeed provoked the dispassionate remark. Loveliness illumined her like a faint flame, seeming to hold its light up to the dusk of Stella's face; a face suggesting twilight, dim and dotted with unnoticeable features; dun, not dark—an early wintry dusk without the stars. Stella had sought to clear this portrait, but she retouched it with a despondent hand. The carefully-accentuated eyebrows and reticently-tinted cheeks could only partially rescue from obscurity a face which Nature meant to be ignored; and she was never unaware that this obscurity was deepened by her sister's luminous proximity, that they enforced a contrast scarcely kind. But now she suddenly flung off disloyalty. This poor little victim, standing there, discarding life, binding itself to a shadowy stake, ready to be burnt up by supernatural fire, could not assume the aspect of a foe. An impulse of compassion, then of rescue seized her, swiftly followed by the conviction of its impracticability. Laurence had put herself out of reach. She was adopting new phrases, twisting her point of view. The things most clear, and, perhaps, too, most dark, to her were those which no one but herself could see. The child, she concluded, must be left to folly, since there appeared to be no wisdom within call profound enough to protest against it, and it was upon this conclusion that she said at last, 'I shall not add to your perplexities, you may reckon me among the few people who will let you be.'

'That makes you my best friend.'

'Or one of your worst enemies. Are you, just now, quite capable of making the distinction?'

She spoke coldly, though not a moment since she had felt the first flicker of warmth about her heart. To think coldly, and so to speak her thought, was Stella's way. On an afterthought, she said abruptly, 'You have a good deal to squander, and of that youth is the costliest part. These are your best years. They will not come over again. You would be wise to ask yourself if you can spare them. But you will not be wise.'

'Oh! I know I am hopeless, incurable', the girl responded lightly, yet with a wistfulness which made the light admission grave.

II

Life had afforded to Laurence Armitage no preparation of petty contests for this momentous one. It was the first—immediate and supreme.

She stood this afternoon, confronting, in the person of her lover, the visible foe attacking that invisible Friend who had but recently, and in so strange a fashion, placed Himself beside her; and at the moment, in the presence of this man, she was acutely conscious of that combative, coercive power from which she had once shrunk, to which, linked with some gentler, but no less resistless force, she had eventually given way. He had not won this girl—whose years passed scarcely beyond the barrier of childhood, whose heart but yesterday had loitered in that garden—without some expenditure of energy and display of skill.

She had loved reluctantly, afraid of love, and yielded sweetly at the last to an allurement shorn of fear, as children will. But now, today, she faced in him again that spectre, shunned by the child she used to be and was no more, with ruth and tears.

'Cannot I keep your pity, though?' She spread her hands out mutely, conclusively rejecting love.

'What have you and I to do with pity? I can't offer you anything more, anything less than love.'

'I would keep that.' She swayed towards it. 'Only to you it means simply possession, satisfaction.'

'To "have and to hold", and all the rest. It means the same to everyone. Why, Laurie, I remember you used almost the same words. I remember the time almost to a minute, and the frock you wore and the way the light fell on your hair and the tune the band was playing;

always afterwards it seemed to be your tune. "If you will have it so", you said, and stopped, and then, "Yes, I am yours to care for and to keep." Don't *you* remember? And now you speak as if it were some paltry version of my own. It once was yours.'

She did not dispute it, dared not pause on such remembrances.

'You slip, then, straight out of my life?'

The attitude of strange detachment in the still white figure by the window quickened his resistance.

'No', he said decisively.

'But you called friendship, when I spoke of it, "a threadbare story". And I think I know you will not be my friend.'

'That was never really your alternative?'

Her hands hung limply down; her lids were drooping, her face pale; she had the aspect of a wind-weary, rainless flower. He crossed the room and caught her hanging hands.

'Laurie,' he said, seriously perplexed, 'you seem to have lost the power to look at anything in a natural way.'

'I have', she answered simply.

'I haven't. I won't take this business to pieces. One doesn't fight with shadows; one steps through them; I step through it—come to you. It is with you I have to do, and I am here to stand between you and your unrealities, to shut them out: I mean to stand. Today, tomorrow, you must see that I am your reality, and you will smile at this new bogey.'

'That is not a good description of my new purpose.'

He loosed impatiently the passive fingers, turned away.

'You would be more human, pardonable, if you wanted to jilt me for another man.'

'I think not,' she said sadly, 'but I know that to no one do I seem either pardonable or human. You put love to my lips, I may not taste it; where did I read it? "Some deep energy compels me to choose hunger." I have no choice but that.'

'A month ago you were yourself.'

'I was my own, or yours, perhaps; or seemed to be.'

'I cannot follow you—I don't pretend to find my way into your maze—the whole thing baffles me. I haven't changed, but you, God knows, you're almost like a stranger, talking some queer new language, looking at me as if there were some tremendous space between us. A month ago, it was you and I, and the world outside.'

'Will you hear me?' she pleaded gently; and even at this moment of peculiar disturbance, it afforded him a distinct, dispassionate pleasure to listen to the high, sweet tones of that meandering voice.

Taking his silence for indulgence, she acknowledged it with a quivering smile.

'I look backward', she began with the sustained intonation which precludes a long story, 'to see that this has always been, in a cant phrase, my fate. As a child, I remember looking down from our high nursery windows on the children, far below us under the railings of the park—vagrants, playing vagrant games, and even then I longed, I think, in a dreamy childish fashion to teach them prettier ways of play. That passed, and then at school in Paris, I used to wish I had the trick of helping wayward spirits, and girls can'—she explained with a little smile—'be wayward like their brothers, though they seem so tame. All this was latent, crude; I saw in it a sanctimonious trait, and tried to check it. It passed, too, unrealized, a vague ideal or "crank", perhaps, and then when I left school we lived too fast for thought; it was a maze of parties and of people with not much room for actual life. It was indeed only a month ago that enlightenment and my summons came.'

'Delivered', he asked sardonically, 'by some sandy-haired parson in the North?'

'No—put straight into my hands by a hectic creature, as I was leaving Euston by the night mail.'

'You don't mean to tell me that your sanity was shaken by a flimsy—tract?'

'If you put it that way, yes. It was flimsy, and I made it absently a marker for my book. That bored me and I read the leaflet through. It contained the usual mixture of sensationalism and inconsequence. It was vapid, hysterical, illogical, and yet it was my message, all the same.'

'Then there you lost your balance? For God's sake don't; you know you're doing that; to leave your world, to cut adrift your people—me! We are bound to see the twist—but can't you see it? For a moment you lost your balance——'

'For a moment I did lose it, but it was not then and there I saw, was forced to see, my way.' She paused, recalling, trying to frame the record of dark hours, and went on: 'A struggle followed. A woman does not reject so lightly the obvious allurements of life; she cannot view loneliness, exile, age and its sequel so easily as that. The prospect was awful and bewildering—more so to me than it can seem to you; and for a time it stunned me. At first I could not face it, but conclusion came at length from some words I chanced upon one troubled night at random, and these struck deeper than the first incoherent call. "Behold, I have set before thee an open door and no man can shut it. . . . Hold that fast which thou hast, that no man take thy crown." I would even then have stopped my ears; I could not; I was haunted, shadowed by the phrase, "no man can shut it"; there did not seem a hint of choice. Such crowns are sharp, press cruelly; indeed, though for myself, I see no shadow of one, I know they can wring blood from the brows that wear them. But it is not a crown I see at all, only an open door.'

'Did nothing tell you', he persisted, in the manner of humouring a child, 'that you were unaccountably possessed?'

'I was possessed', she admitted quietly. 'Visible signs became obscure; invisible things grew curiously actual. The figures of the world retreated as though behind a screen; its voices were a distant babel; my own short life, and time—the time of ages—seemed only a little while; love, even with your image in its eyes, a mortal toy. This did not last; it could not, it appalled me; yet'—the refrain was musical, mechanical—'it was my message all the same.'

'Briefly, you will pick your way to glory, and send me to the devil. That is the plain and vulgar fact. But if I say you shall not? Haven't I the right to say it? Your first pledge was to me; calls and visions do not leave you honourably free to break it. I shall hold you to it. I shall fight, I warn you, Laurie, and stubbornly for my own——'

'I beseech you not.' She leaned towards him, borrowing from her soul a posture, an inflection of acute dismay.

The accent, the attitude was that of a child in terror-stricken prayer. Of old she had denied, resisted, never yet put forth a plea. This suppliance of hers provoked in him a novel consciousness of passion, a dull sense of pity, moving him finally towards her spirit, forcing response to the spirit's plea. To that appeal, some force outside himself, his individual need, his pain, and his perplexity, made answer.

'If I yield tamely,' he said at last, 'it will make your wild way easier.'

'If you do not, you will break me.'

She seemed as he glanced down on her, half shattered now; so tireless and yet so weary, formidably frail.

'How?' he asked, not following her thought.

'I cannot explain. I simply feel that if your power stooped to roughness, it would snap me—like a twig.'

'Your whim—or what you call your purpose?'

'No; just myself.'

'You understand that you have broken me? That doesn't seem to touch you.'

'But it does,' she cried, sweeping a hand across her eyes, 'God knows and pities me, it does. It blinds, bewilders me.'

'Then you still care?'

'There is no "still" in love', she answered quietly.

'You are beyond me.' He grew harsh. 'Dead or dying, as we uninspired people reckon life.'

'One does not die because—one suffers. Everything can kill—but pain——'

She found for this a slow and wavering smile which matched her utterance and provoked him by its difficult composure.

'I will make you live', he broke out almost brutally and stopped. Her pallor startled him, her face of fear.

'God help us both', he ended. It was more an imprecation than a prayer. 'I scare you, and you make me, somehow, half a fool and half a brute. The man that's left can't reach the woman in you. I suppose there's nothing more to say.'

She held her hand out, groping that way towards pardon, but he left her quickly, his farewell spoken in the prosaic click of the closing door. Now she raised her eyes and held him in her gaze; now she laid her heart under his hand to throb its story. Vainly. She might keep him thus, would keep him, in the coming years, his presence never lost, her secret. But with him it would be different. If not present to his sense, his spirit would not feel her by. He would remember her in bitterness, or, losing bitterness, forget. Her old world she saw already in the dimness of the twilight, and the new gave yet no hint of dawn. Upon the space between them, blank and starless, she let fall a sudden rain of tears.

Stella found her sobbing quietly, still standing by the window at the end of the big empty room.

'This is not heroic, Laurie. Has Tony dragged you back to womanhood, reconverted you to common sense?'

'He has gone in anger; justly cold. I have chilled every heart', she mused desolately, shivering at their cold contact.

'Because you will not let them warm you. You used to be so simple, now you have become a rather complex puzzle of which we can't fit in the parts, and if we could perhaps we shouldn't find the picture they produced convincing or attractive.'

'Stella,' the girl ventured suddenly, 'do you not believe in—God?'

A shrug of the shoulders was to have served for answer, but the girl's face called from its clearing mists a glance so newly imperative, that Stella framed a verbal substitute.

'I have never disturbed myself to analyse anything so trivial as my "belief".'

'Then you cannot even partly understand.'

'I don't aspire to. But in my metallic way, I give you credit for sincerity, and some misguided pluck; your distress distresses me, though not to the point of weakness.'

'Oh', the poor child cried, as the mist gathered in her eyes again, 'it is a wicked thing to say, but I wish, oh! how I wish, that some of us were weaker than we are!'

III

Laurence and Lucy Moreton, the pretty typical evangelists, had shut the door upon the crowded room and found themselves on the dark stairs. The party, given by the students in their honour, had been a jovial, rather noisy farewell feast, and Laurence found that to have seen the end of them was an immense relief. For they had jarred—not tonight only—no—for three almost intolerable years. They were so unmodulated she thought wearily, not of her world at all—what Stella, who had seen them once, had called 'betweens'.

The people of her world had jarred in other days—but differently. Their pose and twang was more familiar, lighter and less vehement. It was of vehemence and all the cant of small solemnities that she had grown so tired. Yet they had been, she hastened to remind herself, extremely kind. 'Extremely kind.' The phrase suggested Lucy. Why did Lucy's phrases always sound so ready-made? She turned to her and said abruptly: 'Do you know I am in the mood to fling up everything tonight?'

'That sounds like a whisper from the enemy,' returned the little enthusiast in her conventional pious fashion. 'When you have had your call——'

'Oh!' said Laurence with a touch of irritation. 'There are so many calls. How does one know, I wonder, if one has caught the real voice?'

But as she spoke, she felt her insincerity; had she not almost ceased to hear? Three years ago, viewed from afar, with all its sadness and its severance, what a romantic possibility her sacrifice had seemed. That picture had lost lustre, inspiration, and vitality; its tone tonight was an intolerable grey. And then repenting of the momentary petulance, she added—

'Perhaps it is as well that we are going out together; you see straighter and feel more simply than I ever shall. I suppose it is that I am tired—of—of people and exams, and tea-parties, and all this week's farewells. Good-night.'

And as she said it, she was conscious of being a little tired of Lucy too.

She hailed a hansom and was driven home.

Her soul had lost its footing; she knew that. It beat itself distractedly against a chill, dark air; peered helplessly into obscurity; listened with strained intentness for the still voice to speak again, imperatively, conclusively, as it had done before. Its obdurate silence silenced her; she was not able to send forth a cry. Where was the great Deliverer? Invisible, inaudible; another counsellor was near. 'Reclaim your life,' it urged, 'it is yours to keep and not to cast away.'

Yes, faith was assuredly failing her, and with it, power. Faith will 'remove mountains', but unfaith, to the spirit's vision, will remove them too.

Reaching her rooms, she turned the light on hastily. Oh! she must have light, if only this prosaic, unilluminative glare!

Stella and Lady Armitage were out: they seemed to be always out when she came in. Wherever they might be tonight, she wished herself with them. A hunger seized her, she felt starved; a hunger for the old irresponsible existence, the hum of futile conversation, for the 'swish' of skirts, music, the odour of familiar essences—yet she had never liked perfumes; she sickened for them now, only because they might restore the sense of some extinguished fragrance in the air of life. Her own dress was redolent of smoke and chemicals; she went swiftly into the adjoining room and changed it for an evening gown. Coming back, she began to pace up and down the long, luxurious room. It painted the picture of the easy past in delicately brilliant tints, and all her chosen things were there. She began fingering them feverishly, the costly knick-knacks strewn about it, their contact bringing some tangible assuagement of her hardly comprehended pain.

She stood looking at her little gallery of water-colours, oddly, unsymmetrically hung; at the rich, unlooped curtains, and the shallow, velvet shelves, upon which rows of unframed photographs were tilted in long lines against the wall.

These portraits stared at her in merciless reminder of the barren present, a strange crew; authors and opera singers, known and unknowable celebrities, chance acquaintances, and friends. It had been early a marked trait of hers not to lose memory of faces which had pleased or spoken or impressively passed by; part of a keen and instinctive feeling that she must not let slip even the minor loveliness of life. Now they demanded its retention, challenged dismissal, joining their own to that persistent utterance which breathed 'stay'. The crowd of faces congregated round her, and from its midst emerged the one she shunned supremely; his whose, while her will remained, she must with the last remnant of it shut away. She could, she would not meet it, and her head dropped desperately down upon her hands.

An hour, two hours passed. She lay back listening for the sound of wheels in the deserted street below.

At length the clock chimed two; some minutes later she heard Stella's step ascend the stairs and travel past her door. Would sleep befriend her? Lately it had touched her eyes reluctantly, come loth, aversely, to a sleepless heart.

And speech? she wanted speech, but could not gain the hearing of her own deaf spirit. Was Stella's deafer? She went swiftly out and made her way along the unlit passage to her sister's room.

Stella was lounging in an armchair by the fire. 'Why are you up'? she inquired yawning. 'I thought "your holiness" retired at ten. I suppose you know your limits, but you are making a wreck—to be accurate, an exquisite wreck of yourself. Is it worth while?'

'If you mean my looks, what does it matter? Are they really gone?'

'Temporarily rubbed out. Of course it matters little to anybody, if not to you; but it reminds one for the millionth time of the proverbial irony of life. Now I, for instance, would sell my soul for your beauty, while you are placidly bartering your beauty for your soul.'

'Not placidly; tonight I imagine both might be put up at a low figure.'

'What's the matter? Has your visit to the menagerie brought on a headache? Did the inmates howl?'

'Not more than usual. Stella—I have lost my way.'

'That is tragic, but not final; and as we regard it, scarcely loss.'

'You know what I mean', the girl said wretchedly. 'It was foolish of me to come to you.'

'If you want recuperative texts. I am religiously illiterate. Get Bennet to make you some coffee and go to bed.'

'I know it's late, but would it bore you dreadfully if I stayed here a little while? Please don't scoff. I have a stupid dread of everything tonight; myself, my room, the world outside, the place I'm going to. You know we sail a week today.'

'Sit down', said Stella. 'Try the chair with the green cushions. Now I come to think of it, I don't see much of you. And is it really a week today? You strange unhappy child!'

Laurence pushed the chair aside, advanced and stood before her sister, looking down with burning, over-brilliant eyes which had absorbed all the vitality of the white face from which they shone.

'Stella, I must go on.'

'But not tonight', said Stella quietly. 'Tonight you've stopped. That's obvious.'

'Tomorrow then. I—must—go—on.'

'If that's the programme for tomorrow, you had better sleep tonight.'

'I cannot sleep, or if I do, my dreams are ugly, haunted.' She forced a smile and change of tone.

'That is a nice new frock of yours, one of Félise's inspirations? It seems ages since I saw Félise. Where have you been?'

'Must I exert myself to remember? There—and home, and—Oh, by the way, I met Tony somewhere. He is prepared to make a last attack. The news of your departure has disturbed him. He looks menacing and says ominously little. Isn't his tenacity commendable?'

'He must not come, you told him so.'

'I imagined that to be your business. But, my dear, he will, and having waited all this time, he may be difficult to deal with.'

'I know. I cannot see him.'

'Tell him so.'

'I cannot tell him—Stella.' She threw her hands out. 'If I give way—break down, what should you say?'

'That you have wasted a deplorable amount of energy and time. I should congratulate you with reservations; but unfortunately you will not "give way".'

The girl knelt down and with a dreary, childish exclamation, laid her head upon her sister's knee.

'I could go on', she stammered—'if—if there were anyone to pray for me. Not those people who are always praying.' She flung off the vision of those 'people' with a gesture almost petulant—'but someone—different; you, you know. I cannot; I have missed my way.'

Stella drew off her gloves deliberately and put a hand upon the pale, soft hair. Her voice struck hard on her own ear in her attempt to soften it.

'Failing—er—intercession', she said presently, 'I must substitute coffee.'

And she got up to ring the bell.

IV

'I heard you were leaving England, and I came to say good-bye.'

It was an unconsidered speech and Anthony Gurney stammered over it; it was not what he had come to say. The words were wrung from him; they broke baldly upon a silence, which to his sense struck passion dumb; a stillness unresponsive, mute as death, which like death's delicate presence seemed to pervade the room.

The girl before him held this silence in her eyes, it clung to her pale lips, and lay upon her white, impassive brow.

He could hardly identify this presentment of her with that of the actual being who was to have been his wife. She faced him like the wraith of one whom he had thought to meet in flesh, but met, in fact, remote from it, under the aspect of an unexpected apparition; and he shrank from the strange encounter as the living shrink from death.

She had said once—the phrase was lodged in memory—'if your power stoops to roughness, it will break me'; and it was with this intent that he had come, only to find her unassailable, walled round by this fine silence, and guarded by a serenity which seemed not to belong to any world of his.

He waited, with unaccustomed patience, for her reply.

It came slowly; it sounded slow, even from that retarded voice; the cold prosaic utterance cut through him like a remembered thrust of steel.

'Yes, we are sailing in a day or two; it was kind of you to think of me.'

Was this, she wondered, what he had come to say? Was it against this colourless 'Good-bye', that she had fought so many nights—so many nights?

The haggard hours reappeared, took shape in thought to mock her baseless fear. She might have spared herself that struggle in which she seemed to have spilt her spirit's blood.

It was his moment, had he known it, for revolt against the vainness of victory that had brought her to the verge of a supreme defeat.

A breath of passion would have blown her towards him, swept the fluttering leaf into his hand, but there was something in her distant gaze, her parted presence which forced him, for the moment, to suspend that breath.

A band struck up in the street outside; he listened relievedly to its gasping delivery of a familiar air; the brazen wail restored him grotesquely to external life, recalled the social exigencies of the moment.

'I suppose you will wear the native costume', he ventured aimlessly, at length; 'it ought to suit you, though you are so fair.'

'Yes, I suppose I shall in time; they say the people take more kindly to one, if one does.'

'They will take kindly to you, anyhow. You know'—he smiled mechanically, he seemed to be babbling like a marionette—'you have a charm.'

'I had', she admitted simply, 'but Stella tells me it is growing "beautifully less".'

'A sisterly mistake.' He felt himself becoming momentarily more vapid. 'How is she?'

'As usual; very robust and very gay.'

It occurred to him how often he saw Stella, how in the future he would still be seeing Stella; that carefully draped and tinted personality, so uninteresting, noticeable only as a perpetual reminder of this other woman, now tangible, and near, but soon to be remote and irreclaimable.

An assertive impulse seized him. He must crash through the numbing stillness of her presence, defy it and dispel it. But he had missed his moment, it was passed. The empty commonplaces which they had just exchanged had steadied her, and feeling a frail security, she kept it when, after a pause, he attacked it with—

'I did not come to talk inanities. We are not dummies. Let us be human. I had better tell you what I really came to say.'

'No'! she said, summoning a coldness which seemed to be for her like death to desperate creatures, waiting within call, 'not if it is something which I cannot hear.'

'But you must hear it.'

His hard insistency struck like a blow against her clear reluctant voice.

'You came to say good-bye.'

She found a smile, held out her hand with a conclusive gesture of dismissal, adding, 'Forgive me, I have nothing else to say.'

He felt the flavour of an oath upon his tongue, the dust and smoke of failure flung into his eyes; a faint sweet bugle sounded his retreat, but ere he made it, he advanced a step.

'I have a right to ask one question. Are you happy?'

Her frame, her spirit seemed suddenly stung, then frozen to torpor by a rush of ice-like air.

Her lips were stiffened by it, but she moved them. 'Absolutely happy.'

He accepted it and she was left alone.

V

The door had just closed upon Lady Armitage's impressive figure, clad in sumptuous mourning, an orthodox embodiment of maternal grief. Her temporary absence appeared to Stella in the light of one of life's remaining mercies; she got up and crossed the room.

She caught her own reflection in one of the long mirrors. No, she had never looked, she never would look, even passable in black.

She paused to take note of the new lines with which the last few weeks had marked her face. They did not alter it materially, how should they? Hers was not a face—the knowledge had ceased to sting her—which sorrow or even time could mar. She was not old, and yet she would never be young again. Life was not thrilling, it never had been that; but it was no longer mildly entertaining; and she surveyed the prospective length of it; it seemed so long, she thought, before one might reasonably expect to die.

But this was sheer morbidity. She shook it off and went towards the window, looking out. The carriage was below; she watched her mother enter it and, after some fussy directions, drive away. The great room seemed intolerably empty; and yet this view of it was hardly new. Laurence must long have left a void, only she had not fully realized it before. In her cold and curious fashion, she had missed the child—she always thought of Laurence as 'the child'—and now the child was—where?

She left the window and sat down at a littered davenport, taking from a drawer some covered sheets and a telegraphic envelope. There was no need to reread them; every line was painfully familiar; first the pink message, curt and callously official: 'Laurence Armitage massacred, with others; will send particulars', and above it, the comic, unpronounceable foreign name of the place from which it was dispatched.

She put it down; the words had been so horrible, so startling, a few weeks ago, and this afternoon they wore a commonplace, accustomed aspect, like the ordinary delivery of news one might naturally expect to hear.

'Laurence Armitage'—Laurie, yes; she was going back upon her first stunned reception of the bald announcement; that *was* her sister's name.

The door opened. 'Captain Gurney' was announced. She held out a hand to the advancing figure, but did not rise.

'Please sit down', she said. 'Mamma had to go out. I am to offer profuse apologies, and you must accept them, as I did not tell her till the last moment that I was expecting you.'

'Thank you.' His relief was frank. 'I should have come, but not—so soon. You sent for me?'

She took up the papers. 'There is something that you will like to have. I wished to give it you myself. It seems that she'—love and death make definite and sufficient a bare pronoun—'she wrote a fragmentary note to you. I have it here.'

Without replying, he put out his hand for it.

'Perhaps you will read this first', she suggested, offering him a more closely-written page. 'It comes from Miss Moreton—the girl who went out with her—was with her. I wrote to ask for some remembrances of—of Laurie, and she has kindly and promptly sent me this. It has the twang, but one need not be critical; the girl was evidently fond of—her.'

He took the proffered sheet and read it through. It was headed by the tragic semi-farcical foreign name.

'Dear Miss Armitage', it began, 'as you have asked me, I will write all I can remember about our dear sister who is now—one cannot but rejoice to know—with God. I need not repeat details of the terrible catastrophe; you will be only too familiar with them by now. Some days before the dreadful—yet in a sense, blessed—morning, we had been warned to keep inside the gates—it was considered safer; but she was nursing a little native boy in one of the huts outside, and it seemed impossible to keep her from what she felt she had to do. She was always splendidly brave and fearless, and death came to her in the Master's service. I believe now she must have known she had to suffer it for His sake. We saved ourselves; she seemed to have no self to save. She was truly "faithful unto death", and Christ has given her a "crown of life".

'We feel we have lost less a comrade than a light, for His light shone through her. Her spirit seemed a torch which did not flicker and could not fail. She sat often silent, while we chattered, but her presence was so illuminating we hardly missed her speech. I fancy she thought we "gushed" a little, and I once asked her if that were so. "Ah", she said, "you think me cold, but am I so critical? I hoped I had got over that. I try, in my most wayward moments, to remember that we are all warming our hearts at the same fire".

'Her beauty made a great impression on the people; it was an earthly gift, which she was permitted to make use of in the heavenly work. She promised extraordinary power, and we imagined a great future for her, not knowing it was to be greater than any we foresaw. "The Master is come and calleth for thee." She went willingly at that call. Latterly, her health showed signs of failing, and we urged rest upon her, but she would not take it. She did not spare herself or seem to set any value upon her life. They say, at the last, she might have saved herself, but would not—did not seem to care. We were speaking once of memories and she said, "My sweetest memory in heaven would be of some soul on earth that I had saved." But the Master did not give her time to work for Him. He had appointed her to die. "Dear in the sight of the Lord is the death of His Saints." They met it gladly; it could not touch them, for they had pre-conquered death.

'I think I have told you all I can remember. She said very little; it was only with the people that her reticence took flight. Accept my sympathy in your great sorrow; our tears for her, for all of them, are triumph; even our mourning strikes a note of joy, and that it may be blessed to all of us is the fervent prayer of—Yours sincerely, LUCY MORETON.'

He returned the letter without comment. 'May I have the—the note you spoke of? It may be an answer to a cowardly appeal I sent; how long it seems! and yet it is not more than a few weeks ago.'

'You must forgive me', Stella explained, 'for looking through it, not noticing at first that it was obviously meant for you.'

His glance fell on the page of foreign note which she held out to him; he looked for a moment stupidly at the characters of the clear, decorative hand. The light was retreating, leaving the room to twilight. Stella lit two candles, and placed them on the table, but he went towards the window, preferring distance and a dimmer light. While he stood there, she sat steeped in the heavy silence, staring at the steady cones of flame.

The roll of wheels outside, monotonously audible, seemed, as he read, to rumble in his brain.

The letter started without preface and evidenced haste or agitation; it was undated and began: 'Your note, this morning, lies in pieces upon my table. It is one I could not keep. It seems as if my old life were in shreds, unreadable as that. I think it is. I have not answered you before, because I could not; I felt weak and faltering and distracted;

now something tells me that I must. Why do you tempt me to unfaithfulness so late? You force me, almost cruelly, to turn to you, but if I turn, it is only for a moment and with my body not my soul. If I come back to you—you say I must—I must be sent, as I was sent away from you, by some diviner voice, and that, I cannot hear. I have lost hearing. Once before I lost it, but it came back; it will come back again. I wait. I am alone. I suffer too. Love means so much beyond what we call joy. You say—you cannot mean it? that my "sanctity" as you call it, is purchased by your ruin. Is that true? The thought is terrible. It has bewildered me. Once, as I told you, I saw simply "an open door". I went, or seemed to go, straight through it. But now you have confused my sight. I see two doors; one leads to you and one beyond you, but towards which the divine finger points, I cannot see. I wait for that; a sign—a vision of my way. Be patient, gentler with me. I need patience too. I have my moments also of rebellion and despair. The sense of what I have made you suffer seems more than I can bear. Forgive me, for my life is not my own. The very tears that fall upon this paper seem not to belong to me. Will you be patient? Soon, certainly, clearly I shall see. I seem upon the verge of dawn—not far from some conclusive light. When once my path is plain I shall not waver; I shall go through it, when I find my door. I know you do not understand, but wait, with me—*for* me, perhaps. I send——'

It bore no signature; broke off abruptly; ended there. He folded it, and turned to Stella, holding the paper loosely in his hand. They faced in silence, two dark figures in the darkening room. After a long oppressive pause he came towards her and stood looking down upon the upturned unlovely face, thrown into pale and almost startling prominence by the two tall candles, between which he peered. His was in shadow, only faintly illumined by them, and as she saw it, it looked grey.

'She would have come back—to me', was his first heavy utterance. It seemed so idle Stella passed it by. But he returned to it. 'You don't suppose', he urged, with desperate persistence, 'that she wasn't coming back to me?'

He was used to Stella's unresponsiveness; he took her silence now for acquiescence and went on.

'I feel a clod; incapable of thought, incapable of pain. What are you thinking?'

'Not of what you made her suffer; for God, I take it, loved her better and He made her suffer even more. I was thinking', she answered, with a new note of tenderness, 'of wasted love—and life. And of that "sweetest memory" of hers denied. It seems hard she should have missed the thing she gave her life to gain.'

'But you are rational; you of all people don't believe in "souls" and "salvation" and the rest.'

'I believe in saints. I did not. But I have thought just lately that this—what can one call it?—awful sacrifice, should make of one either a thorough infidel or a thorough Christian. Most of us halt contemptibly between the two.'

'I didn't know you were that sort. I have never gone in for that kind of thing at all.'

'Nor I', she said quietly, 'till now. But this last week it has occurred to me—I don't know why I tell you—what if that "sweetest memory" of hers—you see how the phrase sticks—what if the soul she wanted for remembrance and did not live—but perhaps died to save—were—mine?'

'Good God'! he cried, 'surely this ghastly tragedy has turned you sick. You are not acquiescing in it, preparing to profit by it in some strained, unnatural way?'

'If I did, don't you see, it would be her doing and not mine; her way of coming back and talking over things, of making me share now what in the past I would not share. I should be glad, I think, if things turned out that way.'

A strange antagonism seized him. What if, after all, the dead *had* memories? If she should have a memory—the right to that was his, not Stella's—nobody's but his.

'Pull yourself together', he urged roughly. 'You are getting touched by—by——'

'By the poor child's madness', she finished for him. 'I think not.'

He turned to go, turned back again, and faced her with a new insistence.

'Don't take it that way—any way but that! But no, you don't, you can't take it—that way.'

She moved towards the window and the twilight.

'It's too soon—too strange. I do not know.'

A WHITE NIGHT

'THE incident', said Cameron, 'is spoiled inevitably in the telling, by its merely accidental quality of melodrama, its sensational machinery, which, to the view of anyone who didn't witness it, is apt to blur the finer outlines of the scene. The subtlety, or call it the significance, is missed, and unavoidably, as one attempts to put the thing before you, in a certain casual crudity, and inessential violence of fact. Make it a medieval matter—put it back some centuries—and the affair takes on its proper tone immediately, is tinctured with the sinister solemnity which actually enveloped it. But as it stands, a recollection, an experience, a picture, well, it doesn't reproduce; one must have the original if one is going to hang it on one's wall.'

In spite of which I took it down the night he told it and, thanks to a trick of accuracy, I believe you have the story as I heard it, almost word for word.

It was in the spring of 1876, a rainless spring, as I remember it, of white roads and brown crops and steely skies.

Sent out the year before on mining business, I had been then some eighteen months in Spain. My job was finished; I was leaving the Black Country, planning a vague look round, perhaps a little sport among the mountains, when a letter from my sister Ella laid the dust of doubtful schemes.

She was on a discursive honeymoon. They had come on from Florence to Madrid, and disappointed with the rank modernity of their last halt, wished to explore some of the least known towns of the interior: 'Something unique, untrodden, and uncivilized', she indicated modestly. Further, if I were free and amiable, and so on, they would join me anywhere in Andalusia. I was in fact to show them round.

I did 'my possible'; we roughed it pretty thoroughly, but the young person's passion for the strange bore her robustly through the risks and discomforts of those wilder districts which at best, perhaps, are hardly woman's ground.

King, on occasion nursed anxiety, and mourned his little luxuries; Ella accepted anything that befell, from dirt to danger, with a humorous composure dating back to nursery days—she had the instincts and the physique of a traveller, with a brilliancy of touch and a decision of attack on human instruments which told. She took our mule-drivers in hand with some success. Later, no doubt, their wretched beasts were made to smart for it, in the reaction from a lull in that habitual brutality which makes the animals of Spain a real blot upon the gay indifferentism of its people.

It pleased her to devise a lurid *Dies Irae* for these affable barbarians, a special process of reincarnation for the Spaniard generally, whereby the space of one dog's life at least should be ensured to him.

And on the day I'm coming to, a tedious, dislocating journey in a springless cart had brought her to the verge of quite unusual weariness, a weariness of spirit only, she protested, waving a hand toward our man who lashed and sang alternately, fetching at intervals a sunny smile for the poor lady's vain remonstrances before he lashed again.

The details of that day—our setting forth, our ride, and our arrival—all the minor episodes stand out with singular distinctness, forming a background in one's memory to the eventual, central scene.

We left our inn—a rough *posada*—about sunrise, and our road, washed to a track by winter rains, lay first through wide half-cultivated slopes, capped everywhere with orange trees and palm and olive patches, curiously bare of farms or villages, till one recalls the lawless state of those outlying regions and the absence of communication between them and town.

Abruptly, blotted in blue mist, vineyards and olives, with the groups of aloes marking off field boundaries, disappeared. We entered on a land of naked rock, peak after peak of it, cutting a jagged line against the clear intensity of the sky.

This passed again, with early afternoon our straight, white road grew featureless, a dusty stretch, save far ahead the sun-tipped ridge of a sierra, and the silver ribbon of the river twisting among the barren hills. Toward the end we passed one of the wooden crosses set up on these roads to mark some spot of violence or disaster. These are the only signposts one encounters, and as we came up with it, our beasts were goaded for the last ascent.

Irregular grey walls came into view; we skirted them and turned in through a Roman gateway and across a bridge into a maze of narrow stone-pitched streets, spanned here and there by Moorish arches, and execrably rough to rattle over.

A strong illusion of the Orient, extreme antiquity and dreamlike stillness marked the place.

Crossing the grey arcaded Plaza, just beginning at that hour to be splashed with blots of gaudy colour moving to the tinkling of the mule-bells, we were soon upon the outskirts of the town—the most untouched, remote and, I believe, the most remarkable that we had dropped upon.

In its neglect and singularity, it made a claim to something like supremacy of charm. There was the quality of diffidence belonging to unrecognized abandoned personalities in that appeal.

That's how it's docketed in memory—a city with a claim, which, as it happened, I was not to weigh.

Our inn, a long, one-storeyed building with caged windows, most of them unglazed, had been an old palacio; its broken fortunes hadn't robbed it of its character, its air.

The spacious place was practically empty, and the shuttered rooms, stone-flagged and cool, after our shadeless ride, invited one to a prolonged siesta; but Ella wasn't friendly to a pause. Her buoyancy survived our meal. She seemed even to face the morrow's repetition of that indescribable experience with serenity. We found her in the small paved garden, sipping chocolate and airing Spanish with our host, a man of some distinction, possibly of broken fortunes too.

The conversation, delicately edged with compliment on his side, was on hers a little blunted by a limited vocabulary, and left us both presumably a margin for imagination.

Si, la Señora, he explained as we came up, knew absolutely nothing of fatigue, and the impetuosity of the *Señora,* this attractive eagerness to make acquaintance with it, did great honour to his much forgotten, much neglected town. He spoke of it with rather touching ardour, as a place unvisited, but *'digno de renombre illustre'*, worthy of high fame.

It has stood still, it was perhaps too stationary; innovation was repellent to the Spaniard, yet this conservatism, lack of enterprise, the virtue or the failing of his country—as we pleased—had its aesthetic value. Was there not, he would appeal to the *Señora, 'una belleza de reposo'*, a beauty of quiescence, a dignity above prosperity? *'Muy bien.'* Let the *Señora* judge, you had it there!

We struck out from the town, perhaps insensibly toward the landmark of a Calvary, planted a mile or so beyond the walls, its three black shafts above the mass of roofs and pinnacles, in sharp relief against the sky, against which suddenly a flock of vultures threw the first white cloud. With the descending sun, the clear persistence of the blue was losing permanence, a breeze sprang up and birds began to call.

The Spanish evening has unique effects and exquisite exhilarations: this one led us on some distance past the Calvary and the last group of scattered houses—many in complete decay—which straggle, thinning outwards from the city boundaries into the *campo.*

Standing alone, after a stretch of crumbling wall, a wretched little *venta,* like a stop to some meandering sentence, closed the broken line.

The place was windowless, but through the open door an oath or two—the common blend of sacrilege and vileness—with a smell of charcoal, frying oil-cakes and an odour of the stable, drifted out into the freshness of the evening air.

Immediately before us lay a dim expanse of treeless plain: behind, clear cut against a smokeless sky, the flat roof lines and towers of the city, seeming, as we looked back on them, less distant than in fact they were.

We took a road which finally confronted us with a huge block of buildings, an old church and convent, massed in the shadow of a hill and standing at the entrance to three cross-roads.

The convent, one of the few remaining in the south, not fallen into ruin, nor yet put, as far as one could judge, to worldly uses, was exceptionally large. We counted over thirty windows in a line upon the western side below the central tower with its pointed turret; the eastern wing, an evidently older part, was cut irregularly with a few square gratings.

The big, grey structure was impressive in its loneliness, its blank negation of the outside world, its stark expressionless detachment.

The church, of darker stone, was massive too; its only noticeable feature a small cloister with Romanesque arcades joining the nave on its south-western wall.

A group of peasant women coming out from vespers passed us and went chattering up the road, the last, an aged creature shuffling painfully some yards behind the rest still muttering her

Madre purisima,
Madre castisima,
Ruega por nosostros,

in a kind of automatic drone.

We looked in, as one does instinctively: the altar lights which hang like sickly stars in the profound obscurity of Spanish churches were being quickly blotted out.

We didn't enter then, but turned back to the convent gate, which stood half open, showing a side of the uncorniced cloisters, and a crowd of flowers, touched to an intensity of brilliance and fragrance by the twilight. Six or seven dogs, the sandy-coloured lurchers of the country, lean and wolfish-looking hounds, were sprawling round the gateway; save for this dejected crew, the place seemed resolutely lifeless; and this absence of a human note was just. One didn't want its solitude or silence touched, its really fine impersonality destroyed.

We hadn't meant—there wasn't light enough—to try the church again, but as we passed it, we turned into the small cloister. King, who had come to his last match, was seeking shelter from the breeze which had considerably freshened, and at the far end we came upon a little door, unlocked. I don't know why we tried it, but mechanically, as the conscientious tourist will, we drifted in and groped round. Only the vaguest outlines were discernible; the lancets of the lantern at the transept crossing, and a large rose window at the western end seemed, at a glance, the only means of light, and this was failing, leaving fast the fading panes.

One half-detected, almost guessed, the blind triforium, but the enormous width of the great building made immediate mark. The darkness, masking as it did distinctive features, emphasized the sense of space, which, like the spirit of a shrouded form, gained force, intensity, from its material disguise.

We stayed not more than a few minutes, but on reaching the small door again we found it fast; bolted or locked undoubtedly in the short interval. Of course we put our backs to it and made a pretty violent outcry, hoping the worthy sacristan was hanging round or somewhere within call. Of course he wasn't. We tried two other doors; both barred, and there was nothing left for it but noise. We shouted, I suppose, for half an hour, intermittently, and King persisted hoarsely after I had given out.

The echo of the vast, dark, empty place caught up our cries, seeming to hold them in suspension for a second in the void invisibility of roof and arches, then to fling them down in hollow repetition with an accent of unearthly mimicry which struck a little grimly on one's ear; and when we paused the silence seemed alert, expectant, ready to repel the first recurrence of unholy clamour. Finally, we gave it up; the hope of a release before the dawn, at earliest, was too forlorn. King, explosive and solicitous, was solemnly perturbed, but Ella faced the situation with an admirable tranquillity. Some chocolate and a muff would certainly, for her, she said, have made it more engaging, but poor dear men, the really tragic element resolved itself into—No matches, no cigar!

Unluckily we hadn't even this poor means of temporary light. Our steps and voices sounded loud, almost aggressive, as we groped about; the darkness then was shutting down and shortly it grew absolute. We camped eventually in one of the side chapels on the south side of the chancel, and kept a conversation going for a time, but gradually it dropped. The temperature, the fixed obscurity, and possibly a curious oppression in the spiritual atmosphere relaxed and forced it down.

The scent of incense clung about; a biting chillness crept up through the aisles; it got intensely cold. The stillness too became insistent; it was literally deathlike, rigid, exclusive, even awfully remote. It shut us out and held aloof; our passive presences, our mere vitality, seemed almost a disturbance of it; quiet as we were, we breathed, but it was breathless, and as time went on, one's impulse was to fight the sort of shapeless personality it presently assumed, to talk, to walk about and make a definite attack on it. Its influence on the others was presumably more soothing, obviously they weren't that way inclined.

Five or six hours must have passed. Nothing had marked them, and they hadn't seemed to move. The darkness seemed to thicken, in a way, to muddle thought and filter through into one's brain, and waiting, cramped and cold for it to lift, the soundlessness again impressed itself unpleasantly—it was intense, unnatural, acute.

And then it stirred.

The break in it was vague but positive; it might have been that, scarcely audible, the wind outside was rising, and yet not precisely that. I barely caught, and couldn't localize the sound.

Ella and King were dozing, they had had some snatches of uncomfortable sleep; I, I suppose, was preternaturally awake. I heard a key turn, and the swing back of a door, rapidly followed by a wave of voices breaking in. I put my hand out and touched King, and in a moment, both of them waked and started up.

I can't say how, but it at once occurred to us that quiet was our cue, that we were in for something singular.

The place was filling slowly with a chant, and then, emerging from the eastern end of the north aisle and travelling down just opposite, across the intervening dark, a line of light came into view, crossing the opening of the arches, cut by the massive piers, a moving, flickering line, advancing and advancing with the voices.

The outlines of the figures in the long procession weren't perceptible, the faces, palely lit and level with the tapers they were carrying, one rather felt than saw; but unmistakably the voices were men's voices, and the chant, the measured, reiterated cadences, prevailed over the wavering light.

Heavy and sombre as the stillness which it broke, vaguely akin to it, the chant swept in and gained upon the silence with a motion of the tide. It was a music neither of the senses, nor the spirit, but the mind, as set, as stately, almost as inanimate as the dark aisles through which it echoed; even, colourless and cold.

And then, quite suddenly, against its grave and passionless inflections something clashed, a piercing intermittent note, an awful discord, shrilling out and dying down and shrilling out again—a cry—a scream.

The chant went on; the light, from where we stood, was steadily retreating, and we ventured forward. Judging our whereabouts as best we could, we made towards the choir and stumbled up some steps, placing ourselves eventually behind one of the pillars of the apse. And from this point, the whole proceeding was apparent.

At the west end the line of light was turning; fifty or sixty monks (about—and at a venture) habited in brown and carrying tapers, walking two and two, were moving up the central aisle towards us, headed by three, one with the cross between two others bearing heavy silver candlesticks with tapers, larger than those carried by the rest.

Reaching the chancel steps, they paused; the three bearing the cross and candlesticks stood facing the altar, while those following diverged to right and left and lined the aisle. The first to take up this position were quite young, some almost boys; they were succeeded gradually by older men, those at the tail of the procession being obviously aged and infirm.

And then a figure, white and slight, erect—a woman's figure—struck a startling note at the far end of the brown line, a note as startling as the shrieks which jarred recurrently, were jarring still against the chant.

A pace or two behind her walked two priests in surplices, and after them another, vested in a cope. And on the whole impassive company her presence, her disturbance, made no mark. For them, in fact, she wasn't there.

Neither was she aware of them. I doubt if to her consciousness, or mine, as she approached, grew definite, there was a creature in the place besides herself.

She moved and uttered her successive cries as if both sound and motion were entirely mechanical—more like a person in some trance of terror or of anguish than a voluntary rebel; her cries bespoke a physical revulsion into which her spirit didn't enter; they were not her own—they were outside herself; there was no discomposure in her carriage, nor, when we presently saw it, in her face. Both were distinguished by a certain exquisite hauteur, and this detachment of her personality from her distress impressed one curiously. She wasn't altogether real, she didn't altogether live, and yet her presence there was the supreme reality of the unreal scene, and lent to it, at least as I was viewing it, its only element of life.

She had, one understood, her part to play; she wasn't, for the moment, quite prepared; she played it later with superb effect.

As she came up with the three priests, the monks closed in and formed a semi-circle round them, while the priests advanced and placed themselves behind the monks who bore the cross and candlesticks, immediately below the chancel steps, facing the altar. They left her standing some few paces back, in the half-ring of sickly light shed by the tapers.

Now one saw her face. It was of striking beauty, but its age? One couldn't say. It had the tints, the purity of youth—it might have been extremely young, matured merely by the moment; but for a veil of fine repression which only years, it seemed, could possibly have woven. And it was itself—this face—a mask, one of the loveliest that spirit ever wore. It kept the spirit's counsel. Though what stirred it then, in that unique emergency, one saw—to what had stirred it, or might stir it gave no clue. It threw one back on vain conjecture.

Put the match of passion to it—would it burn? Touch it with grief and would it cloud, contract? With joy—and could it find, or had it ever found, a smile? Again, one couldn't say.

Only, as she stood there, erect and motionless, it showed the faintest flicker of distaste, disgust, as if she shrank from some repellent contact. She was clad, I think I said, from head to foot in a white linen garment; head and ears were covered too, the oval of the face alone was visible, and this was slightly flushed. Her screams were changing into little cries or moans, like those of a spent animal, from whom the momentary pressure of attack has been removed. They broke from her at intervals, unnoticed, unsuppressed, and now on silence, for the monks had ceased their chanting.

As they did so one realized the presence of these men, who, up to now, had scarcely taken shape as actualities, been more than an accompaniment—a drone. They shifted from a mass of voices to a row of pallid faces, each one lit by its own taper, hung upon the dark, or thrown abruptly, as it were, upon a screen; all different; all, at first distinct, but linked together by a subtle likeness, stamped with that dye which blurs the print of individuality—the signet of the cloister.

Taking them singly, though one did it roughly, rapidly enough, it wasn't difficult at starting to detect varieties of natural and spiritual equipment. There they were, spread out for sorting, nonentities and saints and devils, side by side, and what was queerer, animated by one purpose, governed by one law.

Some of the faces touched upon divinity; some fell below humanity; some were, of course, merely a blotch of book and bell, and all were set impassively toward the woman standing there.

And then one lost the sense of their diversity in their resemblance; the similarity persisted and persisted till the row of faces seemed to merge into one face—the face of nothing human—of a system, of a rule. It framed the woman's and one felt the force of it: she wasn't in the hands of men.

There was a pause filled only by her cries, a space of silence which they hardly broke; and then one of the monks stepped forward, slid into the chancel and began to light up the high altar. The little yellow tongues of flame struggled and started up, till first one line and then another starred the gloom.

Her glance had followed him; her eyes were fixed upon that point of darkness growing to a blaze. There was for her, in that illumination, some intense significance, and as she gazed intently on the patch of brilliance, her cries were suddenly arrested—quelled. The light had lifted something, given back to her an unimpaired identity. She was at last in full possession of herself. The flicker of distaste had passed and left her face to its inflexible, inscrutable repose.

She drew herself to her full height and turned towards the men behind her with an air of proud surrender, of magnificent disdain. I think she made some sign.

Another monk stepped out, extinguished and laid down his taper, and approached her.

I was prepared for something singular, for something passably bizarre, but not for what immediately occurred. He touched her eyes and closed them; then her mouth, and made a feint of closing that, while one of the two priests threw over his short surplice a black stole and started audibly with a *Sub venite*. The monks responded. Here and there I caught the words or sense of a response. The prayers for the most part were unintelligible: it was no doubt the usual office for the dead, and if it was, no finer satire for the work in hand could well have been devised. Loudly and unexpectedly above his unctuous monotone a bell clanged out three times. An *Ave* followed, after which two bells together, this time muffled, sounded out again three times. The priest proceeded with a *Miserere*, during which they rang the bells alternately, and there was something curiously suggestive and determinate about this part of the performance. The real action had, one felt, begun.

At the first stroke of the first bell her eyelids fluttered, but she kept them down; it wasn't until later at one point in the response, '*Non intres in judicium cum ancilla tua Domine*', she yielded to an impulse of her lips, permitted them the shadow of a smile. But for this slip she looked the thing of death they reckoned to have made of her—detached herself, with an inspired touch, from all the living actors in the solemn farce, from all apparent apprehension of the scene. I, too, was quite incredibly outside it all.

I hadn't even asked myself precisely what was going to take place. Possibly I had caught the trick of her quiescence, acquiescence, and I went no further than she went; I waited—waited with her, as it were, to see it through. And I experienced a vague, almost resentful sense of interruption, incongruity, when King broke in to ask me what was up. He brought me back to Ella's presence, to the consciousness that this, so far as the spectators were concerned, was not a woman's comedy.

I made it briefly plain to them, as I knew something of the place and people, that any movement on our side would probably prove more than rash, and turned again to what was going forward.

They were clumsily transforming the white figure. Two monks had robed her in a habit of their colour of her order, I suppose, and were now putting on the scapular and girdle. Finally they flung over her the long white-hooded cloak and awkwardly arranged the veil, leaving her face uncovered; then they joined her hands and placed between them a small cross.

This change of setting emphasized my first impression of her face; the mask was lovelier now and more complete.

Two voices started sonorously, '*Libera me, Domine*', the monks took up the chant, the whole assembly now began to move, the muffled bells to ring again at intervals, while the procession formed and filed into the choir. The monks proceeded to their stalls, the younger taking places in the rear. The two who had assisted at the robing led the passive figure to the centre of the chancel, where the three who bore the cross and candlesticks turned round and stood a short way off confronting her. Two others, carrying the censer and *bénitier*, stationed themselves immediately behind her with the priests and the officiant, who now, in a loud voice, began his recitations.

They seemed, with variations, to be going through it all again. I caught the '*Non intres in judicium*' and the '*Sub venite*' recurring with the force of a refrain. It was a long elaborate affair. The grave deliberation of its detail heightened its effect. Not to be tedious, I give it you in brief. It lasted altogether possibly two hours.

The priest assisting the officiant, lifting the border of his cope, attended him when he proceeded first to sprinkle, then to incense the presumably dead figure, with the crucifix confronting it, held almost like a challenge to its sightless face. They made the usual inclinations to the image as they passed it, and repeated the performance of the incensing and sprinkling with extreme formality at intervals, in all, I think, three times.

There was no break in the continuous drone proceeding from the choir; they kept it going; none of them looked up—or none at least of whom I had a view—when four young monks slid out, and, kneeling down in the clear space between her and the crucifix, dislodged a stone which must have previously been loosened in the paving of the chancel, and disclosed a cavity, the depth of which I wasn't near enough to see.

For this I wasn't quite prepared, and yet I wasn't discomposed. I can't attempt to make it clear under what pressure I accepted this impossible *dénouement*, but I did accept it. More than that, I was exclusively absorbed in her reception of it. Though she couldn't, wouldn't see, she must have been aware of what was happening. But on the other hand, she was prepared, dispassionately ready, for the end.

All through the dragging length of the long offices, although she hadn't stirred or given any sign (except that one faint shadow of a smile) of consciousness, I felt the force of her intense vitality, the tension of its absolute impression. The life of those enclosing presences seemed to have passed into her presence, to be concentrated there. For to my view it was these men who held her in death's grip who didn't live, and she alone who was absorbently alive.

The candles, burning steadily on either side the crucifix, the soft illumination of innumerable altar lights confronting her, intensified the darkness which above her and behind her—everywhere beyond the narrow confines of the feeble light in which she stood—prevailed.

This setting lent to her the aspect of an unsubstantial, almost supernatural figure, suddenly arrested in its passage through the dark.

She stood compliantly and absolutely still. If she had swayed, or given any hint of wavering, of an appeal to God or man, I must have answered it magnetically. It was she who had the key to what I might have done but didn't do. Make what you will of it—we were inexplicably *en rapport*.

But failing failure I was backing her; it hadn't once occurred to me, without her sanction, to step in, to intervene; that I had anything to do with it beyond my recognition of her—of her part, her claim to play it as she pleased. And now it was—a thousand years too late!

They managed the illusion for themselves and me magnificently. She had come to be a thing of spirit only, not in any sort of clay. She was already in the world of shades; some power as sovereign and determinate as Death itself had lodged her there, past rescue or the profanation of recall.

King was in the act of springing forward; he had got out his revolver; meant, if possible, to shoot her before closing with the rest. It was the right and only workable idea. I held him back, using the first deterrent that occurred to me, reminding him of Ella, and the notion of her danger may have hovered on the outskirts of my mind. But it was not for her at all that I was consciously concerned. I was impelled to stand aside, to force him, too, to stand aside and see it through.

What followed, followed as such things occur in dreams; the senses seize, the mind, or what remains of it, accepts mechanically the natural or unnatural sequence of events.

I saw the grave surrounded by the priests and blessed; and then the woman and the grave repeatedly, alternately, incensed and sprinkled with deliberate solemnity; and heard, as if from a great distance, the recitations of the prayers, and chanting of interminable psalms.

At the last moment, with their hands upon her, standing for a second still erect, before she was committed to the darkness, she unclosed her eyes, sent one swift glance towards the light, a glance which caught it, flashed it back, recaptured it and kept it for the lighting of her tomb. And then her face was covered with her veil.

The final act was the supreme illusion of the whole. I watched the lowering of the passive figure as if I had been witnessing the actual entombment of the dead.

The grave was sprinkled and incensed again, the stone replaced and fastened down. A long sequence of prayers said over it succeeded, at the end of which, the monks put out their tapers, only one or two remaining lit with those beside the Crucifix.

The priests and the officiant at length approached the altar, kneeling and prostrating there some minutes and repeating '*Pater Nosters*', followed by the choir.

Finally in rising, the officiant pronounced alone and loudly '*Requiescat in pace.*' The monks responded sonorously, 'Amen'.

The altar lights were one by one extinguished; at a sign, preceded by the cross, the vague, almost invisible procession formed and travelled down the aisle, reciting quietly the '*De Profundis*' and guided now, by only, here and there, a solitary light. The quiet recitation, growing fainter, was a new and unfamiliar impression; I felt that I was missing something—what? I missed, in fact, the chanting; then quite suddenly and certainly I missed—the scream. In place of it there was this '*De Profundis*' and her silence. Out of her deep I realized it, dreamily, of course she would not call.

The door swung to; the church was dark and still again—immensely dark and still.

There was a pause, in which we didn't move or speak; in which I doubted for a second the reality of the incredibly remote, yet almost present scene, trying to reconstruct it in imagination, pit the dream against the fact, the fact against the dream.

'Good God!' said King at length, 'what are we going to do?'

His voice awoke me forcibly to something nearer daylight, to the human and inhuman elements in the remarkable affair, which hitherto had missed my mind; they struck against it now with a tremendous shock, and mentally I rubbed my eyes. I saw what King had all along been looking at, the sheer, unpicturesque barbarity. What *were* we going to do?

She breathed perhaps, perhaps she heard us—something of us—we were standing not more than a yard or so away; and if she did, she waited, that was the most poignant possibility, for our decision, our attack.

Ella was naturally unstrung: we left her crouching by the pillar; later I think she partially lost consciousness. It was as well—it left us free.

Striking, as nearly as we could, the centre of the altar, working from it, we made a guess at the position of the stone, and on our hands and knees felt blindly for some indication of its loosened edge. But everywhere the paving, to our touch, presented an unevenness of surface, and we picked at random, chiefly for the sake of doing something. In that intolerable darkness there was really nothing to be done but wait for dawn or listen for some guidance from below. For that we listened breathless and alert enough, but nothing stirred. The stillness had become again intense, acute, and now a grim significance attached to it.

The minutes, hours, dragged; time wasn't as it had been, stationary, but desperately, murderously slow.

Each moment of inaction counted—counted horribly, as we stood straining ears and eyes for any hint of sound, of light.

At length the darkness lifted, almost imperceptibly at first; the big rose window to the west became a scarcely visible grey blot; the massive piers detached themselves from the dense mass of shadow and stood out, immense and vague; the windows of the lantern just above us showed a ring of slowly lightening panes; and with the dawn, we found the spot and set to work.

The implements we improvised we soon discovered to be practically useless. We loosened, but we couldn't move the stone.

At intervals we stopped and put our ears to the thin crevices. King thought, and still believes, he heard some sound or movement; but I didn't. I was somehow sure, for that, it was too late.

For everything it was too late, and we returned reluctantly to a consideration of our own predicament; we had, if possible, to get away unseen. And this time luck was on our side. The sacristan, who came in early by the cloister door which we had entered by, without perceiving us, proceeded to the sacristy.

We made a rapid and effectual escape.

We sketched out and elaborated, on our way back to the town, the little scheme of explanation to be offered to our host, which was to cover an announcement of abrupt departure. He received it with polite credulity, profound regret. He ventured to believe that the *Señora* was unfortunately missing a unique experience—cities, like men, had elements of beauty, or of greatness which escape the crowd; but the *Señora* was not of the crowd, and he had hoped she would be able to remain.

Nothing, however, would induce her to remain for more than a few hours. We must push on without delay and put the night's occurrences before the nearest British Consul. She made no comments and admitted no fatigue, but on this point she was persistent to perversity. She carried it.

The Consul proved hospitable and amiable. He heard the story and was suitably impressed. It was a truly horrible experience—remarkably dramatic—yes. He added it—we saw him doing it—to his collection of strange tales.

The country was, he said, extremely rich in tragic anecdote; and men in his position earned their reputation for romance. But as to *doing* anything in this case, as in others even more remarkable, why, there was absolutely nothing to be done!

The laws of Spain were theoretically admirable, but practically, well—the best that could be said of them was that they had their comic side.

And this was not a civil matter, where the wheels might often, certainly, be oiled. The wheel ecclesiastic was more intractable.

He asked if we were leaving Spain immediately. We said, 'Perhaps in a few days.' 'Take my advice,' said he, 'and make it a few hours.'

We did.

Ella would tell you that the horror of those hours hasn't ever altogether ceased to haunt her, that it visits her in dreams and poisons sleep.

She hasn't ever understood, or quite forgiven me my attitude of temporary detachment. She refuses to admit that, after all, what one is pleased to call reality is merely the intensity of one's illusion. My illusion was intense.

'Oh, for you,' she says, and with a touch of bitterness, 'it was a spectacle. The woman didn't really count.'

For me it was a spectacle, but more than that: it was an acquiescence in a rather splendid crime.

On looking back I see that, at the moment in my mind, the woman didn't really count. She saw herself she didn't. That's precisely what she made me see.

What counted chiefly with her, I suspect, was something infinitely greater to her vision than the terror of men's dreams.

She lies, one must remember, in the very centre of the sanctuary—has a place uniquely sacred to her order, the traditions of her kind. It was this honour, satisfying, as it did, some pride of spirit or of race, which bore her honourably through.

She had, one way or other, clogged the wheels of an inflexible machine. But for the speck of dust she knew herself to be, she was—oh horribly, I grant you!—yet not lightly, not dishonourably, swept away.

MADEMOISELLE

AT first sight you would have said a butterfly with the bloom brushed off; there was a frailty, a brilliancy about her which suggested it, and to go deeper, a hint of wings, a possibility of flight.

But Mademoiselle was not a butterfly, nor was her life a flitting in any garden, nor a matter of many flowers. It was, in fact, a difficult, prosaic business, about which she went with a little mocking careless air that was to make you think it gay.

I suppose—it is a cruel supposition—that when first I knew her she was over forty; you couldn't say her youth had been 'preserved', it had been fought for and retained, a sort of prisoner of war. A slight erect figure, and remarkably bright eyes, with round the mouth, well managed though they were, a few faint lines. But there were no grey hairs, and you were expected to believe there were no grey hours.

Across the road you might have given her twenty-five, across a room, well, five years more, and face to face—? but Mademoiselle never permitted that imprudent face to face. I am sure she always wore a veil, and usually a white one. I cannot remember her without it. There was something symbolic about that veil, so light and so persistent, with the smile behind it; that was Mademoiselle herself—a veil with a smile behind it—and behind the smile? Well, one will never know!

She came and gave us lessons twice a week; engaging little lessons into which she managed with extreme politeness to infuse her profound contempt for the literature of our country, and her keen but critical appreciation for the masterpieces of her own.

She found our romances 'truly desolating', save those perhaps of Charlotte Bronte, *'cette petite Huguenote pieuse et passionée'*, who was, but certainly, a little 'passed'. And for our philosophy—she laughed, and for our drama—well, *mon Dieu!* she wept. For the whole parlous state of everything she experienced—with, but of course, exceptions—shall we say of Shakespeare? Shall we say of Monsieur Meredith, the most obscure?—an acute despair. In a word she had some power of discernment which makes her own romance, to quote herself, 'the most obscure'. The man was so conspicuously small.

The attraction must have been his youth, the cult of youth was so much of a passion with her, and though there were not more than ten years between them, in a wider sense he was again conspicuously young.

She introduced us to him at his studio, one cheerless afternoon in

October, and my impression of that visit is of something curiously grey.

Perhaps it was the room, one of a block of studios just built, in a blind street off Camden Town. It reminded you of a vault, as you stepped down to it from the cramped dark passage. It was fairly large and disproportionately high; but it smelt of damp, and the walls were washed a hard aggressive grey, which again reminded you of tombstones. It had no window, only the top light, and very little furniture; a cheap oil stove which mixed its odour with the dampness, a bed screened off by a dingy cotton curtain, a very new and very common sideboard with a mirror at the back, a deal table, and a few odd chairs.

The decorations put the last touch to the picture. They consisted entirely of the works of Monsieur de St Pierre. Some flat drawings from the antique, a still-life group or two, some studies from the life, extremely French in pose and extremely childish in execution, while, tilted against the steely walls along the floor, were a set of satin-wood panels, daubs of woolly nymphs and Venuses and podgy Cupids, surrounded by trophies of lyres and ribbons and festoons of heavy flowers. These were specimens which he took round or was supposed to take to firms from which he wanted, or was supposed to want, employment; it was this branch of art to which his talents had of late been prostituted. But his faith in the final recognition of the world survived all shocks, and that he was doing nothing at the present moment was merely a proof—I don't remember how he reasoned it—of his superiority.

He was not extravagantly pleased to see us, nor was his linen—what there was of it—extravagantly clean. He was eating watercresses when we arrived, torn from a bunch on the table laid for our reception.

He explained with a smile that he was very ''ungry', and as an afterthought invited us to sit down. To do him justice he was not bad-looking; from a French point of view you might have called him handsome. He had nice grey eyes, and when he was pleased, a vain but rather pretty smile, with a display of even teeth. But he was small. To that one must return.

He greeted Mademoiselle with casual effusiveness; he was really glad to see her: he was very anxious for his tea.

She made a patch of colour, a pleasant stir in the lifeless room, as she set about preparing it. It is impossible to think of her as not busy, or dallying with any task, or even dreaming over it; but this had been one of her full days, and though she moved with her habitual alertness, she looked tired.

When he was not engaged in hurrying her up he allowed himself to be instructed by our attempts at conversation. He wished us to speak English; he was studying English, since without it there were difficulties at the shops. Now and then he jotted down a phrase and took it across to Mademoiselle to have it lucidly explained. But he thought the language heavy—like our art, for example—it had no light touches, no fine shades.

'He alludes', said Mademoiselle, 'to your A B C. He is now acquiring the alphabet—one goes far when one is on the threshold.' And she sent across to him a charming little smile.

Her manner was half protective, half caressing, if you can imagine the maternal with a dash of coquetry; but one could see her raillery was backed by pride; it was the sort of smile reserved for the small vanities of the great.

He made no effort to impress us; he was so sure of his impression. 'These', he said, with a pompous little gesture, 'these are mine', when finally we made the tour of his deplorable productions. 'They are merely trifles. I have never been able to get models suited to my style. I have not yet had the time, the opportunity, to make a mark. *Enfin quelque chose arrivera.* I have the great conceptions—wait!'

'That', said Mademoiselle from her place beside the stove, 'is one of Antoine's little weaknesses, *des grandes conceptions*, and for the great productions, yes—we wait. It is said they do not pay, and first it is necessary—do you say? to make the pot boil before one inflames the world. He proposes a conflagration—when in fact the pot has boiled.'

I don't know how we managed to divine just then that this prosaic task was left to her, unless the quick deterrent glance which he shot back at her assisted us; but subsequent events made it quite clear.

'And it is one of the little weaknesses of women', added St Pierre rhetorically, 'to make nothing of the things of space, to regard exclusively the details. *Question de femme est question de l'amour.* That ends by obstructing the artist—for he is poor if he is great—and that costs much—*l'amour.*'

'It is true', returned Mademoiselle, 'but have you not remarked that when the artist figures in these affairs—it is we always who have to pay?'

'What would you say?' he asked a little sharply, looking up from one of the satinwood Venuses which he was examining with an air of paternal pride.

'But simply, *mon ami*, that there is always that other mistress, who is young with the youth immortal and always also a little difficult, and to be difficult with you others is to be much desired. But regard then—the kettle—at last it boils! Let us seat ourselves. Antoine, you have neglected to place the chairs. That is again a detail, but there are occasions when even the great ones must descend. For me,' she concluded, 'I prefer, if it is a matter of preference, to be small. One requires so much less room, it is less fatiguing, it is not demanded of one to shine.'

Tonight her brilliancy was clouded; there was a shade of effort in her speech and movement which spoke of weariness persistently ignored.

Antoine's hunger was no idle boast. It was the most convincing thing about him. I believe he sometimes passed us things, but I know he was always calling out to her for fresh relays. His cup was empty—or his plate. I can hear him now discoursing, on the utter banality of everything, with his mouth full of bread and butter, and his little half-washed hand stretched out for innumerable cups of tea. I can see him sketching out his great conceptions on the grimy cloth, using instinctively a lump of sugar or a piece of cake for illustration—which he invariably swallowed at the close.

And between his floating ideals and his awful piggishness, as in a cleared and quiet space, I catch a glimpse of Mademoiselle sitting ministering to his material wants and listening to his flowery orations—strangely pleased. One doesn't know how much she saw or understood. It may have been a case of passion which accepts the object as it stands, not altogether blind, but patient and content to wait and hope. But, for my part, I think that he imposed on her his illusion; and if so, that must pass as his supreme achievement. The greatest artist does no more. But of the great—with whom he should have claimed relationship—he had an infinite mistrust. England, at least, possessed no painters. That he made indisputably plain. We mentioned Watts once with tentative anxiety.

'Watts!' he exclaimed excitedly, 'who cannot even draw!'

Certainly Mr Watts had been to Italy. He had learned something—but for teaching—let us go straight to the Venetian School. Admit that he had colour—there he ended, and that was but a clever copy of his master Paolo Veronese.

What was Watts, after all? And Sargent? but he was not to be called English. Character? perhaps—a little—but a mere trick, an accident—and then at best, how superficial!

So on, through the list. One almost envied him the joy, almost applauded the facility with which he plucked the flesh from the most illustrious bones. Granting a point to anyone was a fluke—a plagiarism. There was no originality. This—it was understood—he would himself eventually supply.

Mademoiselle refused to enter the discussion.

'*Dieu!*' she said, 'it is so long since I have heard it all. I passed it under silence. And I occupy myself more profitably', she was at the moment thus employed, 'with the deficient buttons of the coat of the distinguished speaker. About Art, besides, I know nothing at all. I have for it unfortunately only an undisciplined admiration. *La Perfection, où est elle?* Angels support her—those poor devils of angels who have in fact no choice. But for me I am human. I should find her very dull. And what, I ask you, would become of Antoine,' she suggested, gravely, 'if in the end she should present herself? What would remain for him to do, on what then would he make his little speeches? It would be truly crushing. He too—he would find her very dull.'

'Ah! with these women,' he burst out, with a fine flourish, 'it is always like that. To be amused, to be distracted! Of the great truths—the great realities—what do they after all demand? Nothing! and it is I who speak.'

'These great verities, my friend,' returned Mademoiselle, indulgently, 'become great stupidities if you think to put them in your pocket. And for reality, is it so far, or even so seductive that we need disturb ourselves to seek it? I have found it so much an experience of all the days. Antoine has not my acquaintance with the English mamma, who is not entirely a thing of dreams. And her cherished infants—the pupils—they also have something of actuality when they refuse to advance themselves, as happens often. But,' she admitted, 'he has reason; with us it is of the little things the great ones compose themselves.'

'I also, one time had pupils', he informed us, in the tone of one alluding to an abyss from which he has emerged. 'But I abandoned them. I found them insupportable. In their presence it was impossible to work. Of all animals they are the most imitative, and it is not advisable that they should reproduce one's style.'

'Ah! but if only I could persuade them to reproduce mine,' cried Mademoiselle, 'I should be ravished. It would save so much of pain.'

'That is altogether another matter,' he returned, indifferently, 'literature is not my *métier*.'

And as the conversation here diverged to it he relapsed into himself, gazing abstractedly at his compositions ranged along the walls, growing each moment mercifully dimmer with the failing light.

The room was left to dusk; its vaultlike gloom became oppressive and its bareness struck one suddenly as sordid; there was a stagnancy about the place, vaguely recalling to one's mind a disused pond in some deserted spot. But presently the lamp was lit. It was an indescribable relief.

Literature was not Antoine's *métier*, but when some aspect of it touched a point in his reflections he descended to it for a moment and retook himself again into the clouds. Mademoiselle had been performing what she called the 'little interment' of a popular English authoress; her literary animosities were keen.

'I envelop her', she said, 'in a shroud, the precise shade of which she has previously written to the papers to record her preference, and I bury her deep, but most profoundly deep, with all the rites of her own extremely involved religion; but she will come up, I assure you, she will resurrect herself to make the complaint that the letters are not large enough on her tomb.'

'But I—I admire this lady', he protested. 'She has the courage of contempt for an obsolete classicism—she has the divine gift of repudiation for that intolerable criticism which destroys the soul of art. And for one who has attempted to rewrite the Scriptures——'

Mademoiselle politely interposed.

'Permit me, Antoine—I myself am composing this lady's epitaph, and you anticipate every cherished phrase. Let us by all means cultivate the divine gift of repudiation, but first it is necessary—is it not so? for it to be effective that we accomplish for ourselves a public repudiation, and that exacts an ingenuity quite unique. And to rewrite the Scriptures it must be that one is not one but many saints. When you are even half a one, *mon ami,* you shall try.'

But this unfortunate retort launched him upon a favourite theme. I won't attempt a repetition of the hackneyed arguments for infidelity which he poured forth with turgid volubility. He was permitted to proceed unchecked. Once only, Mademoiselle said quietly, 'He speaks without the book', and for the rest, it was a subject which, staunch Catholic as she was, she would not desecrate with dispute.

Now and again she tried to stop him with irrelevant little questions:— 'Were there no more buttons to be attached to some yet more disreputable coat? Would he approach and let her rearrange his tie?'

He chattered on, until the silence of his audience seemed to strike him suddenly: 'Is it possible', he asked rhetorically, 'that I speak to those who still divert themselves with these incredible stupidities?' and paused.

'I have already expressed the wish', said Mademoiselle, with exquisite detachment, 'that you would let me readjust your bow.'

He went across and knelt down on the floor beside her, while she retied the floppy, rather greasy scarf.

'Ah', he exclaimed, 'these ruses, but of all things they are the most transparent! It is evident I may not speak. For me, I have the wider mind. I treat you with more clemency. Are you not permitted to be devout, since in fact that becomes you very well? Do I not permit you to amuse yourself with these little acts of devotion for which I have a contempt supreme, these little follies?'

For a moment she looked down on him, and left a lingering touch upon his shoulder, before gently pushing him away. 'As if', she said, 'it were not the good God Himself Who permits to all of us our follies—yes—blind child—even this of thine—to thee. But we become too serious. *De la gaieté, mes enfants, de la gaieté.*'

We rose to go. He seemed relieved, and then announced it was his hour for supper. He had found a most convenient restaurant quite near. Would not the little pious one accompany him? She graciously declined—there were still some exercises to correct, but she could share our road some way.

Then she informed us that this little festival was almost a farewell. Antoine immediately was going to New York. It had been difficult—or, to be frank—impossible to get work here, and over there the thing was sure—but certain. There was the promise of, perhaps, a great career. He must have liberty, she said, his temperament required room, much air, but fortunately he did not lack confidence, a quality so often missing in the artist.

'It is a parting—yes,' she said, 'but not—it is our hope—for long. The arrangement is that I go out to him when he is *lancé*. Afterwards—our dream is Paris. In my idle hours I make sometimes to myself two dreams. One, it is my entrance into Paradise, that place of no betrothals, no toilettes, but—who shall say?—perhaps of some diversion; the other, it is my entrance into Paris—with Antoine, it is understood. I leave you then to figure to yourself which of the two is the more cherished dream!'

And here she stopped to say good-bye.

Tonight she was again a little pressed.

'Ah! these mammas,' she cried, 'these pupils, and these execrable compositions! If the saints themselves should fail one, these are a sure deliverance from *des fantaisies!*'

With which she turned—passed out of view; a graceful beautifully shod, distinguished little figure, hurrying down the dingy street.

The next we heard of him was of his having sailed.

He had not let her see him off; it was suggested that his emotions were not equal to the strain.

'And he has reason', she agreed; 'these poignant scenes under the eyes of all the world are *inconvenantes*. When he returns it will be quite another thing.'

As time wore on we asked for news of him. At first she said she hadn't heard, the letter must have been delayed. Then later it occurred to me I had some influence with a large firm of piano-makers in New York, who might make something of his satinwood productions; and I asked for his address. But it had slipped her memory. Oh, yes, he had found employment—but to establish oneself surely, that took time.

Not then suspecting that she really didn't know it, in a week or two I asked for it again. But he had changed his lodgings, he made many changes; even she, at the moment, knew not where to write! Nothing could exceed my kindness, but at present he was fully occupied; should he, at any moment, need this generous introduction I should in truth become their benefactor.

It was vague. Something might easily have happened to him, but she wouldn't own up to the mystery of his silence. She preferred to keep it to herself.

She went her way at a much quickened pace, she worked at a tremendous rate, she practically never stopped. And then the pace or something else began to tell, and for a week or two she had to slacken down.

It was about this time—with an extreme reluctance—that she asked for an advance upon her small account.

'It is on these occasions,' she said gracefully, 'one makes the choice. One asks the favour of a friend. But all the same, it is necessary that I make an explanation. M. de St Pierre has a mother, very poor, whom he has left in Paris, and it is fitting that during his absence, while he is yet struggling, she should be maintained. Just now he is in little difficulties, and I charge myself with this affair. Though I have never seen this lady—under the circumstances—it is natural I regard her as a parent. Mine I have lost—it is now many years past—but in Antoine's I shall one day behold another, altogether different, but still dear.'

'You see,' remarked my wife—who didn't hesitate to paint Antoine in the colours of the burning lake—'she keeps the family; where is it going to end?'

That being the case, I said I supposed he would eventually turn up, unless he had met with some unlucky twist of fate. He might, I mildly hinted, have been drowned.

'The Antoines of this world don't drown', she said prophetically. And as it happened she was right.

He turned up four months afterwards in Paris. I ran against him one amazingly bright evening in some narrow street off the Boulevard St Germain, and there was quite a melodramatic little scene.

He hoped he wasn't recognized, and was about to hurry on, but I turned round and blocked his way. I don't suppose I looked particularly friendly. He made no attempt to play his cards; he smiled a little nervously, and threw them down.

'It is unfortunate. Monsieur will not betray me?'

'And so', I commented briefly, 'New York was a conveniently distant city, and you have been here all along.'

'By what right?' he burst out violently, and then seemed to think better of it. 'I am under no obligation to explain myself. It is absolutely my affair—to me.'

'Not altogether,' I replied, 'if I am inclined to make it mine. New York', I pursued, 'was merely an ingenious blind?'

'It served', he said uneasily; 'these things arrange themselves.'

'In this case, however,' I reminded him, 'I mean to have a hand in the arrangement. Do you see? This farce must stop.'

'I do not quite understand, monsieur.'

I assured him it was very simple.

'Mademoiselle sends money regularly to some address in Paris, presumably for the maintenance of a certain Madame de St Pierre. This money is very acceptable to a certain Monsieur de St Pierre. Madame, in fact, does not exist'.

He hesitated; and then remarked with a ridiculous little swagger: 'Monsieur wishes to insult me. Is he prepared for my reply?'

'Quite', I assured him; 'only, in these matters, it is the brutal custom of my country to settle them with fists. But it really isn't necessary'; and I repeated: 'Madame, in fact, does not exist.'

'After all,' he said considerately, 'for the sake of the lady I do not wish to quarrel with any friend of Mademoiselle's. Monsieur evidently has the affair at the end of the fingers. It would be impolite to contradict monsieur.'

'Then it is understood that these supplies must cease. Mademoiselle must be informed—that, too, no doubt, will arrange itself—that madame, *votre mère*, no longer requires to be maintained.'

'And if I refuse?' he asked dramatically.

'Then I shall be under the painful necessity of telling Mademoiselle a very unpleasant little story.'

'Which, in the end,' he said, twisting his small moustache, and with an objectionable smile, 'will have the effect of lacerating the heart of a very charming lady.'

'There you deceive yourself', I said mendaciously; 'but I am not in the habit of discussing ladies in this particular.'

'Mademoiselle is happy in her protector', he said offensively. 'The gallantry of the English is so curious, so difficult to define.'

I could have knocked him down with immense satisfaction, but under no circumstances would it have been worth while. I persisted patiently.

'It is understood?'

'*Eh bien!*' he agreed at length, after a pause of deliberation, during which he regarded me attentively, reflectively, with those really beautiful grey eyes. 'Then, let us say, it shall be arranged. But monsieur will hold to his part of the agreement. He will guard the silence that I am here. It is natural that while one is young—yes, even at a price—one wishes to be free.'

And in a moment he was off. I followed at my leisure, saw him turn into the boulevard, cross it rapidly, and disappear into a *café*.

It was an intensely brilliant night, the lights shone with peculiar brightness, and the trees were blotted almost black against the clear, star-dotted sky. My way back took me through the *cité* and along the Seine, then past the Concorde up to the *Etoile*. And there I stopped to look down the long avenue of twinkling lamps sloping away in the dark. The scene was fine to an indifferent eye, and suddenly it struck me with a new significance. It was, of course, this Paris, with its lights, its trees, its toilettes, and its indefatigable gaiety, the city of her dreams. And here he was, and here he meant undoubtedly to stay.

It is impossible to know if he kept his word. Mademoiselle, on my return, was more inscrutable and even gayer; there were times when few things in the world seemed sadder, in the light of that encounter, than this incurable gaiety of Mademoiselle. She wore it like a *costume de théâtre*. One wondered if she woke and slept in it, whether she ever took it off. She was always before the footlights in those days, smiling and scattering little jests and keeping up her part. The curtain never seemed to go down, and she never seemed to be really tired. But as time went on she got to look shrunken under the spangles, and there were moments when one seemed to catch the tremendous effort of it all. There were moments even when it looked like a very nimble, very graceful little dance of death.

It is now more than eighteen months since I met Monsieur de St Pierre, and Mademoiselle has moved to a less distinguished neighbourhood; the life of the marvellous hats and toques is not so brief, and she admits with a shrug of supreme indifference that she is not so busy, not quite so 'pressed' as she used to be.

And in that gallant fight with youth she is beginning to get beaten. At last she is looking nearly old.

My wife says the suspense is killing her, but I think myself she is one of those who, let life be what it may, will not easily let it go. She seldom speaks of M de St Pierre, she certainly knows nothing of his whereabouts, but when she mentions him it is with a fine assumption of knowing everything.

'But slowly, but surely,' she will say composedly, 'as with his talents must arrive always, he is getting on.'

The last time she alluded to him, plainly with reluctance, but as if she must, as if she were forced to keep him going, keep it up.

'That does not go so well, over there,' she told us brightly, 'but in time—one must be patient—it is merely an affair of waiting.'

Since then I have been away, and this morning brings me a note from a still less distinguished neighbourhood, in which she says at the turn of a charming compliment that absence only renders the friend more dear. And also that she has not been very well—'a little suffering with these devils of nerves, to which we other women, we concede too much, is it not so?' However, with, for the present, a thousand shakes of the hand, and, that assassin of men, the doctor, permitting it, she hopes to make me a visit very soon.

It would seem that Mademoiselle is waiting still.

MARK STAFFORD'S WIFE

I

I HAD promised her mother, blindly, as one makes such promises, to 'look after' Kate, but never found myself quite fitted for the task.

To say that, at the outset, there were moments when she seemed to hang between two worlds, is to make her out less brightly human than she was, but now and then she gave a hint of unreality, or rather of intangibility, which set me wondering how she was equipped to meet those problems which present themselves to most young women of remarkable attraction and substantial fortune, in the course of time.

If she had been, as she was said to be, a perfect copy of my beautiful dead friend, that would have turned the key on all perplexities, but as it was, the likeness ended with her face. The rare tranquillity which had reflected faithfully her mother's temperament, with Kate served merely to screen off an unsuspected fire. One knew it there; one couldn't know what it was burning or might burn, that reticent little flame, so hidden that it was common for a certain coldness and inanimation to be noted as her chief distinction or defect.

She made the most of her reputation, she lived up to it, partly, no doubt, believed in it; at any rate she liked us all to take this view. It was her pose, though no one ever posed less consciously, to despise the stuff of dreams; yet I believe she walked sometimes clad wholly in that gossamer; the air of gay indifference, almost of insensibility, which she perversely wore, while it imposed on casual spectators, remained for me an exquisite mask, a thin protection possibly, but unreliable as unrealities invariably are. If anyone had ventured to remind her how excessively romantic the real Katharine Relton was, she would have given him the lie with fine effect—refuted such a calumny as stoutly to herself as to her accuser's face.

No one can smile more readily than she, poor child, would once have smiled at this presentment of what she was pleased to call her 'simple self'.

'You know, dearest duenna,' she would say, 'you take amazing pains to make a puzzle of me. I can see you turning the inoffensive picture upside down to find poor Napoleon standing by his tomb. He isn't there!'

But it was just this sense of some intention in the picture missed, that made her difficult, even dangerous, to touch.

Her splendid health seemed a sufficient spell against the fashionable curse of nerves. I no more dreaded them for Kate, than I dreaded kleptomania. She was beautifully sound; but in her very soundness there was the suggestive quality of flawless glass, a frailness, a transparency, even a hardness of the finer sort. She would never, under a strain, I fancied, slowly and pitifully fail, but simply break. At her mother's death, one of the cruellest endings to a gentle life, though they had lived entirely in and for each other, she went through those indescribable days with something like a smile, a bright and, as I thought, unnatural sanity; until, going one evening with some message to her room, I learnt how terribly for Kate the night undid the day. From that moment I feared really nothing for her but the test of her own extraordinary self-control.

Afterwards, at once, she wished to travel, not under my wing I plainly understood, but with someone more remote from immediate memories, who hadn't cared and didn't know.

With more reluctance than I showed, I let her go, nominally in charge of a lively American widow, who was not, as she put it, 'one of those terribly concrete creatures who can't see that a tree will make a table', and who proposed to develop her companion on the newest lines with 'rollicking success'. I was not alarmed, and submitted to their long silences and a certain freedom in their choice of people and of places as part of the adventure. After nine months' absence, Kate returned—avowedly 'penitent and improved'. She no longer evaded, she declared, the guardianship of angels, and to put herself in the way of it, agreed to come and live under my roof, at my suggestion; childless and solitary woman that I was, she seemed to throw back the shutters of the long-closed house, letting in patches of the bluest sky, freshening it with a rush of youthful air, and opening my doors to all sorts of charming people, for whom she displayed so admirable an impartiality, that before I had well begun to take the measure of their assiduity or to buckle on my shining armour for their benefit, behold! under my heedless eye, she had become engaged to Charlie Darch.

They had foreseen, these two young people, they protested with confident effrontery, that I was capable of producing some sober, gifted and impossibly eligible person, and in view of such a blunder, to spare me and the shadowy fourth our disillusionment, had settled it themselves.

Prepared perhaps for eventful surprises, I had meanwhile been negligently trusting in a kindly guiding star; and that it was now shining over a young man of no particular brilliance or distinction, did not disquiet me.

Charlie Darch was a surprise but by no means a disaster. For my ideal he was too young, and at first I was inclined to look on him as a nice enough, but rather plain, unvarnished fact. On a nearer view, however, there was a pleasing side to his honest unpretentiousness, his lack of the modern intellectual veneer.

He was so modestly aware that he wasn't, as he phrased it, 'showy', and his recognition that Kate, in 'putting up' with him, was missing chances infinitely showier was touchingly sincere.

'I'm not, and of course I know it,' he said in his literal way, 'your notion, or anywhere near it—of what Kate might have done. She might have done, it's easily understood, immensely better, except', he added simply, 'that I can't believe any man could think so much of her, or be more bent on giving her, every way, his best. I daresay she seems to you, like a delicate bit of china put into rather clumsy hands, not at all, in fact, into the hands of a connoisseur; but you've no idea how tremendously careful and considerate and all that, I shall be. You'll see.'

This was, I think, the only profession he ever made to me. A thing once said and done, with him was apt to be dismissed as needing no retrospect nor reinforcement. He was, as became his youth, a little final, and I had imagined that for me at any rate he would probably stand still. But he advanced. Once on the road to your goodwill, he made his way; you liked him better, found it easier to believe in, to accept him; and not difficult, as time went on, to discover that he shone, though unobtrusively, in human dealings. He got rough but remarkably good impressions; he was apt to catch them instinctively from the sunny side and to be, too, very prompt and positive in his judgement and decisions and appreciations.

Only in one instance he was noticeably vague. He had met Mark Stafford at my house; we had presented our celebrity, not perhaps without some flourishes, and Darch's view of him seemed singularly indistinct; he slipped in speaking of him behind borrowed phrases and struck persistently the impersonal note. His mind—if it was clear to him in this particular—remained for us a perfect smudge.

Stafford was then emerging steadily, though *The Forest and the Market Place* had yet to make its memorable stir. Kate had come across him at Mentone; later he found us out in London and came to frequent our little weekly 'At Homes' with, I was told, a flattering regularity. He made a point of being very nice to Darch. He liked him, he explained, for what he called his bold indifference to subtleties, his breadth of line. 'And incidentally, perhaps', he said, 'because he hasn't read, and doesn't mean to read, our precious books. He's splendidly illiterate; his scorn of current values is a real distinction.'

I wasn't so distinguished. I had submissively run through Mark Stafford's books and didn't care for them. They gave me too much the idea of a vivisectionist at work, the man with the knife, with, in his case, no great end to serve, though I had the assurance of Kate and worthier critics that this incisive touch—this pitiless impartiality was, properly understood, superb.

I grew indeed a little weary of his trumpeted superiority, his unique methods and results and all the rest; clinging more stubbornly, in the full blare of it, to my own obsolete ideals of his craft.

But though, personally, I might prefer the literary artist to the literary surgeon, the man himself was another matter, one with which preference had less to do.

You might hold out, you did for a time, intractably, against the charm which, sooner or later, he would delicately impose, yielding at last more to a sense of your own ungraciousness than to any urgency of his. While in a manner detaining you, until you found the inevitable recognition, he put you exquisitely at your ease, seeming to cover your reticences, your reluctances, and incertitudes towards him with a strong, unfluttering wing. He never swooped, as you felt he could quite gracefully and effectively have done, to hold you in the grip of a mind that knew no stumbling movements nor halting flights, nor any state of unpreparedness. He understood and didn't mind your hesitations, meeting and smoothing them with a rich patience, which assured you that it could afford to wait. So gradual was the influence, winning on you by imperceptible inches, that till quite the end I never guessed to what extent I had given in. He suppressed himself to give you room, kept in the shadow not to disturb your flickering lights; his own, one suspected, burned extremely clear, defined things perfectly; though he had the air of moving about like the rest of us with a delightful vagueness, involved in the general mist.

'If he didn't ignore so charmingly', Kate pointed out, 'his own importance, you wouldn't be grudgingly giving him the benefit of a doubt which doesn't practically exist. He would get from you his due. And I believe he really does. Admit that, in your treacherous, timorous heart, you are half afraid of him, and to meet the case have fallen back on your religious instincts, and are burning little private candles on his altar in self-defence? I burn them too, but openly and with a difference; not to propitiate my deity, merely to come in for a share of the reflected glory—to shine a little too.'

'But isn't superstition', I suggested, 'one of your great man's pet nine-pins—the chief one, in fact—that he's so elaborately setting up for the pleasure of so neatly knocking down?'

'Oh! he won't draw the line as close as that', she inconsistently turned round; 'he won't count himself a superstition. They don't, you know.'

He was not then, I mildly urged, too much above and beyond us all to believe immensely in himself.

'Only with him'—she saved herself—'there is a solid basis of belief.

He can't help knowing that he is bound—whatever he's driving at—in the end, to win.'

'Are you answering for it, that he will in time get Charlie over to his side?'

'He doesn't for a moment want to. Charlie is too straight a path, he hasn't any windings—not the shadow of a turning, and when Mark Stafford's walking in a garden, he makes instinctively for the maze.'

'He finds your young man interesting all the same.'

'For just such glimpses, as unwarily, and incidentally, he may afford of me. That's all.'

'And you don't mind?'

'Not in the least. I enjoy it, wouldn't you—posing for a master?'

'Do you mean he will have the assurance to put you down in black and white?'

'Nothing so crude! There is the deeper joy of pure discovery—and the passion of the chase. The sport comes in for me, in knowing that he will never perfectly "get" me. We shall wake up one fine morning to find he "has softly and suddenly vanished away, for the Snark was a Boojum, you see".'

'Have you made sure of that?'

'It was made sure for me, long ago; when I was born perhaps, that I must *be* myself and stay myself and belong, in a fashion, to myself alone. Even marriage——' she suddenly broke off.

'Yes,' I prompted, 'even marriage——?'

'Well, I can't to anyone open every door; whoever owns the poor little house, there must be rooms of which, to the end, I keep the key.'

'And this is the person who used to talk of her "simple self"!'

'The simplest selves have, haven't they, private corners, quiet nooks?'

'The simplest people don't deliberately pose to their favourite painters, for the purposes of mystification.'

'They don't', she smiled, 'always get the chance, with the rare experience thrown in, of watching them at work, surprising their little tricks; and his little tricks are sometimes, let me tell you, quite inspired.'

It is difficult at this distance, and in the light, or darkness, of all that has come and gone, to be sure if she really thought as much of him as she made out; whether in face of Darch's evasive attitude and my pretence—it was merely that—of antagonism, she wasn't 'standing up' to us from sheer perversity. I am inclined to think she was. One is so apt, in looking back, to tint the glass to the shade of subsequent experience and to see things through it, not in the white glare of fact.

In those early days of their engagement, it is nearly clear to me that the only prominent figure in the landscape was Charlie Darch. There may have been a patch of sky above, and a strip of earth beneath his broad, beaming, genial figure, but the intervening space was inconsiderable. There was no mistaking them, for all their show of taking each other very much for granted, for anything but the happiest pair; their eyes, half-humorously, half-seriously bent on their amazing future, their feet in perfect step—marching, poor children, with a gaiety, a confidence, a blind felicity towards their obscure parting of the ways. Then Darch was unexpectedly called upon to superintend some engineering work in Spain.

Kate declared herself ready for a hasty marriage and the wilds, a scheme which he pronounced impracticable. It was, he insisted, a choice between throwing up the business, or going out for a year, he hoped it wouldn't run to more, alone. Finally, supported by our promise to join him later at some fairly civilized point in Andalusia, if he could manage to snatch a few weeks' holiday, he went.

For four or five months, the bulk and frequency of their correspondence was remarkable. Then it inexplicably flagged and dropped. This turn in their affairs, for me was complicated by Kate's alternate anxiety and reluctance to mature our plans for Spain. Nothing, with her, of course was obvious, only subtly, like a coming change of temperature, in the air. Without allusion to it, one could see, or rather feel her, raising and removing barriers to our departure, weeks before it could feasibly take place.

I can't say how she produced the effect, but simply that she did, for me, produce it, of a person listening and looking for something she hoped not to find, walking on tiptoe, opening and shutting doors. Her fine composure was not outwardly impaired, but running through it like a twisted thread, one divined a flaw in its smooth surface, wondering from what jar in the machinery it came. At length, making a bold attempt at some unravelment, I asked when we should actually start, what we were going to do. She came out quite distinctly with a plan, a prompt—

'Well, if it's manageable and agreeable for you, what would you say to Biarritz next week, and gently on from there?'

'Gently—but definitely where?' I wished to know.

'Oh! somewhere—can't that be settled later?—within easy range of his outlandish quarters. It's to come for him, by way of a surprise. Isn't it enough for us, just now, that he'll be immensely pleased to see us?'

For me, this presumption was not so entirely sufficing. It came to me, at least, as a surprise, her charming vagueness, her confidence that I should, as I seemed to do, incuriously embrace it. We got as far as Paris, even as far as our last evening there, when suddenly she called a halt. I had gone upstairs to pack, leaving her with some friends, whom she had found in the hotel, to settle the question of the Opéra or the Français, when the message was brought up to me that a gentleman had called, and would I, Miss Relton asked, kindly, at my convenience, descend? I was not greatly surprised to recognize Mark Stafford in our visitor. Paris was a place where he would naturally, if unexpectedly, turn up. He had, he explained, only that morning learnt from mutual friends, that we were passing through, *en route* for Spain. He had hastened at the first possible moment to present himself, tentatively to suggest that, as he was also working round to Madrid, we might be able to make use of him. He hoped we should. His plans were elastic, perfectly adaptable, could contract or expand, if we delightfully permitted it, in sympathy with ours. Kate had been standing by the window with her back half turned, a slight white figure, motionless, with something almost rigid in the erectness of its pose—while he was making me his explanations; but at this, she turned with the slow grace of all her movements; with an air of serene premeditation, like an actor taking up his cue. 'I think', she said, with an odd deliberation meant to reach something beyond my ear, 'that it is the nicest proposition imaginable, one of the most alluring, only unfortunately, after all it isn't to be Spain. At the last moment, we have had to give it up.' She paused, and without looking across at me, more rapidly proceeded: 'This is just a little extravagant splash—and we are absurdly going back to—Scotland. Spain, if it's ever to be Spain, is—well—not yet.'

'Yes,' I backed her up, and I felt that I was forcing it, as she had exquisitely failed to do, 'we've had to block it out when it seemed fitted in.'

'But for me,' he faced her, while, though I was obviously out of it, he took me in with an inclusive smile, 'this is a real blow. It takes the wind out of the little sail I was so gaily spreading. What—I am falling back on dreams!—I might have shown you, for I know some of the untrodden ways—what we might have done!'

'Ah, yes', she assented, with a little deprecatory wave of the hand, and quoted lightly

They sailed across the silent main,
And reached the great Gromboolian plain,
And there they play for ever more
At battlecock and shuttledore——

and we are slinking tamely back to—golf! It's very stupid.'

'It's extremely sad', he substituted.

'No' she returned with a faint flush, 'it's not altogether sad, because it's so courageous. Don't you think it is?'

He glanced swiftly across at her, and the flush died out, leaving her unusually pale.

'It's too courageous,' he said, his eyes in full possession of her lovely, inexpressive face, 'since it leaves me out in the cold.'

'It leaves you precisely where you were,' she threw back, meeting his glance with a sort of smiling stare, 'for weren't we, in the first instance, going quite alone?'

'But I had the hope—' he protested.

'Oh, the hope', she interposed, ' "Hope is a timid friend." You prefer, admit it, something braver—more definite—even to the definiteness of disappointment.'

'Miss Relton means', he hazarded, addressing himself to me, 'that you wouldn't have had me after all.'

'Oh, I never answer for Kate. Though for myself——' I left it flatteringly open.

'No one is rash enough to answer for "Kate" ' she challenged him. 'Even you—venturous as you are!'

He laughed.

'I am never that. I am, as you know, the most unconscionable plodder. I potter and crawl. I go extremely slow.'

'Then—that', she concluded, 'must have settled it, if it hadn't been already settled. You needn't be told that my normal state is quiescent, but when I do move, I want to fly.'

'That parts the clouds. I shall scan the sky——' he risked, 'on the chance that eventually you may catch me up. Meanwhile I am keeping you from Calvé, you mustn't let me do that. Down below, I can feel them champing, your impatient friends; feverishly buttoning gloves and consulting clocks.'

'Aren't you coming, too', her tone, never vivid, was at the moment, singularly colourless, but his put on a warmer tint.

'I?—yes—of course. I am coming, too.' She went, at this, to fetch her cloak, leaving a hush behind her in the loud, overlit, flamboyant room.

After a short concession to it, he broke it lightly with—

'So while I pursue my lonely way, the poor young man over there has got to wait?'

'Oh, Kate——' I suggested, 'is a person to be waited for, not by any means to be whistled for, to be snatched.'

'She might so easily be scared, you mean, or spirit herself away? Yes, and one imagines, too, it must be a waiting, in a sense, in ambush; as it were behind one's tree, since fairies don't come out when mortals are abroad. She has, hasn't she, a touch of the sprite, a vague atmosphere of mist, of moonlight, which makes of Darch still more emphatically an embodiment of, well—of the broad glare of day?'

'In spite of which, she will come out for him—she has; it's part, perhaps, of her charming waywardness, that it's for him she has come out.'

'Though for me,' he returned, 'she won't, she hasn't. I shan't, however,' he concluded softly, 'despondently believe that she never will.'

The ensuing silence was for me intensified by the acquiescence, the absorption in it of Kate herself, who had come back and stood reflected in a mirror facing me, but not within his view. She had noiselessly pushed open the half-closed door and paused there, framed in the high opening, erect, elate, with a strange air of victory, sure and silent, her lips just parted in a faint, unwavering smile. Thinking herself unseen, she stayed a moment watching us remotely; puppets, from her dispassionate regard, we might have been, inaudibly discoursing on a distant stage.

So curiously detached, exclusively, intensely in possession of herself, and aloof from us, she seemed, that I couldn't naturally make a sign of recognition. Stafford, however, as though aware of it, broke the spell by abruptly rising, turning and confronting her, upon which she advanced a step or two, coming down suddenly as it were, by some, to us, inaccessible private stair.

'It's not to be Calvé', she announced immediately. 'It's to be Réjane.'

'Your final choice?' he asked.

'Our unanimous decision.'

'And she was giving *Carmen*,' he protested, 'you won't go back?'

'It's too late to go back; and more than time to be going on.' At which he joined her and they left me to make what I might of the new tangle.

Briefly, I made little of it; and Kate, to whom I looked eventually for enlightenment, was disappointing.

She knocked at my door shortly after midnight, entered, sat down, deliberately drew off her gloves and waited apparently for comments I was not prepared to offer. At length, accepting my not unnatural reluctance to launch in untried waters, with her slow, tranquil stroke, she pushed off herself.

'You are justly vexed?'

'I am reasonably puzzled.'

'And of course it won't simplify things to tell you, late enough in the day, that my engagement with Charlie Darch is "off"?'

I caught as closely as I could her level tone: 'This happened——?'

'It happened, dear friend, six weeks ago.'

'All the same, we were, so I supposed, on our way out to him——?'

'It's incredible, indecent', she assented evenly; 'but as you say, we were. You have every right to exclaim that I have behaved, continue to behave, unpardonably; though it's on your patience, your indulgence, I have so much counted for—for'— she paused, got up, walked to the window and came back, 'for breathing space, for room to twist and turn as easily as I may.'

'You can', I assured her, conscious nevertheless that she was stretching them, 'count on them still, I hope indefinitely.'

'I know; you are perfect, which makes me monstrous; but I can't bring the figures out of the mist for you. That was', she pursued reflectively, remotely, 'my notion, in getting incredibly and indecently, as I said, at Charlie—who is not a thing of shadows—of uncertainties, and who might—but now I see, who couldn't'—she broke off and ended with a note of new decision— 'He mustn't be involved.'

'Involved, my dearest child,' I asked, 'in what?'

'In my intolerable vapours, my precious mist.'

'Decidedly,' I concluded, 'we had better, after all, make for definiteness and daylight by way of Biarritz tomorrow.'

'No', she shut it out with a prompt, final gesture. 'Not if you are going to be immensely considerate and kind. And if I can't tonight, nor perhaps tomorrow, make things clear, well—you will give me time? Later, you'll let me return to it; we'll repack and restart—that's roughly my idea—quite peaceably by ourselves.'

II

It was not long before the figure which she could not or would not, that night, bring out of the mist, emerged unmistakably in the shape of Stafford.

She had suggested I should give her time: I did, taking it there had been some temporary hitch, not easily explainable, which time would adjust without my interference; her attitude during our stay in Scotland lent colour to this view.

'It's not imperative', she said, 'since he's so far off—so fortunately out of it, poor boy!—that the lights should be turned on us just yet. I want a few weeks quietly in the shade.'

I acquiesced: it worked in well with my idea that she should want it: Darch, whom I illogically acquitted, would be shortly coming back and they would patch it up. But, at once on our return, she declared her readiness to become for a day or two a subject of discussion, insisting quietly that now it must come out.

'Oh! if it's final——?'

I wouldn't press her, but I didn't hide my difficulty and reluctance.

'You think me horribly light—a leaf in the wind!'

'They have sometimes a way of blowing back?' I hazarded.

'No; they blow on.' She was too positive, and her conclusion had an unusual touch of bitterness. 'After all, if we are as light as that—as inconsequent—as detached—it doesn't greatly matter, our vagrant way!'

'But you are not, my child,' I was throwing at the moment hands out in the darkness, 'as light as that—and if I believed it—'

'Wait!' she interposed. 'You'll see.'

I saw not then, but soon enough, that the door was definitely shut on Darch, and that any movement towards it reopening was blocked by Stafford. He was not aggressively in the way; he was simply there—a substantial, stationary figure which she couldn't or wouldn't pass and made no effort to dislodge. They both seemed to be standing very still, facing each other, waiting, with the space between them not yet bridged—cut clear. My first impulse was to step in and strike out blindly for the poor young man behind the door, but I realized that I had missed my moment, amiably blinking, sitting, it proved, ridiculously still. Now, it was not so much Stafford who tripped me up in my attempt to rise, as Kate herself, with whom I was less than ever on solid ground. She was taking me uncomfortably off my feet. Nothing about her was stranger, when at length they made their plunge, than what, for want of a better term, I must call her assurance. She offered no excuses, for the inexcusable, and appeared to cast no shadow of thought upon a change of front, which, however easily effected, is supposed to have its pensive side. She seemed to have no shadows, no pensive side, so suddenly had she ceased to be the Kate I knew or guessed at. I had said of her once that she seemed to hang between two worlds, giving her then, in thought perhaps, a vague companionship with spirits of a lighter air, but at last she had come down and planted herself on a patch of earth. She hadn't etherealized, she had materialized. Stepping determinately from the path of dreams, shaking away the mists, she stood out an intensely actual figure shining with a hard, new brightness.

For my oldfashioned views, I told her, it was too much of a jump, when almost in the same breath with the announcement of her break with Darch, she wished her new engagement given out.

'But I am quite indifferent', she returned, dismissing me with a brilliant smile, 'to the gaping crowd—the public stare.'

'And to me too'; I couldn't help reminding her. 'To my private stare, which up to now, my dear, I have considerately kept down.'

'If I am not indifferent to it, I can face it. Am I the first woman who has changed her mind? I know it's reckoned more picturesque to change it to slow music, but if I prefer to do without the modulation, to start at once with a crash on the new chord——?'

'It doesn't occur to you that that may strike Charlie as rather harsh——?'

'Happily he hasn't a "temperament"! He will survive; when one knows the worst one can. I liked and like him, of course, amazingly, but—well—God, you know, eventually disposes——'

'Oh, if you mean me to look on Mark as a divine provision——!'

'Can't you? But I see you can't. I wonder why? He is going to be a "personage", and by the same token I——' she paused.

'You', I reminded her, 'will "shine a little too". He will give you, of course, as Charles would put it, "A much better show".'

'A share, for what it's worth, of his little row of footlights, yes—but you are not reconciled, you are undisguisedly displeased. Am I too practical or too perfidious? And behind it all, you are still looking for our old friend the spectre—you won't find him—you never will!'

'You admit at last then, that it's there——?'

'Produce it, annihilate it, and I'll own everything', she challenged me, and with that I had to be content.

They spent the honeymoon—a matter of some months—in Egypt, and the letters which she wrote from there, one by one, as I put them by—and together, as I took them out to reread and reconsider—produced the same crude, unnatural effect: the effect, in fine, of glare. They showed a curious lack of the half-lights and quiet tones and human touches which had been noticeably hers; telling me everything and nothing, they were mercilessly bright; as though for the time, her personality, steeped in and even hypnotized by the immutable relentless sunshine, had caught the tireless, shadeless brilliance and detachment of the East. I was to find however, on her return, that she hadn't left it there.

Within the year, for Mark, who had just brought out what is said to be his masterpiece, the little row of footlights was for the first time in full flare; but it was Kate who at once stepped up to them, taking, with an ease, a certainty, the centre of the stage. Interested, amused, her husband genially retreated.

'It's not Mark Stafford's book, it's Mark Stafford's wife', he remarked quietly, one evening, looking round his uncomfortably encumbered rooms, 'which explains and justifies this distinguished crowd. It's not to something like two years of pious toil, but to the happy accident of the happiest choice, that I owe my little hour of fame. You can see for yourself, if in the first instance it was for me they ventured forth, it's for Kate they stay, and it's for her they come again. And you never prepared me! Was it fair——?'

'Didn't she', I asked, 'ever confront you with the warning that, in a given case, she meant to shine?'

'Not a whisper, not a breath! She sprang it on me. Don't you remember our old notion of her as a shy, reluctant fay, not to be rudely tempted into the vulgarities, the mortalities of daylight?'

'All the same,' I risked, with a sense of touching upon certainty, 'you *were*, as a matter of fact, prepared for—anything!'

'I am now', he admitted smiling, 'for everything, aren't you? And definitely, for the rapid fall of the curtain'—and, as I didn't catch his drift, he added—'for her backing out of it—suddenly refusing to keep it up.'

From our comparatively unobstructed corner, I followed the glance he shot across at her, over the buzzing, faintly scented, somewhat congested company—to be, for the first time forcibly, painfully struck by the unexpectedness, the incredibility of it all. Kate planted there, so vividly reminiscent of, so impenetrably unlike herself, the conspicuous centre of a group of men, for the most part strangers or quite newcomers, intimately held, detained by an influence which I somehow divined to be as far from the spirit of the girl I had known and sheltered as high, quiet stars from the lamps of town.

Never had she looked more beautiful; whatever she had lost—and I can't say how it became chillingly plain to me that some vague virtue had gone out of her—she had gained to a supreme degree, what she had never lacked—distinction.

In her severe white and silver draperies, with her wonderfully dressed fair hair, her erect carriage, her slow, gracious movements, she wore the air of an exiled queen. Her familiar inexpressiveness seemed to be more pronounced, more studied; the repose of her attitude, her voice, her infrequent gestures, was profound—and in its intensity almost provocative of the impression she was obviously and, as I unwillingly conceded to myself, consciously producing.

Her beauty apparently commanded an attention absorbed enough to waive the usual claims of speech. She was listening perfectly, talking little, giving her quiescent charm full play. With an extraordinary rapidity, she had surrendered to some nameless need of prominence, and was finally mounted on her pedestal exposing an insentient surface, while inwardly—I couldn't doubt it—she was breathing some secret flame.

I turned to Mark with an answer pitched as nearly as I could manage it in his own easy key.

'Why shouldn't she keep it up? She has matured; as you say "come out"; she wasn't naturally, going to be left behind. You are both, and I suppose you are mutually aware of it, a wonderful—a joint success.'

I had never prevaricated with a clearer conscience or a more clouded mind. If she were going to keep it up, if this was what she meant by shining, it became for me an important question whether the background wouldn't grow appreciably darker with the increased definiteness of her luminosity. How long—to put it plainly—would it take to turn Mark's indulgent smile into an intelligible frown? Already I was beginning to hear a shade too much and to see too little of 'the beautiful Mrs Stafford'.

I saw more of her gowns, though it was not to her I owed the privilege. Her dressmaker, who happened also to be mine, was not, on my occasional visits, to be deterred from thrusting on me an acquaintance, which I should not otherwise have enjoyed, with her extravagant sequence of 'creations'. Her tastes had been so simple, her expenditure so modest in this direction that, without exaggerating the significance of trifles, I was compelled to add this new departure to the list of her surprises. Later, I sometimes met with the gowns again, but Kate herself was not now, in any sense, to be come upon in *déshabille*, in the intimacy, so to speak, of the morning wrapper. She was rarely to be found alone; with the wave, as it were, of an invisible wand, she had summoned round her a deterrent band, set up an elaborate human barrier, against old privacies and old associations.

She went everywhere and she never seemed to come really back; her few free hours were merely interludes; she was always going on again. She lived, to my view, at the foot or at the head of stairs, getting in and out of carriages, and relaxing, if she relaxed at all, under the eyes and hands of an heroic maid in the intervals between receptions. As time went on, one or two men—mere names to me—were accidentally referred to in my hearing as being distinguished by her friendship and Mark himself had casually responded to my interest in the one I picked out at random—a young Frenchman—with—'Oh! a rising sprig, a painter, one of Kate's retainers'.

The phrase, while its complacency was, in a measure, reassuring, had inconsequently jarred.

Her husband's work—I heard it on all sides—monopolized him, he was too preoccupied apparently to be critical of his wife's distractions, but to what extent his negligence accounted for their latitude I saw too little of either of them to decide. They had taken a house in Scotland for the shooting, and in the autumn for a week or two I was to join their party there. Meanwhile conclusion halted; looking at the whole blurred business through what remained to me of her mother's eyes, I was watching rather anxiously for daylight, when Charlie Darch broke in upon the scene.

On my return from a round of visits, I found his card among the little pile awaiting me, and later heard from Mark that in my absence he had cropped up and they had seen a fair amount of him.

'You'll meet him', he added, 'with the rest, I hope, in September, if he doesn't look you up before. He's just the same old Philistine; an exhilarating chap!'

If this was how he affected Mark, his presence in the big, strange country house subsequently inspired me with frank mistrust.

He was not the same: he was distinctly older and more finished: he had grown the least bit formidable in the process of throwing off the boyish diffidence which, in the old days, had made him more accessible and, perhaps too, more easily dismissible. A day or two sufficed to show me that his interest in Kate had steadfastly survived, but what she made of the discovery was obscure. If she distinguished him at all, it was by a peculiar stillness in his company, as though she were keeping recognition in reserve, while he stopped short of any intimate approach.

The detestably keen eye I kept on both of them disclosed at length that he too was watching her, intently but discreetly and reluctantly. Poor Kate! What were we looking for? It may have been a conscience-stricken fancy that, for all its stealth, she felt our scrutiny and faced it—beat if off with her unclouded gaze, her remote serenity. There was one moment in the dusk, when there seemed to be something like a lurking horror in it.

The nights were sultry, and I hadn't slept. The house was full and, as usual, she was more or less surrounded; the little Frenchman, at close quarters, proved to be no more a matter for uneasiness than the acquisition of a lap-dog, though at the end of a ribbon held by Kate, he was as much a matter for surprise. She seemed to find his relaxed fidelity, the air of weary ardour with which he hovered round her, mildly entertaining. Mark, when he wasn't shooting, drifted, as his way was, to the background; Darch, too, held himself somewhat aloof; he was obviously not concerned with her immediate circle; these people didn't count, he was looking over their heads indifferently, like a tall man in a crowd.

My visit reached its term a day or two before Mark's birthday, for which some elaborate tableaux had been arranged; and on the plea that since I had brought my camera, I must stay on to photograph the party and be generally useful, I was persuaded to extend it.

Kate was to posture as Ophelia to the Hamlet of the little Frenchman, who had been languid as an invalid and difficult as a spoiled child until the idea, his own, of impersonating the morbid Dane served partially to restore his lost deportment and vitality. Darch backed out, protesting it was much more in his line to do the lime-light. Afterwards there was to be a dance.

The night was fine, but heavy, airless, with the heat that comes before a storm, and contemplating an escape from the hot rooms, with the precaution of my years I had gone up to fetch a wrap, was on the point of going down, when I turned back to throw up my closed window. It looked down upon the shrubbery, festooned tonight with paper lanterns. As I glanced out, I was aware of two figures stationed opposite, against the wall of green. Their presence rather than their attitude, for passion has its magnetism even for those who have out-distanced it, suggested my retreat. I was about to make it when the man bent forward, seizing the woman's hands insistently, thwarting what might have been a movement of refusal or withdrawal. It was Darch, and without waiting for her to turn her head, I knew too, that it was Kate. They spoke so low, I couldn't hear what they were saying—I didn't want, or need, I thought, to hear.

Below, I found Mark asking for her and she presently appeared among the dancers. She hadn't changed the gown she had worn for the *Hamlet* tableau, copied from some picture of Rossetti's.

'It suits her uncommonly well', Mark commented, 'but, under our breath, let us confess she beautifully missed the part. Kate has her qualities, but pliancy isn't one of them. You don't get Pure Reason condescending even to look distraught.'

'Is she so purely reasonable?'

'Call it balance. She would be worth watching in a panic—but for this sort of thing,' he laughed, 'if she had had her way, I believe she would have done Ophelia with her hair up! Didn't you hear her, but perhaps you weren't behind the scenes?—I don't know what's your elegant equivalent—damning the straws?'

She had come up behind, and made her own defence: 'Naturally; a woman's more or less at a disadvantage, and a shade disreputable with her hair down. So I was shocking? But of course I knew it. If there had been tragedy in me I must have shown it; I was thinking of supper, and the cook who has an inveterate habit of getting drunk on these occasions. You have your shawl.' She turned to me. 'You are going out? But who's taking you?'

'Only a step or two, and I am not being taken.'

She followed me out on to the illuminated lawn.

'I am not sure if I altogether like this painting of the night', she began, looking round upon the mass of hanging coloured lights. 'One ought to be able to command the moon, it's more distinguished and satisfactory. But on the whole, wouldn't you call it a success?'

I was not in the mood to talk inanities, or to wait for a fitter moment, or to question the wisdom of direct attack.

'What has become of Charlie?' I asked irrelevantly. 'I have hardly seen him all the evening.'

'He doesn't dance, but it may be taken for granted he's doing duty somewhere. He was out here just now.'

'With you?'

'Yes.' Her inflection hinted faint surprise. 'With me.'

'It hasn't occurred to you'—I made my plunge—'that you see too much of him, that he's not a person quickly to resign himself—to forget—and that even if it's wise, it mayn't be kind?'

There was a long and rather painful pause, in which she stood staring at the lit windows, the moving figures, and beating time with her fingers on the back of a seat to the waltz which had just struck up. At length she relieved it with—

'I understand. It's an unflattering inference, but I am not afraid of corrupting my old friend—or of shaking his fine stability.'

'Or of causing him useless pain?'

'You are assuming—what?' she asked dispassionately.

'Nothing; surely my affection for you both is reason enough—excuse enough—if I have over-anxiously misread the situation—'

She interposed: 'If you want facts, it was not I who suggested his coming here; it was Mark. The "situation", whatever that implies, is Mark's affair.'

I didn't pretend, I couldn't, wholly to believe it.

'He was not a friend of Mark's', I reminded her. 'He never frankly liked him. Do you imagine he likes him better—now?'

She was still staring past me at the lit windows. The waltz had stopped, but she went on fingering the memory of it.

'I haven't the least idea; but why not—when it's all over?'

'Is it all over?' I persisted gently.

She turned round and showed me beneath the unreal, festive lights, a white face, intensely familiar, intensely strange—a young face suddenly grown old.

'Is anything ever over?' she broke out, with the first spark of passion I had ever seen struck from her. 'Is even death itself the end? We can't see—can't possibly see—though we *are seen*, and not by any means in a glass darkly. If one was sure—but nothing's sure—that there was at the close—deliverance from this awful light, this uplifting darkness, that we are in the grip of—blind—blind stumblers——!'

Catching at the only thread in this bewildering tangle which I thought I could make use of, I said rather unsteadily—

'We can, at least, see far enough to save ourselves, and others too, from walking crookedly. And Charlie——'

She thrust in swiftly, as if to intercept a threatening blow: 'Before God—I am clear of Charlie. If there's truth in anything, there's truth in friendship; it's a refuge and not a danger; his hands are safe.'

'My poor child,' I said, her vehemence moved, while it alarmed me, 'you are owning that, to some extent, you are in them.'

With an abrupt return to her old expressionless detachment, she discriminated: 'Mayn't one, for instance, own to being in the hands of God without dismay? But all this is extremely lurid; it's more to the point, since we are talking confidences, that I am not particularly, as you see, myself. I can't—to define the symptoms—always think consecutively, and I don't remember my engagements.'

I was successfully diverted. Such an admission, on her lips, with her unblotted record—she had invariably scoffed at ailments—suggested something which might be grave.

'Have you seen anyone?'

'No. You know exactly what they are. We flock to them in our thousands and they wave us off with a great deal of "dear lady" and rest, or massage, or change of scene, according to our purse!'

'I shall take you to Sir Matthew Fenton.'

'A delightful man, and a profound admirer of Mark's. I know; you would arrange to see him privately and elicit the valuable information that Mrs Stafford was an ideal hostess and her husband a first-rate pathologist—spoiled; with the genial afterthought that you couldn't get these charming women to embrace St Paul's doctrine "moderation, moderation"! A pause for the inspection of his new Mauve—or is it Maris he collects? and he would amiably bow you out. We eat too many sweets—in fine—and take ourselves too seriously. *Voilà tout!*'

'But you will see him?'

'Possibly, or someone else—if I don't pull myself together. But I mean to!'

She touched my arm with a light pressure of dismissal: 'Are you coming in? You know I ought to be dancing.'

My night's outlook was sufficiently confused, and the events of the morrow didn't tend to clear it.

Mark and I breakfasted alone together; Darch had been up with the lark, he said, and had gone out early; and when, an hour or so later, he came upon me in Kate's little sitting-room, where I had taken refuge from the general dishevelment, he brought in a breath of outdoor freshness with a vaguely uneasy manner and a look of sleeplessness.

He was promptly definite, blankly candid: it was Kate he wanted to talk over, and his unembarrassed assumption of his right to do so, temporarily overcame my impulse to dispute it.

He closed the door and sat down and came out at once with the bald question: 'Have you any idea how bad she really is?'

I had learned in the past that my conversational strategies were no match for his direct simplicity.

'It was only last night she let me suspect that there was anything the matter, and from what she said—it wasn't much—I concluded that she was thoroughly run down.'

'Is that your name for it—or hers?' He seemed to be summoning patience for the potterer he had to deal with, and went on indulgently, 'but probably she has not been open with you if you haven't decided on any step——'

'Isn't her husband——?' I began rather pointedly.

He cut me short.

'What is the good of these—these absurd pretences? We are old friends, and we are in possession of what, I take it, is common property. Her husband is probably the last person to whom she is likely to confess a weakness, the first, in fact, from whom she would ingeniously hide it. It's no affair of mine, their mutual attitude, except so far as there must be someone to act. You don't suppose it's my choice to move in the miserable business?'

'Don't you think that all round you may be taking an exaggerated view?'

He got up and began pacing up and down the little room with slow, short strides, stopping at length and resolutely facing me.

'I am breaking faith—but it's clear you aren't aware—and you ought to be—that for some time she's been under a delusion, an obsession—I got it out of her. She thinks, poor child! that there's something, some shapeless horror, looking over her shoulder straight, as she hideously persists, into her soul. Not', he went on, with a sort of forced irrelevancy, 'but it won't bear looking into—the clearest pool!—but it's the what—the monstrous thing that's doing it, that's shattering her. And it's not recent. She won't say how long—she says reluctantly—"some time"——'

'She told me last night she couldn't think coherently—wasn't remembering her engagements.'

'That's the threat, if we can't avert it, of a catastrophe: she is beginning not to have any thought outside it, not to remember anything but that. She has made an inconceivably splendid fight, but it can't go on; it's for us to prevent her great success from becoming a great disaster. You have seen her, she's been literally smiling through it; but what a nightmare!'

He made a movement which revealed to me how completely she had impressed him with the actuality of the unreal, how appallingly clear, how irrationally reasonable, she must have been. He was visibly, almost physically oppressed; he looked haunted, too. I laid a hand upon his arm.

'It's all terrible, incredible, but you mustn't look almost as if you shared it.'

'Wait', he said, 'until she tells you herself. Perhaps then you'll be shaken, you'll be inclined to share it too. She must see someone, at once—you are the fittest person to insist. I was pledged on my honour not—as she put it—to betray her, but it's too serious!'

'I must speak to Mark.'

'Didn't he tell you? He had a wire—some business muddle—he's gone up to town. It's a matter, so I understood, of a day or two.'

He made the announcement with a certain grim relief which drew from me: 'You waited——?'

'No', he checked me. 'I simply didn't think of him. I took my cue, I suppose, from—from everybody; they are not spoken of, even paragraphed together; they are independent—' he paused for a word and finally braved it out—'notorieties: will that do?'

'Mark, I remember, used to admire you for your indifference to fine shades. It isn't subtle.'

'No, thank God!' he broke out, 'it isn't subtle! That's not my line; if it were, I shouldn't be pleading for her now. She would be in my hands not in his—and partially in yours. She wouldn't have been brought to this extremity. Have you never asked yourself', he went on more steadily, 'what broke our compact? Have you ever mistaken her since then, for a happy woman? What is it, do you suppose, that has twisted the Kate we knew into—well, the woman who allows that French poodle to patter at her heels? Kate—our Kate, the Mrs Stafford of shop windows—the "beautiful Mrs Stafford"! What is the key to the whole unthinkable change, if it's not some blind instinct of flight, of escape from some intolerable influence or atmosphere? Call it subtlety, if you like! I haven't found, and I'm not particularly keen to find its name.'

'My dear boy,' I protested, 'I can't follow you. You are naturally distressed, upset, and you are taking the most grotesque and unjustifiable view of the whole sad business. I was on the spot and I believe, although, at the time, I couldn't of course approve of it, that she made her choice deliberately. She was dazzled, one doesn't know how a girl's head is turned, by what—you know how the world looks at things—seemed to her a brilliant opportunity. But why go back to it? As to her husband—and oughtn't he surely just now to have our sympathy?—if he is in any sense to blame, it is simply in having left her perhaps too much to herself. And if she, poor child, hasn't used her freedom altogether wisely, it's after all an intelligible weakness. Wasn't she bound, under the circumstances, to make some stir? Mark himself admitted that she was his finest discovery. He was frankly proud of it, that he didn't miss, even in her, his "little human praise".'

He gave me a look which suddenly, decisively, divided us—put an impassable space between us.

'I give it up', was his brief conclusion. 'You are all beyond me—I haven't, as you say, a head for subtleties. What do you mean to do?'

'Mark must be told—consulted.' For the moment I saw no further.

'Damn consultations!' he said quietly. 'What is to hinder your taking her up today?'

'For one thing, Kate herself. And then there are these tableaux people to be photographed this afternoon. Half of them will be gone tomorrow. Don't you see how inexplicable, with Mark too away, it must appear even if Kate would agree to a plausible excuse? She wouldn't—she won't in any case be easy. She is not, you know, a person to be forced.'

'It's in your hands.' He was speaking now from a distance, trying to make his voice carry—to reach me—to move me. 'If it were in mine——'

'If it were,' I urged, 'you wouldn't before it's absolutely unavoidable provoke the inevitable chatter?'

He deliberately turned his back on me, went to the window and stood cheerlessly looking out. There was nothing more to say—nothing to stay for; I got up and moved towards the door. He hastened to open it, remarking as he did so, dully—distantly: 'I am one of the inconvenient people who will be gone tomorrow.' Shutting me out with it—turning into the room again before I had shaped my lips to a conventional regret.

At luncheon, I found it difficult—almost impossible—to fit the picture of my startled thought into the frame of this pitiful disclosure. Her whole aspect of tranquil brilliance, her perfect manipulation of the pieces in the social game, had it not been for Darch's corroborative presence, would have made the dreaded thing unthinkable; but later in the afternoon, the shadow of the cloud took shape. The stage had been left up. Most of the tableaux had been taken, when Kate, who had not come in to tea, and was being asked for, appeared and had her scene set up. She mounted the platform and began rather automatically to strike her pose, when a murmur reached her from below. She had forgotten to change her dress. For a moment she stared, stood still, as if she didn't catch the point of the remonstrance—wasn't going to—when a glance from Darch seemed to recall her to herself, and meeting it, she at once stepped down with a timid, absent—

'So I have. I am sorry. Does it matter? Then we are out of it.'

'Not hopelessly', said Darch, who was bent, I understood, on keeping her attention on the stretch. 'M. Devereux—Hamlet must be done anyway—in solitary distinction.'

'Of course,' she rose to it at once, 'he mustn't be missed, and after all he gains immensely. Please', she called up to him, 'stay where you are.'

He intractably descended.

'But no,' he objected, 'without you—it becomes meaningless, and it must not be that Mrs Stafford alone remains uncommemorated. Impossible!'

'Oh! for that'—she had regained entire possession of herself—'it easily arranges itself. You shall commemorate my stupidity! Will this do?'

She walked across the room and placed herself against a *portière*—a white figure erect and admirably posed—smiling out from the crimson folds.

It seemed as if in this momentary presentment, for the first time since her marriage she confronted me alone, cut off. She stood, to my sense, in a cleared, hushed space, the centre of a far-reaching muteness, indefinable and uninvaded by the chattering crowd. With the click of the camera, she was once more of it, a moving, shining part—a sunlit presence with all clouds dispersed.

I had no more speech with her that day. I never, now I come to think of it, had speech with her again. Whether, that evening, she really evaded me, or whether my own uneasy, indeterminate movements towards her—too hesitant to be frankly met—let down between us the final curtain, I can never be quite sure.

I awoke next morning with a firmer mind, less faltering purposes. Too late! She had slipped through my irresolute fingers. Her maid brought me a note at noon. 'Madame had wished me not to be disturbed.'

I took the envelope from the woman's hand, and, loth to open it under her attentive, initiated eye, dismissed her, divining a disposition to loiter—to be questioned. She left me startled by the simple commentary with which she withdrew. 'Madame had accompanied Mr Darch to the station last night and had not yet returned.'

I closed the door on her and turned to the letter which was going to explain itself. But it was not explicit.

'I have left Mark', it started with that abrupt announcement. 'Charlie is taking me away. I cannot explain or justify our action; but in time the inevitable justifies itself. The world will have ugly thoughts of us; will you be able to find something truer? I am sure only of one sufficient thing, that God will not condemn us—if it were only God!'

And that was all. I sat staring stupidly at the little sheet with its meagre, startling statement, waiting perhaps for some light to flash out from between the lines, upon those two elusive, receding images, of Kate, of Darch, which slowly, strangely enough, as the minutes passed, became obscured, over-shadowed by another; till at length it was Mark alone I distinctly saw. For me, for themselves, they had taken flight, but he remained and I—I who must singly and immediately face him, be arraigned possibly before him and vicariously stripped and judged. It came over me with a force which left me almost indifferent to the other exigencies of the moment, the dismissal or entertainment of his lingering unenlightened guests, of whom I finally disposed as rapidly and adroitly as I could.

Travelling all night, I arrived in London, unreasonably early, but as soon as I felt myself presentable, I set forth and knocked at the familiar door. He was out. The man knew nothing of his movements beyond a probability of his being home to dinner. I left a note and went home and waited the better part of the intolerable day.

When at last, late, he was shown in, the tense silence which served for greeting served too to show me that it was not now on me that sentence was to be pronounced. If it was on her, I was ready with my testimony—my plea.

'You wished to see me?' he said at length, in the tone of one gravely, patiently wondering why.

'I wanted you, without delay, to know all the facts, because they must prove to you that it's not, even now, too late to recall—to save her.'

'Kate', he said, slowly, reflectively, seeming, with this utterance of her name, to summon her, set her visibly, tangibly there between us. 'You have not heard? but how should you? She has saved herself.'

'By coming back?'

'No, by going on'—he paused—'by dying!' He spoke considerately, deliberately, as if—called upon brutally to strike—he found no means to humanize the blow. 'She died last night.'

'How?' It broke from me, an articulate dread, not of the event, but of the manner of it.

'Quite simply and suddenly. They had got as far as Dover—and there, with scarcely any warning, she failed—and ended. They give, of course, some plausible name to it, but it was, as you know, her habit—her nature—to do things very quietly, and this—this step of hers was too violent, too unnatural. She felt herself falling—she did fall, and practically—it killed her.'

'The effort, you mean, to recover herself, the will to return, was there, but ineffectual?'

'We shall never know. She has eluded us to the end. It's terrible, but it's perfect. It's Kate herself!'

His thought seemed to be folded in the present, voluntarily bounded by the day so near its close, as though he had schooled himself to press no further; but I was looking back from this strange deliverance to the unintelligible past, and on to that future with its threatening dusk—averted. She *had* been spared.

'As it is,' I managed to say, 'she *is* safe—her memory—herself——?'

'Absolutely. It's in her face.'

'You have seen her?'

'I could almost believe I had never before seen her.' He stopped, and added after an interval, 'but that's unspeakable. Death is an appalling silence.'

'And an absolution?' I wished to know it.

He didn't answer at once, and when he did, it was with a sort of finality, a weight as of last words: 'They are beyond that—the dead. They are divinely indifferent.'

'If you mean we can't reach them, I don't believe it.'

'It is better to. There is that poor young man trying hard not to believe it. He won't succeed.'

'You have forgiven him?'

'I am bound to feel immensely sorry for him. He will move his heaven and his earth to call her back, and she won't come.' He held out his hand; he *was* final. 'You were anxious to tell me things, but I shall, please remember it, never want to hear them. They are profoundly immaterial, now, the things that can be told. Good-night.'

It was some weeks later that poor Charlie wrote to me, making vivid, in his simple, troubled note, Mark's image of him, vainly moving his two worlds to call her back.

He was the last person, he knew, he wrote, to ask or be granted any sort of favour—but he was asking one—perhaps the most unpardonable. He wanted, of my charity, the photograph of Kate—the last—he supposed I had it—taken that afternoon in Scotland. He had long since destroyed the earlier ones, his own, and had nothing for what—for want of a better word—he would call remembrance. He would take my silence, if it must be, for refusal, and fully understand it. But perhaps I too might understand and—not refuse.

After a momentary hesitation, I replied telling him I had as yet done nothing with it, but if he cared to come and see in about a week's time, I hoped to have it ready for his acceptance. My attitude, which might intelligibly have been less friendly, was partly determined by Mark's sympathetic sketch of him, and partly by a sense of my own shortcoming in having perhaps met imperfectly his earlier and more impersonal appeal. I believe too, I hoped he might have something to tell me, be able to throw some light upon the edges of the cloud by which, in thought, they were both still, for me, somewhat overshadowed.

I had meant some time to elapse before I touched the portrait,—that poignant reopening of a too recent wound, for which, with the grim self-torture of youth, he pleaded. For me, its associations were too tragic, and the curious muteness, the sense almost of suspended breath which I remembered to have felt in it, was too premonitory of what had so shortly afterwards come to pass.

That afternoon, however, I took out the plate and proceeded to develop it. It came slowly, and eventually, as I held it up, I slightly recoiled—was suddenly struck with something wrong about it, unexpected, strange! Beside the face I was looking for there appeared, not—and yet after all it was another—or the semblance of another face; twisting round, immediately behind her, close over her shoulder; not at first to me a thing human or recognizable, but gradually growing hideously distinct, monstrously familiar—the face of her husband—of Mark himself!

For a second I stood frozenly staring at it, and then with a violence, involuntary, uncontrollable, I threw up the window and flung it out, down, on to the pavement below, where it fell in shattered fragments.

My first instinct during the days and nights which followed, as the horror defined itself—unbearably persisted—was to share it—to shift the weight of it, in defiance of reason, in defiance of everything; and it was naturally Darch to whom, in those hours of disorder and oppression, I was prepared to turn, for whom, in fact, I was tremulously waiting.

But when, punctually at the end of his week, he came, his burdened presence steadied me and I forbore.

As he stood there before me so altered, so spent, so inarticulate, my own selfish need declined, my intention of relief at his expense receded; and I understood that that intolerable revelation must be finally and for ever consigned to silence—to the limbo of unutterable things.

He talked for a time inanimately, evasively, of the weather, the opera, the changes in the Cabinet, but while I listened to that lifeless voice of his uttering its unprofitable commonplaces, I was aware of another, a living voice, lifted above it in insistent supplication.

'Not of Kate,' it reiterated, 'let us speak of anything, of everything but her.'

And she was not named between us, she was simply, mutely, unconquerably present—a haunting shade.

At length he got up to go, standing before he made farewell, silently, submissively expectant.

'You will find it difficult to forgive me,' I told him gently, 'but after all, you were not to have it—none of us were to have it, the precious thing you are waiting for. I have—I had—I hardly know how to confess it—irretrievably spoiled the plate.'

He remained silent, looking at me lingeringly, intently, questioningly in the face, and for an instant, I shrank back before that disturbing scrutiny. Was it possible, imaginable—that he guessed—he knew?

But as soon as I found courage enough to meet, to return his gaze, I saw in it merely the fixity, the pain, the incredulity of acute failure and something like despair.

'It was hopeless, impossible?' he asked at last reluctantly.

'It was quite hopeless, quite impossible,' I said.

THE SMILE

AN old woman once lived at the top of a wonderful Tower. Travellers who know the country well speak little of her, telling only how that land is marked by an air of great loneliness; how far off it lies; and of a strange spell, as of some tumultuous peace, which it throws like a garment over those who linger there.

The Tower rose from the centre of a wood. Strangers skirted the dark entanglement. It was a place of tyrant shadows and imprisoned sunlight, melodious with the notes of hidden birds, who shook the boughs, while scents swept down. The Tower was round and battlemented, its summit farther from earth than sky. The great trees round its base, waving their mighty branches, looked, as its height mocked them, like wind-tossed flowers. The steadfast gazer could see this grey giant rear itself against the blue. Dwellers in the town below said sometimes that it was not there. Some, who traced its outline in the twilight, or through the mists of morning, thought it a trick of cloud and sky.

The ascent to this mysterious height was steep and winding.

Tales were told of blood, of blindness, of men who died defeated and fell headlong into the deep and secret places of the wood. It is true men had been blinded by the myriad hues, the changing lights, or by the dust thrown upward by the footsteps of their fellows. Some fell and reached the summit bleeding; and there were dangers which are not told.

But they might sleep upon the way.

The dead who found rest in the wood's green embrace did not ask a kinder bed. Above, the strange old woman wove strange spells round men, wooing them to seek her, singing—ere they climbed madly upward—a magical song. She held gifts in her hands, and her white hair hung grandly round her unseen face.

It was said she wiped the eyes and feet of weary climbers with those soft tresses, before she parted them, to shed her Smile.

Many, in the streets beyond the wood, never heard her voice, nor knew of the gigantic Tower. Others saw it, and looked upward, and passed along. There were legends told in the country of her beautiful Face. None had seen it, for her white locks lay across it.

In the huts and taverns of the town, the people sat at evening, picturing it—while darkness gathered and hid the Tower.

It was only visible by day. At night, the figure aloft on it was hidden, sending through darkness wild and wonderful strains.

He who heard would start from his place and thrust back the casement, standing motionless as the music stole through the still air towards him, over the trees and along the lighted streets.

Then his comrades whispered together, saying: 'He hears the voice.' On the morrow they watched to see him set out towards the wood.

As he stood at the window, they spoke softly of the old woman's ruthless summons, and whispered of his little ones at home. Then one, perhaps, would start a drinking song, lest others heard it and were called away.

'What', said they, 'if her brow be white as the mountain-tops, it is as cold as snow!'

'But her glance', says he at the window dreamily, 'sends brighter gleams than the sun over hills and hamlets, in the break of a dark day.'

'Fool,' they answered, 'thou hast not seen it.'

'Nay', he cried, 'but I may, she calls me', and at daybreak, he was gone.

Lovers, wandering together through the fields, had heard it and fled, warning neither friends nor kindred, who found them, long afterward, it may be, stretched on soft mosses in the wood. One youth missed his maiden's lips for ever, summoned, as he clasped her, by the imperious call. Breathlessly, without farewell, he sped away, while she, forsaken, stood in the darkness, moaning. Thus some children found her, with wild eyes, distraught. For none returned who set out on that journey, save those tossed down to slumber in the silent wood. It was from the heights that those sad souls were hurled. The last steps of the way appalled them—and they fell, struggling to ascend the slant. Barbed stakes in the slippery surface they might grasp—and some achieved the goal, so aided, with torn and bleeding limbs. The old woman stooped to tend them, flinging aside her misty veil of hair.

She bent towards them and her Smile shone out. It may have crept on, as the dawn steals across the shrouded sky, or perhaps, it flashed like some great beacon into their tired and dimmed eyes, and the splendid light fell full upon them, as they, transfigured with reflected glory, met her face to face.

This grand gaze claimed the victors. They pressed up. Those who reached the summit might ask of her what they would. She could steep their soul in music by a whisper in their ear. Above her head she threw marvellous gifts in circles, like a juggler's balls. Below, poor climbers longed for them, but desire was dead and yet undying, in those who met the Smile.

Travellers hasten through that country, speaking little with its people, oppressed by the mysterious mantle, as of some stormy quietude, which it flings over those who loiter there. Some dare not enter it, knowing not what they fear.

Yet it is a place of quiet fields and gentle hill-slopes, where men till, and drive their oxen. Evil is not thought or done there: priests are banished, home is the only Temple found, and wayfarers, always welcomed to the simple dwellings, find them abodes of peace.

Far from the Tower, among the hills, is a little cottage. It stands in the midst of sloping meadows, shut in by trees, which seem like guardians of the lonely spot. A mother once lived there with her baby. It was an ugly child, naughty, and perpetually hungry, and red in the face. The winds, once pitying the tired woman, asked the trees to help them sing it to sleep. But it drowned their lullaby and screamed louder, till they grew wrathful and nearly blew the roof off, and beat the branches down. This frightened the little one, who kept cowardly peace till morning. It woke as cross as ever, and was washed and fed, and its mother tied gay ribbons on it, and bore it across the meadows, and through the town.

All the way, it could be heard crying to be taken back to toast its crumpled feet before the fire.

But its mother, rather, loved to sit on a green mound by the great tree-trunks in the wood, beneath the Tower. Here she came to watch the distant treasures, which attracted her, for she was poor. She shut her ears to the wonderful voice, rising and falling, calling, like the sound of silence, far away. Gladly she would have listened and joined the climbers, but women with babies cannot always do what they would. So she sat knitting, hushing the babe when it was trouble-some, and looking upward when she could.

It has been said that none but the topmost climbers ever saw the beautiful Face, but this is not so, for the baby, who could not even crawl, opened a small blue eye one day, and saw it; unclosed the other, and sat up and stopped crying, and tumbled off its mother's knee. For those who once see that vision, there is no other.

The baby was stupid and tiresome, but it discovered this, and began to puzzle its mother by toppling over continually in its efforts to peer up so high.

The old woman, for a brief moment had grown weary of watching the way-worn travellers up the steep and she glanced down and saw at the bottom the red and puckered baby face. It cannot be told why she was seized with sudden love for it. It happened so.

At first she sent strange lullabies across the wood, and through the town, and over the meadows, to where at night-time the baby lay. She longed for the child to hear her voice, and strung her magic notes, yet the warm little monster only slept heedless, and ceased crying sooner than it used to do.

The old woman said to herself: 'The child will not listen, but if she sees my Face, when she grows older she will long, more than all these climbers, to come up to me.'

She trembled lest the babe might make one of the crowd who saw the Tower, and looked up at it, and passed along. And so she sought to win the child, and thrust her thick white locks aside.

The stars drop dimly down their heavenly glances on mortal eyes, and men look upward at the distant mountains, learning some of the thoughts seated on their high white brows. The child scrambled through the wood's tangled spaces, seeking its Vision, day by day. She lay in the long grass dreaming, watching the wonderful sight.

Years passed, and still she crept to the great tree-trunk, her gaze chained upward.

Through her life, she said nothing of what she saw. She was possessed, enchanted. Toilers from the steep called to her; she listened smiling, and heard unmoved, the low beguilements of the magic voice. She would murmur to herself: 'Poor souls, how far they climb to see my beautiful Face!'

She grew a woman. Her mother, now bent and grey, begged her to stay at home, to work, and sweep, and to train the vine up the cottage walls. Now and again she did some of these small services, but soon the ache for the beautiful Face assailed her, till, leaving the pot to burn, the vine to droop, her mother weeping, she stole away. And through her life it was always so.

Youths in the town would willingly have won her; for the ugly babe was a comely damsel now. She smiled on one. He drove his oxen past their door each morning. Ere the sun rose, she pushed back her casement; and flushed from slumber, looked down on him as he went by. They walked the fields together in the twilights of one short summer. Then she grew tired of a mortal face. Her daily pilgrimage angered him, and he forbade her to approach the Tower; so they parted.

The neighbours laughed, and spoke of her as one who had no understanding. The old folks shook their heads, nodding them nearly off, at the spectacle of her idle, thriftless ways. She was counted, indeed, a good-for-nothing. Yet the old woman on the Tower loved her still, though she began to doubt if her beloved one would ever bestir herself to scale the height. The poor maid had not dreamed of it. Her life was filled with the delight of gazing at the beautiful Face. Who could tell her that the Smile was absent from it; that none but victors may invoke it; that it was indeed their triumph which gave it birth?

And still the years sped on. She dwelt happily, though cold guests came to the lonely cottage, and stripped it bare, and bore her mother to their unknown land.

At length, despairing, in a moment of great sadness, the old woman turned her Face away and the maiden found herself bereft.

She sat heavy hearted in the empty cottage, bidding the magic voice console her, for that she still could hear. Her old lover passed the window. She beckoned him, saying: 'I go no longer to the Tower.' He clasped her, and hand in hand, they walked the lanes once more. But by her fireside, the great ache seized her, and the unappeasable hunger grew. She would start from fitful slumber, smiling from dreams of the irrevocable sight.

One evening, she called her lover to the cottage, and said: 'We spend this night together!' She drew him in and, at dawn, they parted about the hour of sunrise: she saying nothing of farewell. Free of his last embrace, she stood by her door to watch him disappear, a moving speck upon the hills. Then with a liberated cry, she set off leaping and shouting towards the Tower.

She started on the journey. The way is long. Flowers spring everywhere. On other roads to heavenly places, the pilgrim must not note them or delay. Here he gathers one from every plant he sees; or half-way up, at a stream's edge, a tiny creature, wet and barefoot, holds her hands out for the nosegay, ere she leads across the water. She counts every blossom, and nods stern 'No', if stalks are bent, or petals fallen, or if the posy wants a bud. Many go downward, sadly searching, and return long after, with their offerings complete. A thousand hues dazzle the climber's dust-dimmed eyes. Butterflies and birds sweep past him. The air is full of scent and song. As he mounts, he may look down, and see the child scatter his flowers. Travellers pause; she waits for them to present their posies; laughs, examines, and flings them on the stream.

Above her, sits the old man at the cross roads. He alone can point out the upward path. For him, the toilers chase each butterfly that flutters past them. He demands these with unbrushed wings, imprisoned, that he may set them free.

Towards the summit, there is a gate. A bird unlatches it; the password is to end his song. No climber knows, if thrush, or linnet, or wren, will hail him. Hundreds of singers take their turn and he must learn the note of all.

The maiden soon grew weary. Stones cut her feet; she fell; the labyrinths bewildered her. She sank and slept upon the way. Three times, the fairy at the brook rejected her; she dropped her flowers, or brought them crushed. Far below, in the cottage, she had lived listless. So labour was doubly irksome to her. And the climbers may not help each other. Those who will do so, slip backward and are seen no more. Her lover might have wept to see her stoop so painfully, and struggle with spent breath to gain the old man's fee. It was piteous, too, to hear her gasping travesties of the birds' joyous song. She kept on, bent and almost beaten, and neared at length the last steep slope.

Men named it the despairing spot.

She saw poor climbers, from afar, afraid to clutch the cruel stakes, spin in the air, ere they fell down, down into the wood.

She rested, spent and scarred, her eyes seeking wildly the well-known Face.

Her comrades greeted it, lifting their hands as if in prayer. They raised glad looks, illumined by the splendour which shone down. Her eyes rained tears—so near it seemed. Summoning ebbing strength, she fought, blood-stained and broken, up the last awful path. Men, uncheered, had never trod it, but she pressed on desperately, mounting to the topmost height.

Safe through the battlements, she tasted victory. But the beautiful Face had missed her triumph. The old woman stood, her grand white locks wound round her, looking another way.

The maiden threw her torn arms upward, and then sank lifeless with a desolate cry. The old woman heard, and turned to her beloved, raising her, and sweeping the stains from breast and feet. She called, in tones unknown to earthly music. They rang melodious paeans to dumb distance. The toilers in the fields below, the busy citizens, and on his mountain slope, the maiden's lonely lover, stood still to hear.

The old woman stooped, pushed back her shadowing hair. The maid's stark eyes met hers. In that encounter, the Smile broke, and wavered. Then the ageless light went out.

Travellers tell of the great loneliness that wraps that land; how far it lies; and speak mysteriously of the spell it casts over the dwellers there as of some tempestuous calm. Some have seen the Tower, and a strange white figure at the summit, clothed in tossed hair. It stands, they say, for ever speechless, desolate, striving to waken a burden in its arms.

A FATAL FIDELITY

MR BAGOT put down his watering-can and, whistling softly the while, stood back to cast an approving glance on the neat, if somewhat laboured, wreath which adorned his modest grave. But no!—tilting his head slightly sideways and closing one eye, he perceived a flaw, and stepped briskly forward to give the flattened blooms a few final dabs. Then, turning his back on the achievement, he proceeded to scan expectantly the little churchyard.

Planted round the tiny church with its old wooden tower, in the midst of flat, green fields, which stretched between it and the rich, red suburb half a mile away, it might still have kept its air of ancient peace, if Balling, opulent, progressive Balling with her spruce villas, her princely Broadway—lately exhilarated by the hoot of new electric trams—had not laid a prosperous hand upon it.

To be just to Balling, she had done her handsomest; pink and grey granite monuments held their expensive heads almost level with the little tower; glaring white, and heavily-carved marble crosses, broken columns and polished obelisks reared themselves high in costly splendour above the paltry, weather-beaten head-stones of the past. Modern provision merchants and fancy drapers, many of them retired, had shown up the meanness of an earlier day, and shone forth in the glory of lavish grief, while those old, scanty memorials of the long-forgotten dead lay huddled and crushed beneath the weight of it.

And Mr Bagot, as he gazed around upon these triumphs of the mason's art, was vaguely conscious of the greatness of his native suburb. Why,—he remembered the time when the place was just an ordinary oldfashioned country churchyard, with nothing that he could call to mind to strike the eye, and now it was, so to speak, a regular monumental exhibition. He regretted, in passing, that his own exhibit could not 'compete', but, being of a cheerful and practical temper, assured himself that the late Mrs Bagot had no reason to complain, the coal and potato business, like all businesses at present, being what it was. His reflections at this point received a check, from the appearance of something beyond the hedge, which he was not ungallant enough, even in thought, to call a blot upon the landscape. In his mental phrase it was a 'figger', and to be precise, it was a very short and extremely solid figure, which, having reached and wedged itself successfully through the narrow gateway, advanced towards him panting, and waving a welcoming handkerchief, deeply edged with black.

'Late again!' said Mr Bagot, in a tone of genial reproach—adding, considerately, as the lady was still too spent for adequate response—'Take your time, Mrs Widgery—take your time.' Meanwhile, he crossed the path to refill the watering-can at the tap under the hedge, returning to relieve his companion of a basket of dahlias which hung upon her crape-trimmed arm, and to busy himself with those little attentions which were, in fact, the seed of which this acquaintance was the tender shoot.

'It was the clock', said Mrs Widgery at length, apologetically, 'having been done up, and always losing from twenty to forty minutes afterwards. But I hoped you wouldn't wait.'

'Don't say that', said Mr Bagot, cordially. 'It's a pleasure; you know it is.'

The lady turned back a heavy veil, and disclosed a countenance more remarkable for breadth of surface and ruddiness of hue than distinction of feature, and allowed a smile, tinged with becoming melancholy, to overspread it, while she removed a pair of tight kid gloves.

'Well, I am sure it's very kind of you to say so, though I question whether it's suitable to be talking of pleasure under the circumstances. Not that I can't but feel your thoughtful attentions with the watering-can and such—without mentioning hints on the making up—has been more to the point—and more soothing', she added with conviction, 'than what passes for sympathy elsewhere. I won't say who,' she pursued guardedly, 'but there are those with whom it seems nothing but a mockery; while you, Mr Bagot, have most delicately contrived to make yourself in a way of speaking, part of the bereavement.'

'As a fellow-mourner', returned Mr Bagot, modestly. 'I look on myself as happy in the opportunity of having been on the spot. The road to success in business, or pleasure, or what-not lies in being on the spot; such is my belief,—but in your case, Mrs Widgery, I take no credit for it. I look upon it as a piece of luck.'

'Your views are so free and manly', was the warm reply, ending, however, in a sigh. 'Now Mr Widgery, who was a thinker, held there was no such thing as luck. He considered it as a blasphemy connected with card-playing for which, as he often said, the pit was yawning. Deeply religious he was, and always had an answer ready. The causes of things, he used to say, may be put down as entirely due to the Almighty, though the effects may only too often be attributed to our Arch Enemy, the Devil. I could seldom follow him, but his words always made a deep impression. Such is the power of Faith.'

'Come—come,' urged Mr Bagot, kindly, 'we mustn't brood. We must get to work', and hitching up his trousers, preparatory to joining the lady, who was now kneeling on the sward, pensively placing dahlias in a circular zinc receptacle,—he ventured: 'Two whites and one mauve look a bit blotchy to my idea, if I may say so. If I may take the liberty to count 'em, I should prefer alternates as more tasty, though, recollecting what you have produced, perhaps I'm wrong in presuming to interfere. Two—four—six—eight', he continued, counting—'does it, to a hair!'

'Oh! I can trust your taste', said Mrs Widgery, acting on the suggestion, 'from what I see across the path. Your grave is always a perfect picture, and if you could hear the remarks I have heard passed on it, more than once, you would feel repaid.'

'I do, when I hear yours', responded Mr Bagot, gallantly. 'But the fact is, you get quite tricky over these little jobs, once you do 'em regular. I take no credit for it. Practice *makes* perfect, as they say.'

'Practice don't make an artist', returned the lady, with flattering intention. 'But I was not only alluding to your floral successes. There's the stone and the inscription, always such a test of character, it seems to me, for them as has the gift of choice.'

Mr Bagot got up, wiped his wet hands on the lining of his coat, and throwing the débris of leaves and stalks, which he had carefully collected, over the hedge, admitted candidly: 'As to the wording, the late Mrs Bagot picked her own. It was quite an amusement during her illness, looking 'em out, and making up her mind. Naturally I carried out her wishes as they stood, but if she'd lasted another week, I don't doubt it would have been something different. There seems to be such an assortment, one as good as another, from what she showed me; it would have fairly puzzled me, and wouldn't have satisfied her, if I *had* been called upon to decide.'

'I think you mentioned she was a bit fanciful towards the end?'

'Full of whims, full of whims, from first to last,' he agreed, meeting the upturned glance of sympathy, 'but timid as a linnet. And for a shrinking from unpleasantness, I never knew her equal. Rather than differ from you, she would leave the room half a dozen times a day, without remark, till you came round to her opinion. She resembled a bird,' went on the widower, reflectively, 'a bird in confinement, I should say, having none of their activity in the natural state. Give her her seed and water regular, and refrain from teasing her, and chirpier company no man could expect. But when crossed, her mope was painful, and nothing short of a little present in the shape of a bit of finery or an outing would bring her round.'

'*You* never crossed her', affirmed Mrs Widgery, with pleasing certainty. 'I know you better. You considered her in every way.'

'A good wife has as much call to *be* considered as a good customer, and more—and more', repeated Mr Bagot, generously. 'I can't conscientiously say I crossed her; it made things too uncomfortable, and comfort before contradiction was my motto in married life.'

'And your faithfulness to her memory does you equal credit', observed Mrs Widgery, accepting his proffered help in her attempt to rise, and leaning heavily on his outstretched arm.

'Let credit be given where credit's due', he returned, frankly. 'I laid myself out to remember Emma, and, thanks to you, I can't say I have failed. I won't deny at times, it has cost me an effort; but habit's everything and you have given me the habit. You have kept me up. You would be surprised to know how you have kept me up to the mark. Many a Sunday morning, when I have been tempted to lay in bed and persuade myself that recollection would answer the purpose, your image has acted as a stimulant, and got me out. "No," I have said to myself, "Mrs W. will be there faithful to her time. Mrs W. will want her watering-can, and be wondering what's become of me!" '

'Late last Sunday, and late again this', Mrs Widgery reminded him, in a tone of deep reproach. 'You are forgetting that.'

'Once you have formed the habit, you have won the toss,' said Mr Bagot, brightly confident, 'and it comes easier, almost natural. If you was to be late again next week, though I should be the loser, it would hardly signify, and my obligation to you would remain the same. Sooner or later I should expect you to turn up.'

'After what you have said,' returned Mrs Widgery, with feeling, and presumably referring to the clock, 'I shall put it on or take it back to the shop, rather than run the risk of being behind-hand in what, for the future, I shall look upon as a sacred duty. But perhaps it's time we was turning? Yes, you are right as usual,' she concluded, looking down on their joint arrangement, 'the alternates has a more tasteful effect.'

'I always think you get your money's worth out of dahlias', observed Mr Bagot, following her glance. 'There's more substance in 'em, and more wear. I like 'em as well as anything, and if he was in a position to see it, the late lamented ought to be justly pleased. Did he favour any particular bloom?'

'Well, no,' said Mrs Widgery, reflectively, 'he didn't altogether approve of flowers. He was a scholar, and saw no use for them in creation. Vegetables he could account for, and fruit—to which he was very partial, but flowers baffled him, as a thinker. I have heard him suggest they might have been intended as a snare.'

'Perhaps he sees otherwise now', said Mr Bagot, cheerfully.

'I doubt it,' replied his widow, dubiously, 'he wasn't one to change, and it's on my mind sometimes that he couldn't hold the expense. He was always against extravagance, in all departments; the carefullest of men. Most men, he used to say, would wear their collars until soiled, and then fling 'em reckless to the wash. But he turned his, Mr Bagot, as regular as he wound the clock, and made one do the work of two.'

'Did he now?' said Mr Bagot, with interest. 'I should never have thought of it, but piety puts you up to all sorts of dodges. Emma was friendly, for a time, with one of these churchworkers, who used to pick up cigarette ends and such like for some old gaffer in the parish. Now I should never have thought of that. Half an ounce of shag paid for over the counter would have been my way out of it,—and less trouble, and nicer smoking. He was in that line, I think you said?'

'On the contrary, he was a strict Baptist,' said Mrs Widgery, 'by profession, and dead against the Church and all its works. His outdoor evangelical services, which he conducted of a Sunday evening, was a great success and source of interest to him. I won't undertake to say how many young ladies of the town chiefly employed in the drapery, he didn't bring to a sense of sin, and he was never so happy as when thus employed. One would generally accompany him home, and he would sit wrestling with her in the parlour, while I got the supper, the girl being out. Well do I remember his last address, which brought tears to the eyes of many. "There's too much buoyancy in the world", I can hear him now; "there's too much holler joy." The empty joke and the idle laugh he would not countenance, and as he lived, he died. "Don't let me find you among the goats, Mathilda', was his last words to me, and at first I thought he was wandering, but it was only his wealth of imagery. A born orator, Mr Bagot; the stationery business was beneath him, though it brought him into contact with the studious. He saw to the accounts himself, but he left the stock and counter work entirely to me.'

'And a lucky feller to be able to do so', commented Mr Bagot, unfastening the little gate which took them out into the fields. 'The business went so much against the grain with Emma, I could never get her to put her nose inside the shop; had to have ground glass put in the connecting parlour door to shut it off. There's the difference in people in general, and women in particular. I had hoped, in marrying, to combine a little fancy greengrocery with the heavier job, but I soon saw that was not to be. However,—bygones must be bygones. What about this affair of the memorial to Mr W. Has Daniells sent you the estimates and designs? He promised me to bustle up about it.'

'Friday night, by the last post,' said Mrs Widgery, 'and I can never sufficiently thank you for all your trouble. I selected Number one, head- and foot-stone, as being moderate and suitable. Widgery would never have lain happy under a great outlay, and anything churchy with a cross on it like the other patterns Numbers two and three, would have turned him in his grave. I left the inscription to stand over to ask your advice. Mr Daniells recommended "*Resurjam*" as novel and appropriate, which, according to him, means: "I shall rise again." But I shall be guided by you,' said Mrs Widgery, graciously, 'having been so successful with your own.'

'*Resurjam*', repeated Mr Bagot, reflectively. 'Out of the common, certainly, and might mean anything, if you don't put the equivalent alongside. But it don't sound restful. I should favour something more resigned. Why not "At peace" now?'

'I never liked it—over a husband', replied the lady with decision.

'I don't press it,' said Mr Bagot, amiably, 'it's only an idea; or what of "Not lost, but gone before"?'

'Not that neither', said Mrs Widgery, emphatically. 'My notion is something dignified, but not too desponding, with a dash of feeling, and preferably in poetry,—though cut in lead it would come expensive.'

'I couldn't toss you up anything of that description on the spur of the moment', said Mr Bagot, after a meditative pause. 'You might look over some old memorial cards, or take a train across to Kensal Green, and see if there was anything there that took your fancy. I couldn't oblige you with anything of that nature on the nail.'

'Why not come round again, as you did last Sunday evening, and have a bit of supper and talk it over comfortably', proposed Mrs Widgery, with sudden inspiration. 'Two heads are better than one.'

'Nothing could be nicer', Mr Bagot accepted heartily, and having crossed the two flat green fields, at the edge of which the country ends and the rows of red bow-windowed villas come abruptly into view, they parted with friendly handshakes, expressions of mutual indebtedness, and a hope expressed by Mrs Widgery, and echoed by Mr Bagot, that nothing would occur to prevent their meeting again at half-past eight or nine.

The pleasantest of human plans are, however, liable to disarrangement at the hands of Fate, and when at about eight o'clock the dreamless doze, in which Mrs Widgery was wont to indulge on Sabbath evenings, was rudely broken by the sound of the door-bell, followed by an aggressive double knock, she sat up and braced herself for the unforeseen and untimely visit, which that loud sustained attack upon her knocker heralded. No one, as she said to herself, between the admittance and entrance of her guests, but relatives or the tax collector made 'such an uproar, and anyone with an ounce of consideration would have wrote to say that they was coming; but, pounce upon you when least expected, was always Maria's way.'

'Please, m'm, Mrs and Mr Saunders,' announced the small domestic, in a confidential whisper, 'and the little b'y.'

'Ask them to walk in', said Mrs Widgery, with dignity. 'Mind you remember the extry plates and glasses.'

'Don't put yourself out for us', said Mrs Saunders, with meaningless civility, since it was her invariable custom to time her arrival towards the hour of repast; a meal, as she reminded her husband on their way from the station, being the least, as own sister to the late Mr Widgery, they had the right to expect.

'All I say is', urged Mr Saunders, sensibly, 'don't annoy her—more than you can 'elp. No good comes by annoyance, leastways, not legacies. While they're 'ere, you are at liberty to make things unpleasant, but when they're gone they're in the position to 'it you back. A worm may turn, as the saying is, and make you wish you 'adn't spoken.'

'Oh! Mathilda can hold her own', was Mrs Saunders's inflexible retort.

'Well, all I say is', repeated Mr Saunders, resignedly, 'it's ill-advised. If for once you was to go by me, you would get the boy 'ere to make 'isself agreeable to 'is aunt.' He jerked his thumb in the direction of the hope of the House of Saunders, who, heavily encumbered with and conscious of his Sunday clothes, was trying to keep pace with his mother's rapid stride, and added: 'It would be more to the purpose to appeal to the feelings of a relative through 'im, and leave 'er private affairs alone.'

'*Her* private affairs!' echoed Mrs Saunders, resentfully. 'Say ours! Am I to sit and look on while a designing potater merchant swallers up pore Sam's hard earnings, before he's hardly cold in his grave?'

'Come to that,' said Mr Saunders, practically, 'she kep' the business together, and made it what it is.'

'That's right,' was Mrs Saunders's bitter rejoinder, 'belittle the dead and gone, if it serves your turn, but don't suppose it'll hinder me in my duty of showing her what I think of all I hear. Visits from gentlemen, and turning night into day! If that's your notion of correct behaviour in a widow, it's far from mine. Nor shall I disguise it, Albert.'

'As you please, Maria, only don't round on me afterwards, and say I didn't warn you', was Mr Saunders's final word, which brought them to the door.

Mrs. Saunders had just completed a critical survey of her sister-in-law's apartment, settled herself on the sofa and motioned her husband to a chair, when the door-bell rang again, and, as if connected with the agent at the other end by some mysterious wire, the posture of Mrs Saunders, never pliant, became suddenly rigid, while she directed a glance charged with meaning at her husband, who disloyally evaded it. Her hostess, however, had marked with feelings of uneasiness these outward and visible signs of an inward and spiritual exasperation, and at once put forth the conciliatory, if not strictly truthful statement, that she had ordered sausages, knowing Maria's partiality for that dainty, on the chance that they might drop in. Mrs Saunders received the information with an incredulous and unpleasant smile.

The door opened. 'Please, m'm, the gentleman who was 'ere last Sunday', was the young domestic's tactless intimation that Mr Bagot had arrived.

'My sister-in-law, Mrs Saunders, and husband, Mr Saunders', said Mrs Widgery, ceremoniously, when, after a prolonged and hearty handshake, Mr Bagot had been invited to find a seat.

' 'Appy to make your acquaintance', said Mr Saunders, politely, but with a touch of nervousness, while his wife, compressing her lips and almost imperceptibly inclining her head, offered no response, aiming her first shot, guided by the instincts of sex, at the lady's head.

'Well, Mathilda,' she asked, militantly, 'and how's business, or perhaps I *should* say, how's pleasure?'

'I don't foller you', said Mrs Widgery, coldly; 'business is business, and consequently not all that could be wished, but pleasure to a bereaved woman is similarly out of place.'

'So *I* think', agreed Mrs Saunders with intention.

'Come, come, 'Arry', broke in her husband, pacifically. 'You 'aven't said 'ow-de-do to your aunt yet. Run along and give 'er a kiss, like a good boy.'

Harry, however, remained motionless, and continued to stare apprehensively at the black object, towards which his fascinated attention was needlessly directed.

'He looks poorly', observed his aunt, with a show of affability. She liked and pitied Mr Saunders, whom she regarded as the victim of a great mistake.

'Wants bracing up', replied Mr Saunders, diplomatically. 'Perhaps the air of Kennington ain't what it might be for a delicate boy. But you're 'igh 'ere. 'E always seems the better for a trip to Balling, short as they are. The breeze up by the Reservoir is equal to Clacton-on-Sea, without the expense of the fare.'

'Good for the spirits, it certainly seems, whatever it may be for the health', was Mrs Saunders's pointed contribution.

'They go together', said Mr Bagot, pleasantly, vaguely aware of some oppression in the mental atmosphere; 'when one's down, the other's down, and contrariwise the same.'

'Quite correct, sir', said Mr Saunders, hastily, with sense that this was dangerous ground. 'Now, 'Arry 'ere—as I was saying——'

'Oh, let the child be', interposed his mother, tartly. 'Children know as well, and better, than their elders when they're welcome, and when they're not, though the causes may be fortunately beyond 'em.'

'You're full of mysteries tonight, I must say', said Mrs Widgery, with forced forbearance. 'I'm always pleased enough to see the child in season and out of season. He's harmless, if he's not over affectionate. But in my opinion you keep him up too late. Pore Sam never used to think he'd make old bones.'

'Oh! Widgery always took a unreasonably downcast view of things', commented Mr Saunders, glancing, however, a little anxiously at his drowsy offspring, who, apart from a pallor and puffiness common to his mother's side of the family, showed no sign of imminent collapse.

'Who knows what his reasons were?' hinted Mrs Saunders, darkly. 'Men of his serious cast of mind frequently has an insight into the future, if the present is not sufficient to cause depression. What was my very first words to you, Albert,' she enquired, turning for tardy support to her husand, 'on receiving the telegram of death?'

'I can't say that I recollect exactly', answered Mr Saunders, treacherously. 'I don't hold with taking account of anything let drop by people when they're upset. Why, look at my brother James, when 'is wife was took! He set to and accused 'isself of all manner of things, far better left to the imagination. 'E cried like a child, and——'

An imperious glance from Mrs Saunders arrested these revelations, to which Mrs Widgery, who had conceived and not hesitated to express a deep if vague mistrust of the gentleman in question, was beginning to lend an attentive ear.

'Naturally I was upset,' pursued Mrs Saunders, 'but I was collected with it; I knew what I was saying, and why I said it,—and my words were: "Well, he's happier where he is!"'

'Thank you, Maria', said Mrs Widgery, shortly.

'That's not what I call a compliment to the widow certainly', interposed Mr Bagot, thoughtlessly, with no wish, as he subsequently explained, to stir up strife.

Mrs. Saunders 'pierced him', as she said afterwards, relating the incident to a friend, 'with a glance of disgust from head to feet', and having failed to make any obvious impression on the object of her injurious regard, responded with marked offensiveness: 'Plain-speaking and fair dealing being the custom in *my* family, I have no scruples in leaving flatteries and their fruits and results in more practised hands, from which, as I am given to understand, the added obstacle of matrimonial restraint has lately been removed.'

'How you can dare—' broke in Mrs Widgery, flushing, and finally roused, 'in my house!——'

'In my pore brother's house, you mean', corrected Mrs Saunders, with provoking composure.

'There you make your mistake, Maria,' returned her sister-in-law, 'as Albert and others can bear me witness, though it would never have passed my lips, but for the drift of your last remark. And if there's anything in it, that don't please you, I needn't draw your attention to the natural course for you to take. But while here, while here,' repeated Mrs Widgery, firmly, 'I must request you to cease insinuations calculated to cast a slur on me or those that, from motives of delicacy, I forbear to name.'

Mrs Saunders rose, repeated the piercing process—this time on her sister-in-law—tied the bonnet strings which she had loosened on arrival, and with the air of one unable to breathe another moment such a tainted atmosphere, announced that whatever Mr Saunders's intentions might be, she and the child were going home.

Mr Saunders, coughing apologetically, moved reluctantly, and passing a hand indecisively round the crown of his hat, observed with a lame attempt at pleasantry that sooner or later the best of friends must part, to which Mr Bagot goodhumouredly responded with a slight deflection of the eyelid, intended to convey a sympathetic grasp of the situation.

'*You* might as well stay and have a bit of supper, Albert', replied Mrs Widgery, amiably; 'though if Maria's in such a hurry to get back, I won't be the one to press her to change her mind.'

Mr Saunders wavered, but only for an instant. The discipline of years is not so lightly set aside, and the counsels of harsh experience won the day. The door closed after them with a defiant bang.

'Pore Albert,' commented Mrs Widgery, 'I pity him. His spirit's completely broken: what there ever was of it! Anyone could ride over him. The most pitiful young woman, with a cast in her eye, was riding over him when Maria stepped in and took him out of her hands. She was in feeble health and had a little something, but he had no voice in it from the first, once Maria had come to her decision. Widgery used to say the family owed him a debt of gratitude, but he wasn't responsible, pore young feller, nothing but a sheep to the slaughter, unwilling to the very last.'

'In cases of that sort, if a man can't save himself, nobody can save him,' said Mr Bagot, sententiously, 'unless he has powerful female relatives at his back, and then the natural instinct is to distrust 'em, perhaps rightly; all said and done, you never know where they'll have you. Who would have thought now I should be the innocent occasion of ill-feeling, and spoiling a pleasant evening?'

'Oh! it's not over yet', said Mrs Widgery, with returning cheerfulness. 'And you behaved with perfect taste. I only wish I had half your self-command, but Maria's behaviour is beyond everything. As if I was to be under her instructions as to who I am to entertain!'

'She can't have been herself', was Mr Bagot's charitable supposition.

'That's your noble, generous view of things,' replied Mrs Widgery, 'and utter ignorance of her disposition. She has always been a thorn, as long as I remember her, and seems to get more stand-and-deliver with advancing years. But this time, she has defeated her own object. What are widows?' asked Mrs Widgery, rhetorically, 'but the prey of all? You can feel for me. If you had been taken, and Mrs Bagot left, she would have been in the same defenceless position. I never felt it to the extent I have done this evening, and perhaps I never should, if Maria's conduct had not brought it home to me, showing the contrast between self-seeking and uninterested sympathy, such as yours.'

'I shouldn't dwell on her, if I was you', advised Mr Bagot, kindly.

'Nor do I, unless compelled,' returned Mrs Widgery, 'if for nothing else, for the distressing reason that her painful likeness in features and complexion to the late Mr Widgery frequently poisons the recollection of the lost, while with you, Mr Bagot, on the other hand, the contrary has always held. I have hardly thought of him during the last few months, as a memory—you grasp my meaning—rather than a fact; memories being so much pleasanter, without connecting him with you and all your kindness and attention.'

'Don't make anything of that,' urged Mr Bagot, modestly, 'being as we are quits in that respect; something curiously similar being the case with Emma and yourself. The idea of one calls up the other, like debit and credit in a ledger. The prop is mutual.'

'It was a providential chance,' said Mrs Widgery, reminiscently, 'our meeting as we did, on that very spot, at that very hour, and my not being able to turn the tap but for your timely assistance. It seems as if it was to be!'

'Precisely', agreed Mr Bagot. 'Luck give the stone a push, and all we have got to do is to keep it rolling.'

'Though no effort will be spared to stop it', replied Mrs Widgery, with a note of despondency. 'I can see that without seeing far.'

'A word from you,' said Mr Bagot, impetuously, 'and I could make a proposition, which would lay the dust and clear the road of anything of that sort. But without knowing how it might be taken——'

'I have leant on you, Mr Bagot, as I have leant on few,' said Mrs Widgery, solemnly, 'and never regretted the following of your advice; but if it's connected with Maria, only those who have felt the serpent's sting can realize the full effect of it.'

'Well,' ventured Mr Bagot, thus encouraged, 'it has struck me, to be open with you, only within and consequent on the events of the last half hour, that if you could bring yourself, in time, to think of re-entering the married state, it might simplify matters and be a means of keeping us both up to the mark. Springing as it does from a mutual interest in the two departeds, they would have no reason to feel slighted, rather the reverse; two heads, as I think you observed this morning, being better than one, and why not two hearts, or feelings? I don't press it—' pursued Mr Bagot, 'as you may wish to think it over, though as far as I am concerned, it seems a workable idea.'

'If you would be so kind as to touch the bell,' said Mrs Widgery, with delicate detachment, 'I think we might as well have the supper up; it's more than time. That is the only fault I have to find with Emily: a habit of doing the things to death, and the most unpunctual girl alive.'

'Certainly, with pleasure', said Mr Bagot, rising with alacrity, and adding, as he regained his seat: 'I see I *have* struck you a shade too sudden.'

'It is sudden and unnerving,' answered Mrs Widgery, gravely, but without displeasure, 'and finds me totally unprepared.'

'Well, I'm in no particular hurry', said Mr Bagot, easily. 'When he's spotted a good thing, a sensible man ought to be willing to wait for it; if the ladies prefer to take their time.'

When the date and the place (it was to be Southend) of the honeymoon had eventually been fixed, the further question naturally arose of the weekly tribute to the memory of the respective predecessors of the faithful pair.

'I had thought of asters,' proposed the bride elect, 'being in season, and a hardy flower, as we shall be absent for at least one Sunday.'

'Or everlastings?' suggested Mr Bagot, 'in case, by any chance, we was to stay the fortnight.'

And everlastings they decided it should be.

THE WHEAT

'DON'T LET them cut the Wheat', he had said, sitting up in bed and falling back on it, his face towards the window opening on to the row of windows opposite, in the brickwork of the London street. All through his illness there had been no delirium so that this touch of it at the end seemed strange to them. 'Up to that moment he was quite himself and they were so unlike him', Amy said to her Mother repeating his words about the cutting of the wheat.

No one had known, and half the time he had hardly known himself, but lying there, taking medicines and being read to, he saw how, on and off, it had been with him ever since he was a boy, that Something behind him which he hadn't got at and that other sense of not being altogether Here.

Work took it off and he was always at it, in or out of the house, but ever at the Bank, taking in cheques and handing out gold across the counter, now and then it came to him that it wasn't he who was doing it; that he was really somewhere else and that the cheques and the scales and the sovereigns were not real things. He hadn't much, but all the same he hated money—the look, the feel, the idea of it, perhaps because he stood in a bath of it (someone else's bath) all day from 10 to 4.

Fishermen now——! They had little and kept no hours. He would have liked to be a fisherman. He had watched them, once, on a holiday, from the ferry steps, taking the boats out, hoisting sail, and tacking, sometimes from one side of the harbour to the other, an hour, two hours—getting in. And out at sea, too, out at Sea!

Or a farm hand. He would have liked to follow the plough. There was something about a furrow, the smell of the earth, the give of it under your feet, the brownness, the evenness, the everlastingness of it, up and down—which got hold of you like the sea; the smell and feel of the water, the blueness, the distance, the everlastingness of that. And then the horses—the team of the plough. He could have lived with horses all his life. Sometimes he thought he would have liked to be an animal. Take cats for instance—lying about, blinking and dozing; they had a secret worth knowing if it was only how to get all the heat and stillness and happiness out of the sun.

Those men and animals he fancied had it—the thing he hadn't got at, which was somehow in the sunshine and the night: in lights, too, lamps along the winter streets, and shadows cutting across the parapets of the bridges.

Music would bring it, the band in the Green Park on Sunday evenings; and words from anywhere, in the pages of a newspaper—words like Victory and the Shepherd's Star and the South of France. There was another too which music brought, in which for him all loveliness had once been painted and blotted out, a woman's name. Everything about her had been dreamlike and a fragrance; and at first it was as pure loveliness he saw her, not a thing to touch, simply to wonder at; but later he would lie awake not sure if he could stand it if he didn't touch it; wishing that she would come to him through the night, and show him how to touch it; it was too bewildering alone.

One day he tried to say this to her, and it was difficult: she was arranging flowers. Suddenly he looked up and found she wasn't listening and he had never wanted to speak to anyone about anything again.

And he had married Amy.

After that, as time went on, he came to have only one desire—to be alone: but with Amy you could never be alone, even when she wasn't there: he hoped some day he should get used to her as he had got used to the scales and sovereigns at the Bank.

It was a month or so before his illness that it occurred to him he must have spent his life in sleep, because all at once, things were beginning to stand out for him in a new sort of daylight, so near that however far off they were he seemed almost able to touch them, and so clearly that he might have been looking at them through a pair of field-glasses.

And then one afternoon he discovered that there were only three things on this earth: from the Bank steps, even from the house steps he found them in nearly everything except in his street and over there, on the counter, in the notes and gold.

Everywhere else—and they were in remembered things, the bronze of the seaweed against the grey of the quay-wall; the sweep of a man's hand broadcasting along the furrow: the throb in the breasts of things that ought to be flying but could hardly hold their heads up in the boxes of the bird-shops.

A little while ago he had thought there were a hundred things but now he knew there were just these three which he was beginning to get hold of, and the place where they seemed to him most to be, all together, was in the fields. In the grass, the greenness, the wave of it in the wind, and the life in every blade.

And then he was struck down.

For weeks these women had rustled about the room, pouring stuff down his throat and talking about him in whispers behind a screen; and an Angel of God could not have got them out; but what chiefly worried him was being there shut in.

He broke free, in a way, by thinking of walks in bygone holidays—before his marriage—the roads and the footpaths; and one day he asked Amy for the stick which had gone with him on which he had notched things in memory of the places, but she didn't bring it up.

The next day he asked her Mother for it who said 'Oh, I think she has given it to Tom' (Tom was Amy's brother), and after that when the Nurse came in to tell him how nicely he was getting on he laughed and took no notice of any one of them again.

He simply turned round and lay still and got over a stile into the fields and went on and on.

Sometimes it was spring there and twilight was over them; he liked that best; but this morning it was the August sunshine and they were August fields.

Fields—fields, quite endless, mile after mile of gold; they were the real gold—the wheat, stirring gently, with just above it the green, the line of the hedge and higher up, over it all the blue.

They were there, all three, the only things: the gold, the stir and the folded ear; they were in the wheat and his hand was passing over it and it was passing something into his hand.

All that there was or ever would be—he wanted to have it, to keep it: he was afraid of losing it: that was terror. It made him start up, it made him cry out almost as if he had seen them doing it—he didn't want them to cut down the wheat.

A WEDDING DAY

So doth New Life, olde Life bereave,
  And leave behind, alone to die,
That she, with new-fledged wings may cleave,
  New-'companied, the new-hung sky.

AT the top of two long meadows, which slope upward to the gate, stands a grey cottage. Bleak winds sweep round it when summer is gone, and the ghostly trees, their lullabies forgotten, stand shadowy sentinels of the lonely spot. A yellow plant overspreads the loosely-built walls of its tiny garden: hundreds of chrome-coloured eyes laugh out from a pale opaque green face. There are finer flowers within; but these give you first greeting. Beyond the gate mignonette and woodbine will clamour a second welcome; and stand but a moment in the porch, the sweetbriar will have its say. In winter, long after this hour, the robins utter their first sharp calls, and hop along the rounded walls, as their habit is, trying to out-sing each other, when their friend Nature grows weary of them, and bids them run to man. The berries of the holly-tree beneath the window, peer in to mock the unlit kitchen fire; and the frozen pathway, much in the same humour, might exact warm kisses from unwilling lips in the cold dawn. A little patch of grass would perhaps be veiled in white, in semblance of the snowy pillow from which you had just risen. Its spotlessness might urge you for a moment to seek the chilly bed.

But on this morning of early summer nothing tempts to slumber. The window is set wide open, and the sun about to rise. The birds are shaking the trees around the house under a united stir. They announce their superiority to lazy mortals by calling each other in crescendos of agitation, least any should oversleep themselves. A slothful chaffinch has just flown out, stupid and dishevelled, in answer to indignant twitterings, and a little martin hops to the Bride's window-sill and peers curiously in. He listens disdainfully to her gentle breathing, has his peep, and decamps quickly, to join a company gathered outside the Bridegroom's window, many fields away. He arrives there late, to find his comrades loudly reminding that personage of the wedding finery he has to don. These officious, but kindly little people are no unlearned advisers in the matter of bridal dress. What marriage morning has found them unready, undecked or silent? Despite their friendliness, they are slightly scornful of the stalwart mortal who, at their bidding, arrays himself so soberly, and meets his mating-time without a song.

Gently the sun prepares to rise, chasing grey shades of timid dawn, and spreading, for it is a bridal morning, the tints of love throughout the sky. He, himself is an ardent lover. Evening will show the tears of blood he sheds over the earth he parts from. This is the first flush of greeting, but there is to be a passionate leave-taking by and by.

The daisies, catching his colour on their half-shut lids, pretend it is their own. But alas! the maiden blush will soon forsake them as they grow older, and stare upward with cold bright eyes. Is the bride more modest, since she seems to shun this crimson welcome? No, such a red dawn will flood her waking face, when this has passed, and softer rays steal from those closed white lids, now shrouding the two deep mirrors whence her lover seeks his light. But she should rise to greet this wonderful morning spirit who creeps with so much tenderness and solicitude to her bedside. The gentle visitant stands patiently awaiting her with open arms, and cool benignant breath. Still she sleeps! (Brides, I hear, often lie thus unconscious at the outset of their wedding-day.)

The trees round her casement whisper softly of her sloth, the flowers below are drowsily submitting to their morning bath of dew, and the birds grow noisily impatient of a sin they cannot share. A robin perches on a neighbouring twig, and calls out sharply, till a comrade answers. They start a rival song. The challenger pitches his note too high, struggles to attune himself, fails and flies away. No matter, it was but a ruse to waken her. At night he will return to the same twig and end his morning lay. An old woman, in the porch below is chanting hers. Who hears it? God perhaps; the birds and the Bride, Nature herself, will take no note of such a silent song.

It is early for her to be astir. She stands surveying the narrow path which so soon the Bride must tread. It is wet, but with no tears of her shedding. Thus does Nature our weeping for us, that we may go about our business with clear eyes. She picks off a sweetbriar leaf to smell—it is a country fashion—and bends back a young woodbine tendril—possessed with youth's adventurous desire to stray—as she waits with beautiful patience (Time's best endowment), for the little maiden who should soon be here.

The fire in the tiny living-room is lit—and along the white wall is ranged a shining row of pots and pans, which catch in winter its first gleams. Now the sun is up, they send back to him defiant rays. These are the old woman's books; unless they are spotless she finds them undecipherable; so there is a mighty rubbing of them day by day. Some of us read Nature—badly truly;—others con, for pastime or instruction? their own hearts' poor secrets. The Bridegroom's favourite primer is an old cathedral psalter: the Bride's—his face. But for our old woman, her pots and pans suffice, and they say more to her as the years pass. They serve her for music too, and though she could never listen patiently to the simplest air, the jangle of her beloved metal generates in her some pure delight. One of her favourite sayings is of the kettle, hissing on the hob, 'Hark! it has changed its note'. (The Bride remembers how she used to dread that domestic monster, and used to peep fearfully from behind stiff cotton skirts, to catch his first mysterious hiss, and the sight of his ghostly steam.) Besides these inspired saucepans, the old woman has yet another volume—a big holiday Book, in the glittering of whose pages she feels she has no part. On Sabbath afternoons, she sits with it before her, on the low window-seat, glancing from it to the bright row of shining metal, turning the leaves idly, one by one. Perhaps she tries to read it, if the day is dull, and the pots and pans not very bright. As she stands at her door now, on the brink of her life's morning, she might, so placid is her aspect, know nothing of tumultuous slumber. Yet she has been tossed in it, and awakened from dreams of earth's longest night. Her step is as firm as that, the Bride knows better than any other, her eyes are as bright as those of the child, who will lurch up the path with the heavy milk bucket, by and by—yet long since they saw the snow spread a pall of pallid indifference on the green face of earliest love. Her smile says, 'It has been always summer, and winds, when they came were but the gentlest breezes, sweeping off with cool fingers a too loving sun.' But they had been boisterous enough to bear all hopes of weaker hearts away. Her lined brow will not inform you that the lights beneath it have been set as beacons to many baffled travellers, but the firm line of lips bears witness that it has let through no ignoble cry. Her history is simple. Those stiff, brown hands, clasped patiently, may tell as much of it as man may know. These, ere the pots and pans first knew her, lay across the restless eyes of a man (he was her lover) shutting out the world from him, that he might search his soul for a glimpse of heaven. They closed those same eyes, later, when earth had become all he cared to see.

Then, when they had been conquerors in a fight with hard existence, they found a gentler care. Early one winter morning, a half-frozen baby woke on the threshold, which today the Bride must cross. Had it forgotten to wake, the Bride would not be sleeping now—but this, she is never to know. The being who keeps the secret is seventy years old, bent and grey; but those tireless hands of hers are loth to yield their charge into another's keeping, as they must do, today. (The Bride would tell you, how children who never saw their Master's face, might have felt His blessing through their touch, but they shook their curls from the contact and ran away. She herself has pushed off, with unmeant cruelty, the passage of those knotted fingers through her hair—charged with passion, it conveyed a sense of irritating mystery, unendurable—and the dumb endearment was a dreaded thing.) The last event of this short history was the coming of a stranger to the cottage, a woman whose nights denied her the vision of any dawn. She sought the baby fingers she had once disentangled from her breast, and found these stronger ones. They raised the fallen being, and she left them drenched in her first flood of human woe. From this baptism they will never be free. Such is their brief record. They will guard a grand heart when it beats no more.

Three fires of love burn brightly this summer morning, and the sun will extinguish none. What wonder if the Bridegroom's leaps and dances, asking more and more fuel as the Day wears on? The Bride has yet to trim her hearth. The light plays flickering round it. Indeed her fire has not long been lit; it struggles fitfully to answer the Bridegroom's exultant flames.

There is still another. It has burnt through a long day. Here it is, if life chilled me, I would choose to warm myself. Its glow is greater than the Bridegroom's fiercely burning, or the Bride's transparent gleams. This has the sun's power to sustain or paralyse existence, for those who come within its range. It can be neither summoned nor repelled. Its beauty is terrible, its strength divine, but its manifestation is a mystery still, though it has hung for centuries, to human view, upon an ancient cross. Passion passes—Affection springs in unexpected places. Love may be the sun of life, but it takes long to pierce the mists of this unhappy earth. It strives for outlet in the dear old woman's eyes. The Bride threads her needles: and since she cannot see the clock, the birds outvie each other, eager to mark her waking hour. She says sometimes, how kindly all take care of her. The flowers guide her up the path, and the sweetbriar stops her at the door. All this to keep obscurity from those clear windows that the light of heaven may struggle through! Kindly it beams upon a little figure, staggering under a heavy milk bucket, coming up the path. The gate swings behind it. There is a lurch, a splash, and the path is wet again. The child sets up a wail. It rises to the open casement. The Bride starts up, and rushes bewildered to the window, to arrest the note of woe. This wail is no fit cry for a wedding morning, but the Bride's appearance quells it, as she sends a swift smile downward to the puckered face of the small culprit who is seated forlornly in the midst of the white pool. As she breaks through, bending forward, a cobweb hung across the window is turned by the sunlight into a gold thread. Her tresses surpass its glitter, blown by the breeze about her face. Grey gleams begin to flash in and out the yellow spaces, as she looks laughing down. Thus a game of hide and seek begins between eyes and hair. The child detaches a buff sun-bonnet, and shyly draws a veil of curls across her two blue windows of woe. While the game proceeds the two spectators (for it is only the child who is playing) see a vision. The Bride at her casement, and the old woman at the door. Before them stretch long lanes of magical childhood, and they find no solace there. Eternal sadness hangs over them with the stars. Small feet, once the Bride's (fancies the dreamer at the door) send dying echoes down them, and a wilful sun-bonnet (once the Bride's) takes, at the road's end a turn out of view. There is a sound of baby laughter and then a cry. For to the eyes beneath the sun-bonnet the moor looks lonely. The little figure disappears, the wail, to old ears grows faint, and dies away into those old skies of deep untroubled blue.

Those same skies hang over the Bride's picture. At the top of the same road she finds herself. Before her stands a bent form, this, till today, she never noted, set like a beacon in the twilight of groping youth. Its arms are for ever stretched towards her, its eyes for ever beckoning, and she hears dreamily, mingled with the little milk-maid's laughter, the warning of its eternal voice.

Up and down the familiar highway, people pass and pause and loiter, but the same figure stands steadfast and radiant, a stern refuge, waiting her return. Mists rise and shroud it, a storm gathers and sweeps round, she feels herself a sun-bonneted truant, growing cold. But at length, raising a drenched head, she finds the familiar form visible and patient. And then to the Bride at her window the light grows dim. In those old childish skies the sun begins to set. A soft red tints the white locks of the old beckoner, as the tiny maiden she once was runs towards chastisement and rest. The shadows lengthen, and heaven grows pale. Beyond the hills lies some mysterious morning, one we know the Bride was not awake to greet.

The empty milk bucket, and its small owner go through the gate. As the Bride watches them, the old woman below sends a glance up to scan her face. She finds there a loveliness which other eyes will never see. The Bride is young, but she was only once beautiful. It was when her lover, on their betrothal morning, told her he found her so. The being who now meets her glance has no such power. The window frames a smile, (it is time the Bride arrayed herself) the old woman is defying tears.

Pictures still hang before the eyes of these two dreamers, when they meet in the cheerful living-room below. One is painted in tints of spring, merging into gorgeous summer, the other, in white shades of rime, in hues of pale death and delicate decay.

The sun is sole spectator of their last meal together, there is no intrusion because no interest in his gaze. He views it with a warmly indifferent air. He takes little note of the chamber he illumines; the Bride's transfigured face, and the grinning pots and pans above it, are equally significant to him. It is only to the old woman's fancy that his glare grows brighter, as the Bride steps forth, and stands irresolute, beneath the sweetbriar canopy. The king of light looks down, and the queen of love looks up, but we know the sun's bride is a swarthier maiden, and this one seeks a lover who will dye her cheeks a deeper crimson with a cooler gaze. Erect, she pauses, scents surrounding her, uncertain of her fate. Fear rears himself before her, an ungainly giant, out of all proportion to the actors in such a simple scene. She scans him, startled.

Meanwhile, the frail being behind her gives unwilling place to tears. Through a mist of them she strives to see. What is this strange company stationed along the path which the Bride seems unaware of? She sees plainly, a shadowy babe clinging to the low gate. Its fingers clutch the fastening, while a steadier, but still tottering child plays with it, shaking a golden head. A sedate little person sits knitting near them, her brilliant wools look dazzling in the sunlight. (Did not the Bride claim them, we might conclude the rainbow mats and cushions strewn about the cottage parlour were her handiwork.) So engrossed is she, that though the two babes beg her to join them, she nods a negative, without lifting her busy head. A taller girl stoops to rest a hand on this industrious worker's shoulder, while she watches the children with clear and quiet eyes. Immediately behind this slim figure stands the Bride, whom all these unsubstantial beings persistently resemble. Truly, the baby's hair is paler, but it mimics comically the waving tresses; the maiden just in front of her regards the shadowy assemblage with identical grey eyes; and the little person knitting assumes her serious smile. Each robs her of some obvious lineament. Let us call them her fairy bridesmaids,—that should she see these sweet despoilers, she may bear them no ill-will. As yet she is indifferent to them, startled by that image of the unknown, clothed in the robes of Terror, which she sees beyond the gate. Dismayed she turns suddenly to kiss the clouded eyes behind her. This caress shuts out the fairy vision—it vanishes away.

The now invisible procession leads to Church, while the two mortals follow, hand in hand. As they go down the path the Bride stoops to gather a bunch of mignonette, and an over-open rose disperses petals on her head. She shakes them off smiling; one pink flake clings, loth to be dismissed, but as she rises, drops sadly down. Since the little bridesmaids forgot their duties, the roses see that the path is lightly strewn. Her progress will not lack spectators. This morning with their million eyes, the daisies are staring upward, and tonight, when these grow weary, the stars, with their million eyes, will be ready to look down. The breeze, her airy page, lifts her skirt off the dusty roadway, and the birds wave gently the trees' green banners, as she goes.

At the top of the churchyard steps, the Bridegroom waits them. Between the quiet sleepers they take their way, the lovers leading, while the old woman lags behind.

Within, the sunshine greets them. Gold streams through the shot holes of rent colours, hung in the chancel. The very shreds speak glory's message to our victorious man. The fair and mighty foes that mocked his boyish claims have vindicated them. Woman is won today! The tattered flags proclaim it. With a true victor's gallantry, he leads his first sweet captive, a hostage from her fellows, gently up the aisle, turning a tender, if exultant, glance on her, which says, 'Wonderful, vanquished stranger, thy race is won with thee!' She misses it; her eyes have caught a fancy of the sunlight, playing with flat shields upon a tomb. The upper corners lie in shadow, leaving the centre roughly heart-shaped, and the symbolic trifle pleases her. The Bridegroom does not see it; his gaze is fixed once more on the torn banners, and the old woman has found the fairy bridesmaids, dancing in and out the rays of sunlight, and longs to catch the tiniest to her breast. How dare they play thus—these laughing children, or demurer maidens, while the Bride, in whose face are mirrored all their fleeting glances, stands still and pale?

A kneeling knight, confronting his cold ladies, prays stiffly a blessing on the scene. It is beneath his dignity to recognize them, but his more observant mates are watching them with half-shut eyes. A few feet away, two little cupids peep roguishly from behind their patron's classic robe, longing to join the dancers, but they dare not brave the wrath of the colossal virgin who stands behind their lord. Perhaps, they whisper wistfully to each other, when she decides to place the threatening laurel wreath upon his brow, they may steal off. They must amuse him till he gets it. Then they remember vaguely, as the little bridesmaids mock and beckon, she has been half a century making up her mind! The three mortals stand in the chancel now, beneath the tattered flags, beside the poor little gods of love and the bygone gentlemen's chilly wives.

Hearts are lovely mechanisms, but what playthings! The good old priest at the altar knows nothing of their structure, and dallies dreamily with his Father's magic toys. But an end to pastime: its hour is past. Oh! you poor little shadowy bridesmaids, where are you now? Was it that new look on the Bride's face that banished you? She is your sister, you think, no longer; and you will never come back again! 'No matter', say the cold beruffed dames to their stately spouse, 'the years will bring her plenty more'. He ignores them courteously and still prays on.

At the bottom of the two long meadows, which lead upward to the cottage, at noon, the Bride pauses to say 'Good-bye'. 'But for a day,' she whispers to the stern being before her, who has dealt finally with tears. Silence encircles this parting. Those wrinkled hands, whose history we know, make an appeal. The Bridegroom clasps them. They credit his assurance. And what of the Bride? Her lids are lowered. Lately the lights beneath have shot strange gleams—flashes her old guardian could not answer, though she strove pitifully to reply. She found no key to those bewildering glances, in the Bride's childish eyes. Now drawing the lovers' hands together, she yields that new-born womanhood to him who claims it; the mystery leaves her keeping, as she creeps, a lonely figure, homeward. On her way she catches up a burden. It is like that which taught her first the spell of baby touches. Can it be one of the truant fairy bridesmaids? Yes, the tiniest of them all! Its little staggering feet kept poor pace with the others, and in their haste they must have left it. She rocks and clasps it, singing as she goes. But when at her fireside, she stoops to kiss it, it is cold, and its eyes are shut.

The lovers, sealed one, walk far. Life rears itself before them, a gold-tipped height. The Moon is breathless, greeting the morning in their hearts, with warm embraces of dreamy ease. The lanes wind for them to pastures where the streams say, what they cannot, of eternity—of the indissoluble union of currents when they reach the sea—love's great ocean, on the waves of which they care not if they rise or fall. In the hedgerows, the roses mock, with reticent maiden scorn, those rival ribbons starring the Bride's dress. This is no time for recalling lovers' quarrels, but she remembers suddenly a day of storm, when she tore off these gay favours to arrest the fatal ceremony of today. That black afternoon, she pictures herself as she sat mentally disposing them on a cap the old woman was to wear. This, on subsequent joy-denuded Sabbaths, was to remind a slighted maiden of man's frailty. But with the roses, these pink rosettes resumed their posts, stationed by absolving fingers, and the admonitory headgear was never worn.

Then a faint breeze, stirring some willows, murmurs jestingly of a bygone winter night. 'Beside this winding stream, now despairingly you parted! You,' they whisper to the Bride, 'chose for yourself endless slumber, and a sheltered corner in the churchyard, tossing in warm sheets to cherish the aspiration—? and you (the bridegroom winces) sought the Blue Boar with a certain wild complacency, and went to your rest more heavy-eyed than sad.' Thus the road tells old tales to them, inviting comments of new love.

At intervals, they speak of the lonely cottage and and its occupant. But here, Union, a colossal figure, plants herself in their path. She puts an indignant finger on their lips, and points with threatening meaning to the Solitary Spirit standing beside her, and bids them choose between her and her naked foe. Eventually she triumphs, and the Solitary Spirit strides off, a grand loser, scornfully indifferent. The lovers wander on in wedded silence, pondering life's great 'Yes', while one, sitting by her hearth in a far-off cottage, is learning, with motionless lips, to frame its 'No'.

The Solitary Spirit looks in at the open window, and breathes a message through. Is it a blessing or a promise that falls so lightly on the great Book's open leaf, lying on the old woman's knee?

It is late afternoon. The descending sunlight slants across the floor. Its rays catch the brass corners of an old wooden workbox. The neat and polished exterior hides a lining ill-pasted, with the corners bogged. The workmanship is that of clumsy childhood, so let it pass. Its owner is thinking of its unaccountable disappearance and triumphant return, placed in her lap, while baby hands shrouded her view; how many years ago? She reckons slowly. Countless incidents of uneventful youth present themselves to aid the calculation. She makes it, at length, and a smile claims her at the memory of the cunning plot and tottering diplomatist, until tears claim the smile. She feels a sweep of curls across her cheek, the touch of the hot and over-tired fingers, relaxing hold of hers in arbitrary slumber, as if she was sitting again holding the tiny burden, in the twilight of that winter day. Surely this is sweet companionship? But she will tell you, she is not thinking of the Bride. The hours go slow? The book before her lies unread, and the pots and pans dazzle her attempt to scan them, or is it the mist before her eyes that makes them seem so far away? The shadows will not fall. The sun who rose so early seems loth to set. Stay! something brushed her forehead, like a kiss. The cool red authors of it must be just behind her. Those lips were smiling too. She has slept, she tells herself, while this sweet rape of solitude was planned. Yet the touch clings with feeble magic. It may be but a curtain edge, frayed and swaying in the gently stirring air.

Her lids begin to sport with slumber, for this sensitive oblivion is not sleep. Shall she rise and discover the dear intruder? Ay, there is her morning maiden come back again, stooping slightly forward in the doorway, arms open, lips apart.—Gone! The Book falls at her tragic start. It is recaptured with a poignant vision of lovers sitting on the bridge, perhaps embracing—many miles away. Breathe in her ear, 'Dear soul, the child still loves thee!' It is useless—she will say soberly, that it is tea-time—she was not thinking of the Bride at all.

But oh! the hours go slow!

She rises to prepare the meal. Her pots and pans beam tenderly upon her, but she does not note them. She has heard a distant sound of footsteps. They pause, and stagger—she must not banish them by motion, and stands still, listening. Perhaps the fairy bridesmaids are coming back. Whisper softly, 'Dearest heart, indeed they come!' This too, is useless. Mark her gesture, courteous but imperative. You wronged her. She had quite forgotten the Bride. She was not even thinking of the little feet that might soon be starting from eternity to meet her; though she had spoken of such a fancy to the Bridegroom only yesterday. She fumbles among the crockery. The kettle rings for her the change on his persistent note. She takes no heed of it. At last, a cup steams fragrance into the warm air.

She can taste nothing. Oh! lovers' feast, the gods of joy attend you! I hear the Bridegroom, far away, magnificently spare a eulogy for their beneficent sky, while the Bride bends to tie a shoe. Generous young man, stint not your praises! Heaven may hear them, though it hangs over other realms than those of youth. A fly finds fate in the old woman's teacup. She rescues it with trembling hand. This impotence is new, but she welcomes it, as one should a stranger, with unquestioning grace. Yet the sense of unfamiliar weakness makes her restless. She knows not how to entertain the unknown comer, and she grows mistrustful of, almost angry with, this self, which plays her false.

A strange, insistent anticipation steals over her, of one expected, she knows not whom. She rejects the feeling until it becomes masterful, possessing her. Then with characteristic decision, she goes upstairs. The steep steps make new demands: she mounts slowly, and rests exhausted at the top of the short flight. When she has summoned enough energy to don the clean cap and apron, for which the ascent was made, she makes a long and thoughtful choice, hesitating (for the rank of her mysterious visitor is doubtful) between degrees of finery. At last she decks herself, with curious care, painfully delayed by feebleness, in her finest and most spotless garb.

Preparing to descend, a thought arrests her. The Bride's bed has not been made. This neglect of simple duty tortures her. She asks, is memory forsaking her, or has absence begun so soon to plunder love? The little chamber is disordered, the bed-clothes thrown back hastily, as the late sleeper left them, startled by the little milk-maid's cry. The old woman stands in the doorway, leaning against it, her gaze travelling out through the white-curtained window, and back again to the dishevelled bed. The pillow, pushed aside, shows an impress of the sleeper's head. The spectator sees that wakened sleeper start up, as she does each morning, at the sound of the well known footfall outside the door. She sees the bright being cast off slumber with involuntary welcome. 'Tomorrow morning'. Implacable Thought says slowly, 'she will not be here'. It is incredible. Will God withhold the dawn? It seems likelier. She accords Thought placid scorn.

But what allows her to parley thus, while work waits to be done? She is ready to attack it, but stops, seized suddenly by a convincing witness. The room itself assures her, as she enters. The Bride wakes and sleeps here no more.

It is true then, and God does keep back the day! the place is infinitely empty. She falls, flinging wild arms across the bed, the slave of anguish, tears and utterance forsaking her. She rises in a moment, her bent form almost erect, and looking, with dry, scorched eyes across the meadows, she sees her darling's true yet alien resting-place, hung with those gay curtains which she helped to sew. Dare those gaudy blossoms mock this snowy waste from which none spring? She strokes the flowerless hangings, absently, and leaves a caress on the deserted pillow. May the Bride, tonight, as she yields to others, be spared the revelation of one she leaves behind!

The room is left untouched. Tomorrow—A voice breaks in, 'your guest will soon be here'. The old woman goes down wearily, she smoothes the spotless apron and adjusts the cap. Downstairs, the pots and pans perceive her faintly, a dim figure in the twilight, sitting passively expectant, her hands crossed, the big Book, for which she seems to have forsaken them, open, unread, upon her knee.

It is growing late. Through the fading hours of daylight, the birds are all astir, warning the Bride and Bridegroom of the hour. As the sun dies, their evening song grows fitful, but there is much twittering discussion, mingled with scraps of melody. Gradually, they sink to silence. The daisies are already sleeping; the stars look down from distant fields of blue. The lovers stand in the deepening darkness, hand in hand, in their small bridal chamber. Tomorrow, if they do not close the casement, they will hear together Sunday bells pealing across the dewy fields. 'Tomorrow', says the Bridegroom, 'they must make amends for the solitude snatched today'. 'Tomorrow' lies on the Bride's lips unspoken. Her heart holds no tomorrow—it cannot pass the mystic circle thrown around tonight. It is well. The present is eternity. Nature has obscured her loveliness, that they may find it only in each other's eyes. With shrouded hand has she demanded silence, that when passion becomes too breathless, even for love's whisper, they may hear the beating of each other's heart. And so there is no sound. A few little flowers may sigh perhaps, beneath their window, 'lamenting some enforced chastity', but this they do not heed, the breeze will not bear it, lest the very breath that fans her cheek should not be his. Thus let us leave them. We forbore to waken the Bride this morning, we will not now intrude upon the Bridegroom's hour. We bid them (or may their angels for us)—Good-night.

As they stand embracing, the moon seems to be watching them, but she is looking on another sight. Her wan face smiles back at her dimly from the pots and pans in the cottage where the old woman waits. All is quiet there. She sits, stiff as the white apparel she donned for her unknown guest. And when, at last, the moon's pale face grows tired of watching, and sinks wearily back to its blue pillow, she still sits motionless, and does not stir.

For her watch is over. Some time between midnight and morning, the great angel came. Softly he stole across the radiant floor. She stretched out arms of welcome ere he reached her, and meeting his eyes, her own grew blind to any other sight. He laid a hand charged with eternal rest upon her heart, and smoothed with a kiss the lines on her clear brow. With a silencing finger he sealed her lips, parted to welcome him. In her ear he breathed a secret, and hearing it, she cared to listen to no voices of earth again. Willingly her spirit fled with him, but she bade him leave her body lest the Bride might wish to bid it farewell. A great stillness hangs about it. Yet we need not whisper. The birds will sing as lustily as ever when they wake. Nor need we to tread softly, though those who know less of the night's quiet doings may. This grand guest chamber should not be darkened. Never did its lonely tenant shun the daylight less. Yet tomorrow (the Bride's morrow) there will be some, eager to hush earth's purest music as they draw the faded curtains to shut out day. They will not notice how this frail being sits boldly fronting dawn. Nay, they may even pity one, who met thus, alone and smiling, the terror of men's dreams.

THE BRIDEGROOM'S FRIEND

I HAD returned to London after two months' absence from it, when George Derriman greeted me with the announcement of his prospective wedding, and a request that I should support him during that ceremony in the character of 'best man'. The news astounded me. It was sudden and from other lips would have been almost incredible concerning one who had met the thrusts of matrimonial destiny with affable obduracy for so long.

'It must be a case—' was my first sincere ejaculation, 'of Dieu le veut?' But he assured me, smiling, that the superintendent deity was entirely maternal, and I accepted the amendment with a sense of its propriety and my mistake. 'The lady's name?' was my next question. 'Oh, Miss Evelyn Desborough—doesn't your mother know them slightly? You will like Veva—very peaceful, a kind of filial reaction, handsome, fair, and doesn't make demands.' The latter trait seemed in the circumstances an auspicious one, and I began to picture its unknown possessor, whose part, whatever it might be, in this arrangement determined her for me, a common type. The notification of this unforeseen event invited retrospect, and I mustered three distinct estimates of the bridegroom's personality for review.

The first, intrinsically worthless, was formed at the earliest date of our acquaintance, when I had just vacated the maternal nest and fluttered agape, more perhaps from habit than actual craving for any crumbs of adulation falling to my share. He was the first to note the hungry fledgling and instruct its flight; and though the inducement has indeed been strong, I do not now attribute to his restrictive teaching my own inability to soar. On my half-opened eyes he dawned a towering and omniscient figure, striding intrepidly through the labyrinths of a dazzling city, where his protection became my unfaltering staff and his philosophy a lucid chart for the narrowest passages of a very broad and bewildering way.

But in the growing light which he uncurtained, I soon saw my hero dwindle, I began to doubt his guidance and recant his gospel, until at length he assumed in my unstable mind the posture of a foe. Grandly I decided that I owed to him experiences little comparable to their cost; and mentally arraigned him for an influence insidiously pestilent, if not intentionally corrupt. This intermediate and puritanic measure of his character was more puerile than the first; and it was too, as lacking in generosity as only a very graceless gallant's largess to his worthy lantern-bearer may be. Time lent me wisdom; I encountered men, shorn of his redeeming vices, sowing their paltry store of virtues with a more niggard hand than his; and finally, some ray of early admiration reappeared, and better focussed, produced a likeness of him, in the form of a good comrade, even in small emergencies—of a potential friend. He was too limitable to be aught but trivial, and too trivial to be bad. Marriage on his part was an unimportant and inevitable exploit, which had missed my mind. The tints of comedy had been predominant to the spectator of his lighter unions; but of such hues, foreboding whispered, this one was to be bereft. I myself was ready to affirm that tragedy must hang aloof from it, and even many worlds away. I grew mildly anxious to inspect these women, whose joint prowess entitled them to such a social prize; and for a day or two a gentle savour stole into certain tasteless evenings of diversion, while I strove intuitively to identify them. Not, however, until several misguesses had begun to daunt me, did the objects of my avowedly impertinent search appear.

The entertainment was labelled 'musical', and as I entered the crowded room a lady, mounted on a distant platform, had just ceased contending for supremacy with a drum and fife band passing in the street below. She seated herself panting, partially triumphant, while the sounds of pipe and tabor died defiantly away. Through the open windows, and above the hum of tutored converse, rose rude and intermittent reminders of the insolent, indifferent street. To these our fine assembly sent back modulated murmurs of habitual disdain.

Furnished with the description 'peaceful' and unfettered by imaginative speculation, my glance travelled round the chattering auditory to fit it to some present guest. None there wore it easily enough to lure me towards further blunder. Most of the people too, I knew. One girl, consummately young, a stranger, usurped my attention, offering a spectral semblance of the thing I sought. I scanned her rapidly. Her personality at once invited and repulsed regard. Peace, in the lines of that indubitably lovely form had never lain, nor could those limbs have outlined ever a posture of positive unrest. I needed neither features nor facial expression to confirm this certainty. Even the white folds of her drapery hung in definite denial of turbulence or ease. Her attitude was motionless. That of sentient death might well resemble it. This tall white figure distantly presented to my wandering vision gave an impression of perceptive sleep. A stillness, as of sunshine seemed to fill her veins. A puncture, I thought fantastically, might release a ray and so determine the recovery or extinction of this noiseless life. I sought her face. It was profoundly pale: the features exquisite and regular, wore for the hasty onlooker a listening—it was a deceptive—air. The parted lips and quiet eyes revealed on closer scrutiny a mental languor, far removed from actual concern or questioning repose. This being to my sense, was mute, burdened with an infant's dumbness, or the inarticulation of impendent death. She was insuperably placid, bereft of spiritual tranquillity, yet bodily invested with a cloak of baffling calm. Her eyes met mine, and for some moments negligently detained my gaze. I seemed to be viewing through those mortal chinks some everlasting desert of the soul. It stretched from empty future to unpeopled past, a limitless and solitary plain. I was disturbed by the first chords of a great March, as they were launched into the buzzing air.

The musician's touch was masterly. He realized that the dirge accompanied no earthly bier. Only to mourn a spirit's dissolution could such strains be born. The recurrent crescendos, like despairing footsteps essayed to mount a stair or two in desperate incredulity, and then leaped backward to the level monotone of tragic fact. An episode succeeds, picturing with acute fidelity the course of the ethereal, just ended life. In the halting poignant melody, the spirit reappears in sound, living again its exquisite, half-apprehended dreams, until the march of shadowy death breaks in bewailing, and proclaiming them no more.

Between this music and the striking creature fronting me, my mind tried to trace idly, half unconsciously, some vague, chimerical analogy; quite involuntarily I looked towards her again. She stood impassive, sightless, indifferent it seemed to any phase of speech.

The people near me were dispersing, making roughly for the door. I stepped back, leaning against the wall, to protect my person from the starving mob. Someone addressed me suddenly above the tumult. 'Mr Aston—Miss Desborough. I think you know each other though?' I peered, beheld my white and silent stranger, bowed, and strove to wake myself to pilot her across the rustling throng. If this, I thought, were George's future partner, it was at a strange enactment that I had promised to assist. But my companion claimed attention. She spoke slowly and without animation, her pronunciation was exceptionally and unstudiously distinct. George, she said, could not be there tonight, or he had promised himself to introduce us. She thought her mother knew my people, years ago, before her father died, and mine. Yes, they must have met in Rothshire—she was then too young to recollect it—and she envied me my country home. I smiled at the prosaic contrast of reality, remembering the fantasies of five minutes ago; and having won some honour in the battle for refreshments, suggested quitting the field.

The rooms through which we passed were almost empty, and each seemed hotter than the last. I found a covered balcony, from whence the clatter of the combat was inaudible. It was untenanted. Refusing a chair, she turned a corner of the awning back and stood staring into the street. I offered a trivial comment on the atmosphere. She bent her head. I plunged.

'You are fond of music?'

She moved slightly, and then turned undisguisedly to measure me. 'I do not know'; she said at length, 'it knocks at my door—but I may not admit it.' She added: 'it is my misfortune to hear nothing above an uproar, and to see nothing between the openings of a crowd.'

Her manner justified my comment. 'That, in a rushing life like this, means—death.'

Again, with a characteristic motion, she signified assent. I had ventured boldly, but was unprepared for further advance. She remained standing, raising the heavy canvas with a long white arm, lovelier and not more pallid than her face.

The stillness deepened round us. Her presence enclosed me in some circle of magic and unrestful calm. The quiet became sensitively musical. I thought I heard it, and waited breathless for the last note to be struck by her departure. A gentle inclination of her head directed my notice towards the street. Opposite, leaning against some railings, a bent and evidently aged figure was discernible; a street lamp flickering down accentuated the stiff helplessness of posture. Two girls, mimicking a drunkard's gait, and laughing harshly, staggered along.

'Near though they are', she said, continuing a thought I had not followed, and indicating the dark objects, 'we cannot touch them. As one whirls through life such forms detach themselves from the great crowd of unseen wretchedness, and strike our sight and pass, and one knows nothing of their world, save that it exists. Isn't it so with beauty? Here and there a ray escapes, a note resounds, and these hints of the undiscovered vanish as irrevocably as the poor passers-by.'

I glanced down the dark pavements and another picture sprang to view. She dropped the curtain on it, and sat down.

Response came tardily. Was I to utter platitudes upon elusive loveliness while it stood captured and incarnate by my side? Within the room the guests had reassembled, for the verses of a song reached us with muffled emphasis, familiar words set to a strange air:

> It was not in the winter
> Our love lot was cast;
> It was the time of roses.
> We plucked them as we passed.

The closing lines brought aid to fumbling thought. I listened idly to the ballad, and this refrain impressed itself again.

Applying the light couplet to our semi-serious dialogue, I said—half smiling, 'Listen, the singer answers you. If we want nosegays, we must make our own. It is an obvious maxim. Seize your notes in fact, and stop your passers-by.'

'Naturally, but, if one's hands are tied?'

'Then?'

'Then one must accept the gathering of another, or go without.'

'One more alternative—' I said: 'to free oneself.'

'The best, potentially,' she admitted, rising. 'I think, if you will take me, I must go in.'

Across the threshold of the open window, we stepped into the warm and dazzling room. A lady of majestic proportions propelled herself towards us, flinging forth exclamations as she came. 'My darling child—you here? I quite despaired of finding you. We *must* be going. You know we promised to look in on the Seaforths before going to the Butts. Mr Aston? Ah, of course, one of dear George's greatest friends. We have heard so much of you. Most charmed to meet you. I knew your mother years ago;—has she quite forgotten me? You must come and see us. Veva of course is painfully busy—but we shall expect you, positively, some day with George. *Good*-night.'

This animate personage bore off her pale incongruous companion, and I watched them from the room. Then I stepped back into the empty balcony and untied the awning and looked down. At length, from the porch below stepped two cloaked figures; one, loudly voluble, gesticulated to a heedless comrade. They impersonated well oblivion and vociferation, in the world's masquerade. A moment after my identification of these two specimens of masked humanity, the linkman's voice corroborated it and they were swiftly driven away.

For some days afterward, I steadfastly frequented Derriman's society, swayed by a desire to re-inspect him. He presented the same aspect of genial soullessness that I had always known. At this period his orthodox entanglement was sufficiently novel to afford him interest: and he discoursed untiringly upon the topic then master of his mind. He related unreservedly the details of what he termed his 'capture', and spoke with a sportsman's admiration of Mrs Desborough's methods, invariably alluding to that lady as 'Mama'. 'Captain Desborough', he informed me, 'died two years after she married him—at sea. Everyone says he knew the voyage would finish him, but he wanted to get out of the world quietly and was afraid it couldn't be managed at home.' Conversationally, George compared the lady to a circus arab; remarking figuratively, 'If she throws you, you've got to get up again and dust yourself by the next time she gets round. She don't stop for you.' And after one or two encounters, I verified his judgement.

Manfully I strove to keep pace with that dizzy eloquence, until the effort produced mental exhaustion and defeat. We met her almost daily. She was a phenomenon of perpetual motion. We might come across her anywhere and at any hour of the day, but she was always going somewhere else. Her only justification for eventual slumber must have been that she was going to wake. None but a moral suicide had ventured to arrest the course of this human locomotive, to whom the signals of cessation were incomprehensible and unknown. She dedicated her mornings to the exercise of millinery, initiating her daughter ruthlessly into the arduous splendours of that sport. Sometimes we met them at the entrance of some select establishment, 'Mama' in a state of physical and mental exhilaration, Veva unstimulated, pale and listless, shaping for our greeting a slight and tired smile.

'The dear child,' Mrs Desborough affirmed, was 'so apathetic. She lacks enthusiasm, without which, *nothing* can be done. She persists in white or red or blue or—"anything". Has a distressing mania for simple colours and absolutely *no* head for combinations. I don't know what she *will* become. My health is being *drained* over the trousseau, Mr Aston. We tried on eight, or was it nine, separate gowns last week, which Veva *thinks* will do—and they *don't* do. "Days and moments quickly flying", as the song, or is it an anthem, says? and doubtless the alterations will be even more unsatisfactory. Positively, for a fortnight we haven't been able to have lunch at home!' Restaurants, she thought, were actually injurious—she made an effort—rigorously confined herself to lamb and salmon, but her 'poor darling' starved!

Why, I wondered had a kind Providence given this incurably enterprising creature but one offspring to exploit? My friend's fiancée rarely visited my conscious thought, but once or twice I had surprised myself measuring the hitherto unnoticeable attitudes of other women by a standard obviously singular and new.

One afternoon, a fortnight after our first meeting, I joined the lady and her mother at a picture gallery. George, a necessary, though perhaps unsuitable appurtenance, was there. He used two modes with women. This was an occasion for the superior method which regarded them as children to be propitiated, openly admired, and when their hour was over to be coaxed off to bed. He wore, not inelegantly this manner of a semi-conscious benefactor, noting the effect of sweetmeats tendered. I watched the pale recipient from my seat beside her mother, where by the force of an invincible fluency I was stayed.

The girl received her companion's humorous sallies with tranquil and inactive sweetness. A summer's day gives such unruffled audience to the human and distracting noises which attack in vain its unassailable serenity. Her motions satisfied my eye. She passed in and out the oscillating crowd, a figure insensibly supreme. Occasionally, as they paused before a picture, he interpreted it with assertive gestures, while she, regarding it, stood silent, intimating from time to time a gentle recognition of his clamorous proximity. Not once did she glance towards me. I was content to feel her permeant presence. A thousand might stand beside her, they were powerless to annul her unsuspected and invisible companionship with me. I had no longing to possess her favour or to beckon her regard. She was merely a unique and vital picture, moving among the canvases surrounding her; more puzzling and actual, nearer and yet more distant, decisively a masterpiece, which I was not to bid for or pronounce upon, but which, unless sense failed me, I meant to grasp and bear away. I did not care to clasp the hand that pointed with such slight uncertain fingers mysteriously to its guiding mind: nor to keep pace with feet whose motions were recording vaguely for me the sluggish passage of a soul.

In this attraction there was no allurement. She appeased rather than provoked my senses. I was as indifferent to the ownership of this being as to that of the incomparable Madonna facing me in its massive frame. So long as I might view these rare possessions, I cared nothing for their ultimate disposal or intrinsic worth. They were priceless; no matter, for the moment, they were free. I determined to satiate my innocent infatuation, (for such I now acknowledged it to be) to miss no possible indulgence of it. This human symphony or picture (I could not label it) might for a few weeks longer minister to my delight. A musician perhaps had longed to strum it; a painter to reproduce it; a wealthy burgess to possess it; I asked only to enjoy.

'Dear Veva is so quiet, almost *too* serious, and George such a merry fellow.' Mrs Desborough was babbling on. 'Are they not exactly suited—complementary—you know? You see I look upon you as a friend.' I expressed myself as touched but diffident, while she continued; 'I conceal my own feelings for the dear child's sake. I shall keep up until, as some poet says, doesn't he?—"She has crossed the bar", and then I know I shall be prostrate. Evelyn has never been parted from me in her life.' I murmured, 'If that were so, she must be deeply sensible of the separation.' 'And you know they go abroad for two months after the wedding; she was curiously obstinate about it; though she has always had a great distaste for travelling; and they were offered Madely Grange—Lord Railton's place—such a charming spot, of course you know it? The refusal is most vexing. Now could you have suspected such a restless notion from my placid child?' I suggested that my acquaintance with Miss Desborough was scanty. 'Oh! you must know her better.' This was my intention, but I expressed it in the language of desire. She rose, saying: 'Let us go and find them. By the way, you have seen nothing, not even the Madonna, and everyone is talking of it. How thoughtless of me, and so selfish. I am too worn out to think of pleasure myself. A mother's work, Mr Aston, may not be heroic but it is wearing.'

'In some cases', I agreed readily, 'it must be painfully so.'

'Ah! you are so sympathetic. Here they are. Dear child, come here. I cannot let George monopolize you, absolutely. Poor Mr Aston has seen nothing, devoted himself nobly to your forsaken mother. Take him round. I want a little talk with George. And in ten minutes, not a moment later, we really *must* be off. What a rush life is! doesn't someone say something about a "cot beside the hill"?' I heard her demanding as we left her, 'such a charming aspiration, but alas! we cannot always indulge these higher impulses. Billiter—' The name of a refractory butler thus courageously rebutted the seductions of Arcadia, and the conversation, to our hearing, died away.

Three groups of people round us, engaged affably in asking each other to dinner for a variety of mutually impossible dates, obstructed our advance; and with the easy insolence characteristic of this class of pleasure-seeker, they ignored my civil efforts to dislodge them, and continued to consult their respective note-books with bland smiles.

A sudden recollection seized me, and I said affirmatively, 'You find this crowd intolerable; shall we leave the pictures unconsidered? There must be some sculpture somewhere, and along with it, a little breathing space.' Roughly dispersing the most imminent impeding party, I made way. We turned towards a comparatively empty hall, where in the centre was a fountain playing; and there paused. The faint sound of the trickling water seemed to accentuate the stirless presence near me; and the wan whiteness of the marble flesh around us gleamed in sickly contrast to the healthful, but persistent pallor of my companion's face. This seemed to curb its rosy sources of suffusion, to reserve them for some final exigency. By what rod, I wondered dreamily, did I divine their spring?

'Now we have put the frames and canvases behind us, we can talk of pictures,' she proposed. 'I have been trying to construct one. Mama tells me, that she knew your mother, years ago, when they were girls at school, and after—before my,—and your,—father died. George says she is a "model invalid", and that she never comes to town?'

'No, she prefers the country; it encourages her little hobbies—gardening and a tranquil study of humanity. There is a jest between us, that she is compiling a volume on the higher and lower forms of vegetable life, in which the classification is to be startlingly new.'

'I cannot picture her,' continued my companion simply. 'I have tried; possibly my materials are inadequate.'

I offered supplementary shades and outlines. 'She must be painted very delicately,' I replied, 'in colours borrowed from her flowers: and in the background, don't forget to place a long succession of "companions"—amiable young persons all, but each one too mature to satisfy a white-haired old lady, whose wrinkles won't obliterate persisting characters of youth.'

'Your touches are venturous and brilliant for a beginner:' she said with the incisive clearness that lent significance to her most unimportant utterances,—'but I will put them in.'

Two careworn, crumpled-looking youths lounged past us, pronouncing some ostentatious expressions of relief. 'Those gentlemen', observed Miss Desborough as they retreated, 'think the Madonna in the next room, "humorous".'

'Indeed!' I said, 'they have just closed a disgusting exhibition of their own.'

'I know,' she said.

'I hope you didn't see it?'

'Oh! yes. Mama goes everywhere. They sent us cards. I was wondering (in the next room I mean) what a Madonna would think of them.'

'Don't wonder', I said abruptly, 'don't think—'

A rustling apparition stopped me. 'George advises me to give him notice,' it burst forth suddenly. Then perceiving me, 'I beg your pardon, but perhaps Veva has told you of our trouble with Billiter—no? then pardon me; it has been so much on my mind, an *idée fixe*, as the French say, for at least forty-eight hours, since the dreadful developments about which I have been consulting George. Now we must positively *tear*. *Good*-bye.' She shook a valedictory finger, dragging him away for a last word. I followed with Miss Desborough to the door. There, while I held myself instinctively aloof and bowed farewell, she left me with a smile so imperceptible, that later when I summoned the features of that lovely face to bear their testimony to it, each disclaimed it gravely, and the night discovered me scanning strange countenances to refind it, in the world of dreams.

Our next meeting revealed me in an unexpected attitude. My avoidance of actual contact with this impervious personality was no longer passive, as on that quiet afternoon. The idea of it had become definitely repellent. I felt incapable of handling, however lightly, the casket containing the inexplicable power that was seducing me. The delicate contents, were it ore or perfume, might at my rude touch escape, and I was loth to spoil my mysterious and fragile toy. And yet, I wished to dally with it further, to pursue unchecked, the harmless pastime of research. I had elected to attend this dance, at which I knew the lady would be present, for the purpose of observing her enforced to vigorous action; and my whim was gratified. She danced untiringly, and as she constantly repassed me, I noted that her limbs retained, in animation, their essential distinctions of external but unreal repose. Her motions could not be marred by incidental circumstances; every gesture, each immemorable action, was wrapped in some corner of her own illusive garb of calm.

I began to take a barbarous pleasure in watching other men clutch boldly, that on which I dare not let my finger rest. George afforded me a lavish enjoyment of this grotesque sensation. He was in his manner almost ardent. As he whirled past me, swinging his precious burden, I caught fragments of familiar phrases, pruned for the occasion into conventional form. At length they stopped beside me. He was lamenting a lost programme.

'My dear girl', I heard him asseverate, 'I tell you, I don't remember a single name. The next waltz is green and lilac. Oh! here's Aston! Aren't you dancing tonight? Why not?' I turned to his tall partner, overcame reluctance, and made the required demand. 'I leave you in safe hands,' he said to her, departing.

She may have guessed my feeling vaguely, or perhaps unknowingly I had solicited her comprehension; for she immediately declared herself unwilling to dance again, and bade me take her from the heat to air. We left the ballroom and found a seat in a recess of the wide staircase. From that dim post a trailing mass of colour was discernible below us, as the merged particles of individual brilliance shifted to and fro. My eyes forsook it for the form beside me. A large white fan concealed the face; above the rim of curling feathers, I could just distinguish in the shadow, a line dividing two soft ridges of faintly waving hair. Seated beside this motionless and silent being, I felt like a watcher of some distempered sleep, eager yet unentitled to surprise by question the secrets of an unguarded mind.

At last she spoke, slowly, in a voice that seemed to have travelled far. The words were clear however, and imperious. 'Speak to me of the country, show it me without the people who have always made some chattering compact to flap it from my sight.'

Promptly and mechanically I obeyed, summoning the voices of lovely places which had spoken to me in the past. I chanted the droning songs of noon, the whispers of murmuring evenings, the painted silence of slow sunsets, the dirges and starry lullabies of luminous or murky nights. She listened, her face still hidden, without comment or reply. I paused. She moved her hand, and rested it on the seat beside me; it was gloved I noticed, and I recollected quickly that I had never seen it bare. A slight gesture bade me proceed. With a supreme effort I swept humanity from mead and height, and planted each before her, not desolate but grandly solitary, untrodden and echoing to no cry. The sun played his own part in my inspired picture. The roses bloomed and fell unseen, the waves called and answered far away. Man and his scattered homesteads were banished as by a whirlwind; and his annihilation left no void, affecting the world from which he vanished less than the uprooting of a single tree. He fled, his cries were lost in irresponsive space, he disappeared a moving speck upon the hills; a vagrant and a stranger having no real home there till grass covered him and daisies grew above his head.

'I knew it must be so,' she said at length, lifting her face and turning her eyes upon the stream of people passing up and down. 'I never saw it. Man has revenged himself on your disdainful nature in this city built upon her ruins, and made her a beautiful alien where she was once supreme. But he is an ignoble victor; he glories in the stunted remnants of her state. For my part—' she continued evenly, 'I cannot bear to hear the wretched sparrows chirping on their enclosed and captured trees, or to see flowers hung like trivial favours on brick and mortar, or on human revellers, taunting the vanquished with her fall.'

I said: 'You may see her reigning. She is not inaccessible.'

She indicated the crowd of people still pushing up and down. 'They have always shrouded vision. They form an impenetrable veil; one I have no force to raise, no power to see between—' She stopped, and then went on, 'Solitude is exclusive. She doesn't bow to loneliness, they walk different sides of the way.' Again she looked wearily at the gay guests, saying, 'Since childhood, I have never been free of them. They draw a curtain round my life.' I imagined George's jovial density forming an even more effective screen. Her tone was monotonous, her words almost lacked inflection. In another woman this lassitude would have been insupportable, but she justified it in an inimitable way. 'We live in crowds,' she proceeded, hardly addressing me, 'we worship in herds; our bits of glorified pasteboard, for one day in the week serve the humble office of marking their august owner's places in the house of God; the Temple—you know it—in which we kneel weekly, is strewn with these passports to prayer—'

'But in the country—' I interposed.

'In the country', she repeated, with a first note of bitterness, 'we talk a little louder, grin a little wider, and—if we can manage it—are more disingenuous than in town. Isn't it so?'

I protested. 'You can live—'

'I have never lived,' she averred. 'Not at least since I was a child; my dressmaker and my engagements don't give me time. Once you asked me, did I like music? I never hear it. You watched me staring at those pictures—when was it? a month? a day? a week? ago. I never saw them. I cannot sandwich these fine things and taste them, between thick layers of millinery and mankind. Recall the night of our introduction. Dimly I remember, someone played a sonata. Surely you heard it. I tried to hold a strain of it above the roar, but four hours more of vapid entertainment once for all dispelled it. We reached home that night—morning it was—at five.'

'Then', I said somewhat cynically, 'was your time to recapture your few bars of melody, to read your poem, in colour or in verse.'

'No. I slept. Days don't end, or one might lengthen them; they prelude others.'

'It is possible to relinquish this existence.'

'It is impossible,' was her decisive answer.

Then I remembered George's retort anent maternal fate, and

realized that it had not been solely repartee. This creature, apparently, was born for liberty without rebellion. She had said truly, 'I have not force to lift the curtain.' Nor could she strike for self-deliverance.

I experienced a sensation of cold pity, with the recognition that destiny had chosen her a gaoler who would tighten with unfailing raillery her impalpable chain. He approached us, mounting the stairs slowly and sporting a social smile, to claim his fiancée for another dance.

She rose and took his arm saying, 'I have been amusing Mr Aston and he has been instructing me.'

I followed them downstairs and into the glaring room. It seemed impossible to leave her; yet had she beckoned me by any sign, I could have experienced no desire to stay.

It was some days later that I met George and Mrs Desborough in a fashionable thoroughfare. 'Mama' was rampant, George evidently harassed and preoccupied. They informed me that Miss Desborough was not well. The doctor had ordered perfect quiet and country. 'As if', cried the devoted matron, 'I could conceivably leave town at such a juncture! Veva in this condition, everything falls on me. It is the need of action that alone sustains me; whether I shall survive the strain or not, I do not know.' We jointly prophesied the happier alternative and supported the heroic mother home.

I was not prepared to see Miss Desborough, but she rose from an armchair as we entered the drawing-room. Her aspect startled me. She was visibly changed, and even haggard; her usual tint of healthy pallor had assumed a sickly hue. She smiled faintly, holding a book towards me, saying, 'You see I am reading my poem—in verse—today.' I took the book: it was a selection from Browning, and the page opened by chance at 'The Lost Mistress'. I made some stupid answer, and hastily returned it. She slid a finger between the leaves and leaned back wearily in a low basket-chair. George bent over it, assiduously jocular. I sat, bearing a receptive part in a conversation with Mrs Desborough, at the other end of the room. But the inert figure facing me seemed mystically near. Why, I demanded of myself impatiently, was I no craftsman, capable of embodying for myself this being, in some enduring form? Imaginatively I strove to sketch her in bold lines that mocked reality; to set her person to a baffling air; to conjure words and frame a metre that should ensure her actuality to groping sense for ever; but music laughed; colour arched rainbow brows of scorn; and rhythm danced derision at my impotent essays.

Derriman pleaded an engagement, beckoned me, and we left together. He was apparently disturbed, and eager for my society. I was about to offer a reassurance on the matter of his lady's health, when he disclosed an embarrassment of quite another kind. He reiterated a fervent wish—as was his habit in recurring difficulties—that he had not been such a fool, and solaced himself, at intervals, with the time-honoured consolation, that he was about to thumb a cleanlier page.

He wanted my opinion on the possibility of his leaving town in the present state of affairs; and as his business was sufficiently disreputable, I counselled a personal and immediate settlement of it at any cost. This arranged, he discoursed at seemly length on his fiancée's indisposition; and while he floundered on, I formed a hasty project. My mother, I said, would doubtless gladly receive her for a week, if he would insist on an acceptance of the invitation when procured. I pointed out the merits and exigencies of this suggestion, in view of the approaching marriage and the doctor's advice. He readily acceded. It might be made, he rapidly discovered, to fit his own maturing plans.

I did not analyse my action in making the proposition, conscious that pity formed a large ingredient; but journeyed home, and drew for my mother an undecorated outline of the case. She watched me, I noted with amusement, closely during my performance, but at length assented to the abrupt proposal. My final requirement was that the poor girl might not be harassed by surveillance, but mercifully left alone. Her respite, I concluded, would be brief, and she must return perforce to a thickening fray.

'I know Marcia,' said my mother pregnantly. 'Poor little boat if that barge is towing it!'

'It flows', I said, 'resistlessly along. Miss Desborough', I continued, 'has, her mother says, "no head for combinations", so you might give her the white room.' This chamber overlooked surrounding pastures, where the sheep grazed on lovely steeps. It had no view of road. From the larger bedroom, I remembered, the villagers might be seen all day, dotting the distant hilly street.

Next morning, before breakfast, I stepped on to the terrace and looked down upon our almost perpendicular garden, with its slopes of brilliant flowers; then I climbed upward to the spot we called the 'desert'; a high, tangled place, from which was visible a glimpse of sea. The prayer gong sounded. I descended to find my mother in the long old-fashioned room, her didactic volume open upon the window-seat, waiting my appearance. The stiff personage in brown, was, I surmised, the new 'companion'; not yet permanent enough to be stamped with the full approval of the row of exacting potentates in lavender cotton gowns.

Peace dwelt here, I thought, securely; and I pictured the tall travesty of it standing, a gentle challenger, at the open door. How would she fit this new environment, I questioned? The desire to observe her in each novel situation had become almost a passion. It was impersonal,

I mentally contended, and consequently harmless; but, in the character of host, I should be obviously forbidden the indulgence of it; therefore I determined, (uttering a mechanical 'Amen') to spend the period of her coming visit in town, and there to await the issue of the brief realization of her dreams. Would she return transported or dejected, the owner or the slave of rest? Thus wondering, I departed later, and with no purpose to return.

A letter some days afterward from my mother informed me that her guest had achieved a veritable welcome. 'Why—' queried the writer, 'did you paint me one of your fashionable lugubrious studies of my visitor; and where in the name of honesty did Marcia pick up such a child? I imagined her the modern, artistic monstrosity you drew; but she is charming; a beautiful human picture—without a date. She roams about unchaperoned, as you desired, though I have had some battle with Miss Bodmin (the brown lady) on this score. After tea we sit on the terrace and talk (occasionally) of you. Your little bit of philanthropy has brought a delightful experience into my lonely life. Can't you better it, and manage to come down, at least on Saturday. I want you to see my patient, and your mother wants to see you.'

This last plea was potent, though I had often resisted it before. Yet had I any sound excuse to offer now? London was unbearable, and I was enigmatically restless, haunted by some spirit of immobility and silence, which outward noise and movement seemed not to nullify but to substantiate. My reasons for refusal to go down were quite phantasmal, my interest in Miss Desborough purely aesthetic, and had I not been long pledged to its gratification? Why play with quixotic scruples now? a few days more and we must meet in town, in two weeks she would be Derriman's wife; and thus, during one sultry afternoon, I wavered, knowing not why. Reason at last assured me that tacit doubt implied some danger, and there could be none. Saturday came, and found me in a state of inexplicable jubilation—and on my way.

My mother greeted me at the little ancient doorway at the bottom of the steep winding path. 'Dear boy, this is a surprise. We had quite given you up, thinking that silence must mean No. Veva—Oh! yes, I have arrived at "Veva"—is in the morning-room.' I asked after her health. 'Oh—recovered—not robust. She declines to speak of London. Last night she said, "You remember what Maggie Tulliver says; 'I feel quite wicked with roses, I want to smell them till there is no scent left'? That is how I feel about my days with you." Her simplicity is perfect. Why did you make me fancy her such a complicated and uncomfortable being? You don't know her. I must introduce you anew.'

We mounted together, stopping now and again to comment on ornamental beds and backward fruit-trees. The scented quiet of the place was paradise after the stifling tumult of the city just forsaken. The terrace reached, we went into the house. A door stood open. Through it, I saw the figure towards which I had inevitably journeyed. She stood by the window with her back towards me. The room was scented with carnations. She had just placed a bowl of these flowers on the ledge in front of her, and was finishing its adjustment. Then she turned. Her movement I had mentally anticipated, but her greeting surprised me. 'We have been expecting you.'

'For how long?' I said, since some rejoinder seemed imperative.

She smiled. 'Until you came.'

Neither of us had advanced. I remained standing on the threshold; and her clear words reached me across the long low room. Apart from physical restoration, I apprehended at the moment some indefinable alteration in the well known form. I went forward saying lightly, 'And what has happened since the evening when you "amused" me, and I "instructed" you?'

She held out her hand. 'That night—must I recall it? I think I must have been asleep and have awakened since. I do not find your sunsets silent. The sky last night, was eloquent;—it spoke of everything in life.' I waited. 'Do you insist? It is untranslatable. Above was blue. I read it life celestial; and before us the crimson lights of passion—edged with gold. Behind the deep dark grey of commonplace and burdensome existence.'

My mother joined us, laughing; 'Veva is great at sentimentalizing nature, but she will ignore the stars. They came out late last night, and she would not notice them.'

'They remind me', the girl said slowly, 'of my crowds.'

These vagrant fancies were uttered with the unreserved simplicity of childhood. Her limited sojourn in this place of peace had marked her, more than I had fancied could be possible. She was still mysterious, in slipshod phraseology, 'original', but no longer inharmonious; the element of conflict, which had so vividly impressed me at our first meeting, had almost disappeared. Her intricate discordancy had found some, at least an intermediate resolution. It might hang thus suspended, or proceed.

We sat that evening in the twilight. She, I remember, on the low window-seat of the carnation-scented room. I took up a book from the table and began to cut the leaves. It was the latest volume of a popular poet, which I had brought with me from town. My task ended, she reached a hand for it, and glancing at the title, demanded, 'Can you read this man?' I asked, 'why not?'

She replied with the clear and quiet intonation which gave her words their curious decision. 'Because he has desecrated life. He leaves no fragrance anywhere. All his scents are essences, his very winds as warm as human breath.'

'Nevertheless', I said, 'he gathers flowers.'

She assented, 'Yes, they are all plucked. None blows sweetly in the meadows. His verdure may pass with uncritical humanity, but it is not sweet enough to content the least fastidious cow. Even his roses—and he is fond of roses I believe? tell no better story than those on a lost lady's cheek—that "all that's bright must fade". Everything he touches has the human taint, its primary characteristic is corruptibility,—or so it seems to me.'

I reclaimed the book and fingered the leaves to find a refutation, but she stopped me with the conclusion, 'I do not see heaven even in his children's eyes.'

This sweeping and very youthful commentary startled me. I regarded the speaker suddenly, and for the first time seriously, as Derriman's future wife. Involuntarily, I recalled, then quickly banished, the nature of his recent errand, and the muddy current of his past. I had seen these two together often enough before, yet never till this moment had I realized their mutual relation. Following hard on this deferred disclosure, there rushed a recollection poignantly, exactly representative of that sensation of savage apathy which had possessed me on the night of the memorable ball, as she passed and repassed me in his arms. I asked myself, now with a note of loathing, if the man who had stood there callously regarding them had borne my name? That mazy scene of far off sound and colour surged, and engulfed the neighbouring twilight, ere it melted out of view, and our well known room emerged from darkness slowly as I grew conscious of the disappearing glare. I glanced at the dimly-defined figure opposite. The profile of her face was outlined blackly against the fading yellow sky. At last I might enjoy my picture unmolested. I had stolen it, the truth admitted, for this hour. But it denied me; and avenged its master by a sudden assumption of humanity and was there set before me in transformed and forbidden shape. Stunned and mute I sat, revolving evidence against an undefended self. I had cast for myself in this poor drama my own ignoble part. How sharply had I noted and condemned my friend's habitual attitude towards the girl who was to be his wife; and yet he had but treated her, after his manner, as a child. I, after mine, had contemplated her, with cooler insolence, as a marionette.

Sitting there in the encroaching darkness, keenly sensible of her presence, there came to me the revelation of her as a woman, stationed above and beyond us both. Never in life before had I been so conscious of my clay. She addressed me little, talking intermittently and gently to my mother or the prim brown lady whom we were often tempted to forget. My thoughts enjoined me silence, and I maintained it. Going to the piano, I sought the sole means of outlet for them; but my mother pleaded, after a space of patience, 'May we have something by an older master now?' I crashed out the last chaotic chords of egotism, and slid into a melody by Mozart. 'That again, please,' petitioned a clear voice from the window. I repeated it pianissimo. Then the lights were brought in, and I went from the room, out into cool obscurity, having suffered enough illumination for one night.

The next morning, as I awoke, the bells were tinkling for some superfluous service faintly across the fields. I dressed hurriedly and went down stairs, mastered by the strange conception that this day had dawned for my possession. As I passed the window of the breakfast-room, I stopped to identify a figure standing by the table. It was Evelyn with a letter in her hand. I waited for a recognition, but she did not see me. From the high terrace where I stood the postman's bent figure was just visible descending the distant hilly street. I turned again towards the open window. She had put the letter down unopened and stood regarding it with a glance unmistakably disturbed. Her hands were clasped before her, her whole posture testified affright. She brushed a hand quickly across her eyes, and then uncovered them to discern with a forlorn gesture, the miserable paper square. She pushed it from her, and at length hid it, the ruse was childish, beneath a plate, and remained with her eyes fixed upon the porcelain circle, summoning a wretched little deprecative smile. It was time, I thought, this pantomime concluded. I tore down a couple of climbing-roses from the trellis behind the casement, and strode in to end it. The scene oppressed me. Had it been altogether merciful, or even lawful to quicken this creature's hunger for a serenity which her destiny was going to deny? The flowers in my hand diffused a haunting fragrance, and I remembered how she had used the phrase of a recorded passion, to express her own desire to extract the utmost sweetness from her precious hours, which were so soon to end. The unavoidable letter demanded her return to town on the morrow, and beyond this plain admission of its contents she mentioned it no more that day.

I passed the hours dreamily. Branded with the disclosure of the previous night, I had grown critically numb, sensitive solely to the one consuming fact; that the shadowy image with which I had been playing was substantially subsistent, and for the moment, mine. The knowledge sent me leaping back to childhood. I became again a winged and wandering spirit, wonderstruck in that enchanted land. My pedestrian soul and the prosaic world sustaining it suffered this miraculous transmission undismayed. I could not measure the timeless length of that summer day. Sitting in a brilliant corner of the little crumbling church, I tasted the immortality of which the poor preacher, from his high post of vantage, was tentatively fingering the rind. I know not by what right I viewed the golden city, which he was chalking up so clumsily in colours founded of dingiest clay. But the gates were open, and I looked within. A wheezy instrument aloft bade me proclaim my vision, and I chanted it to the row of red and shining faces fronting me with an inquisitive stare.

Thou hast no shore fair ocean,
Thou hast no time bright day,

I wrapped closely round me the mantle of mysterious contentment, fearing to discard it, lest I lay bare beneath it the scars of a naked soul.

Evelyn too seemed absolutely happy, as oblivious of the future as of the past. We spent the afternoon strolling along wide highways and through drowsy fields, saying nothing beyond required commonplaces; yet then, if ever, utterance was free. Speech perhaps but offered us the fatiguing rites of a communion which must have long been ours. She seemed to have imparted to me something of her slumbrous spirit, for I did not notice her, although I felt her keenly. Like the warm atmosphere and the interminable sunshine, she pervaded me. Once in that endless afternoon, we came upon the sea, and then she spoke. 'I must go and bathe my hands in it. I cannot watch it coldly and leave it without one caress. Some contact is imperative, even if to gain it I must be borne away.' She went to the waves' edge and came back with wet, glistening fingers spread out towards me.

'Are you content?' I asked.

She smiled and shook her head. I too, was on the brink of a treacherous ocean, but I lacked her frank abandonment, and halted, blinking on the shore. We stood listening to the loud splash of the waves for a few moments, and retook our road. It wound for me through the new country of romance, that wild place closed to the earnest seeker, which laughs at man's pilgrimages and marks for each its own capricious boundary line. He who plants even a momentary foot there must forget life's terminus: banishment follows the first recollection that the soul can die. I apprehended only that mine had sprung to birth.

With dying sunlight, this trance ended. As we climbed the steep garden path, light was escaping swiftly. Candles flared within the house and we were welcomed to a retarded meal. This over, we sat again in the carnation-haunted room, my mother dozing in a low seat by the window, Evelyn seated in the embrasure by her side. Her beauty, that night, was breathlessly appealing; her limbs, her features had lost every trace of contest, and were marked only by a superlative repose.

Hitherto, I had been curiously loth to touch this shell of spiritual seduction, but this hour exposed in me a craving to destroy. Passive delight and sensual timidity had been but steps to this base summit. I meditated indeed no gross material onslaught, but plotted an internal wreck. I did not doubt my power to move this woman, but I had sunk to the need or urging from her a cry. A brutal inspiration whispered music. I went to the piano.

She murmured something that was inaudible. It must have been spoken very low.

I wheeled round and met her quiet gaze with fixed involuntary cruelty. 'Listen', I said, 'and I will draw some pictures for you.'

She inclined her head. I struck the first slow chords of that March into which I had tried vainly, at our first meeting, to infuse her baffling personality. The primary notes of death were not to be insistent, they were simply to suggest a shrouded life; the dirge at the outset might even convey a sense of sleep. It ended. I gained the first halting notes of the spirit's sweet and transitory existence; then all of loveliness my fingers held, went free. I seized, but by what means I know not, and thrust into the melody, the finest utterances of life. Its brevity was certain, but the limit was not mine. At its close, I paused, to beckon from futurity the darkest harbingers of annihilation. Ere they came, she had risen and stood beside me placing a hand that did not touch me, a hair's breadth over mine.

'That was death—and life,' she said. 'I thank you, but doesn't it end there?'

'No,' I said relentlessly. 'Another death succeeds.'

'It may,' she answered, 'I know the sequence, but not, I think, tonight.'

'As you will,' I said closing the instrument.

I felt a look I could not meet, as she affirmed quietly, 'I listened for your pleasure; it was a poor one, you will discover that.' I had already done so, in a flash of self-disgust.

'I cannot thank you', she said later to my mother, 'for these days. Life is very long, I think sometimes, but peace, if one has known it, must look the same all through, as lovely at its outset as at its end. It is an ageless thing that you have shown me. There is no other comrade, it seems, with such a changeless face.'

'My dear,' the old lady answered gently, 'you should find others now more beautiful. Thus we think when we are old and life is over, but you are young.'

The girl said nothing more, but stooped and kissed lightly the wrinkled hand resting upon her arm.

On the morrow, George arrived boisterous and important, with a countenance betokening relief, and took his fiancée back to town.

At parting she put out a hand to me, saying, 'I shall see you?' She had scarcely addressed me since the preceding night.

I replied mechanically, framing my answer on her question; 'You shall see me.' But the promise was not kept.

I stayed in the country till I could no longer support its unconquerable stillness, the placid loveliness of earth and sky; and then I left it, and never did a harassed citizen welcome sweet pastures and the waves' white spray with a more grateful passion than that with which I left them, nor bathe his spirit in clear and peaceful streams as gladly as I plunged mine into the tainted eddy of clogged and crowded life. Towards London my steps, even in thought, had never turned. The cover of a chance time-table displayed in large characters the name of a foreign city, and thither mechanically, I went.

If I was flying from reality, fate sent me wisely to that metropolis of a puppet world. It seemed the refuge of the aimless, the home of the moral vagrant, the playground of the smiling sinner, the burying place of the living soul. Thought there was reckoned the short road to folly, so after the manner of that city, I eschewed it and followed the mindless footsteps of the wise. The place seemed infinitely finite, the people so definitely mortal that their final goal appeared to be but half an hour's journey off, in the pretentious suburban cemetery of which they were so proud. Yet doubtless, beneath their dominos, each of these gay-hearted masqueraders hid more of eternity than I had brought with me. I flung myself upon distraction. The irresponsible surroundings soothed me. In the midst of the mimic vitality, I threw off easily the ponderous fact of true subsistence and tripped lightly across the druggetted and footlighted boards of life.

A letter from Derriman cut short these capers. He wrote, 'Whatever are you doing with yourself? when are you coming back to a Christian country and respectable society? I am out of my hole, it wasn't so serious as I thought. "Mama" is positively revolting, Veva not at all the thing. They say she will pick up when we get away. I suppose I shall see you before the 21st? "Mama" will certainly survive that date, but "nous autres"—we must wait and see. Till then, eat, drink &c. This millinery humbug would be a d—d nuisance if it weren't the only thing that keeps "lovely woman" alive. Eh! It seems to be doing the other thing for Veva. Perhaps she is a feminine exception. Horror! and perish the thought!'

I traversed the brilliant streets that morning bathed in continental sunshine, with George's letter in my pocket, while a sentence of it repeated itself idiotically in my brain. 'She—will—pick—up—when—we—get—away.' The reiterated phrase at length grew meaningless. The disconnected fragments of it danced before me with exasperating agility. I caught at them as they went twirling by, marshalled them in place again, shifted them before me in an obedient row, as I paced the shady boulevards; and at length subjected them to an absurd interrogative analysis, reason frowning mockery at my side.

A few days before the wedding, almost as mechanically as I had left it, I returned to England, and took up the suspended threads of being with a determination to let them loose no more. Derriman haunted my rooms in various characters. The benignant lover, the harassed bridegroom, and the doomed bachelor, chased each other up and down my stairs incessantly, and I could not deny these hunted beings sanctuary from a pursuing tailor and a sentinel mother-in-law. Veva, he said, would go abroad, although she seemed in no fit state to travel, and 'Mama' would not hear of the wedding being postponed. 'She'd rather', he said with fatalistic certainty, 'marry me by proxy, though by Jove, when I've given my word to plunge, I shouldn't shirk it at this time of day.'

While he spoke, I became conscious of an alien presence. Did it environ me or stand far off on the borders of a half discernible dissolving world? Did it come to banish or to beckon me? In vain I asked its will, as he went on: 'It's not too late to change our plans. You haven't seen Veva. I wish you would. I fancy she likes you. You might talk some art-jargon to her about its not being just the time to see just the proper things, and so on. Tell her the Madonna season's over for the present, that Italy's artistically beastly, or something of that kind. I make such a hash of it, but you'd know what to say, and she'd believe you.'

I expressed mildly a disinclination for the task, and reiterated dully, 'She will pick up, you know, when you get away.'

'Oh, you think so? that's all right; that's what the old lady says. The fact is, Aston, the poor girl seems so seedy, I rather funked taking her away.'

I repeated automatically the hackneyed reassurance, and it seemed to satisfy him.

I shunned rigidly the meeting for which he was so anxious, and cheated my mind with the notion that the lady I was so systematically avoiding was not in town. My mind refused to picture that tall figure rising each morning to confront the image in some mirror, of its fading and attenuated self. Determinately I built up the certainty that miles of many-coloured fields waved between me and re-finding her; and our greeting (it was dreamily decreed) must thrill across a low-roofed, scented chamber, where diamond panes obscured the lustre of a golden sky.

The wedding would take place on Friday, and on Wednesday afternoon, so soundly had I schooled myself, I did not feel it near. But disillusionment was close upon me; I might well have felt its breath. Towards six o'clock, I left my club, and in this visionary mood, forgetful of prosaic caution, turned into the park. As I dashed into the thick traffic, threading a maze of wheels, a premonitory instinct bade me stop. The mandate was unquestionable; waiving danger, I obeyed it, and among the mass of strangers spinning by me I became aware of the arrestive form that barred my progress, leaning back against a flame-coloured cushion, motionless and white. There, in that circle of menacing death, my life's face flashed before me, wan, ethereal, pathetically radiant, gazing, it seemed, through a thin veil of flesh towards me, from some divine and distant world.

In one transcendent recognition our eyes held each other; and it must have been my heart more than my vision that then caught and registered the haggard lines of cheek and brow. A pallid echo flung them back to me, and my tense senses took their impress as the carriage rolled away. The body's plaint was eloquent, and overbore the urgent solicitation of the soul.

Physically, I apprehended she was in no condition to endure superfluous excitement. The natural and divinely appointed guardian of this delicate mechanism had worked it too sedulously to leave it any capacity for accidental strain.

Reason thus admonished me to gentleness, but impulse pealed across its faint persuasion, sonorous and assertive Noes. Above these voices rose a murmur, into which neither blended, infinitely tender: its wild music conquered the contending notes of counsel, and pointed clearly a sweet way of daring; but I could not take it; the time was past.

I quickly regained the streets and made towards home. Entering my chambers I reminded the porter emphatically that I had left them, and ascended to my room. There, I locked the door and breathed a prayer for privacy, sitting down to the undisturbed entertainment of my mistress, Fate. Face to face we sat; I had done toying with her, but she had still a game to play. My day for handling her was over, and I could not condescend to parley. I suffered her mocking presence coldly, answering nothing to the taunts and threats, nor even to the blandishments she offered. After an hour she swept past me with a stinging curse and smile of latent malice in farewell.

I was left to weariness and began watching stupidly the well known details of the room. One by one passed under a continuous scrutiny, from an exaggerated acquaintance they grew strange. At length no object there was recognizable, each had become inexplicably foreign. My own face, seen in a neighbouring mirror, seemed unknown. The remnants of a recent visit, apparently from George, were scattered about the table. I noticed a photograph, a pocket-book, some fragments of correspondence, together with some bills and a stray visiting-card. These were doubtless evidence of a hurried search for something missing which he had rushed away to find. From my seat, I saw the pictured face, lying sideway amid the litter, tilted on an unsmoked cigar. The features only were familiar, the glance and pose were rare. Thus, at least, I mused, in life she had never looked at me! On the torn pieces of the note, her clear intelligible characters seemed ineffaceably analogous to that conclusive intonation which I had marked and knew so well. I read idly, half-sentences and severed words;—'the usual message—' 'Mama'—'myself'—'aedeker'—'you tomorrow'—Evelyn Desbo—'. Overtaken by a sudden provocation, I got up angrily and swept the table bare. A silver case hidden under the debris fell noisily to the floor. A sick feeling crept about me; my eyes travelled hungrily round the luxurious apartment as they had done about a bare school study, years ago, for hints of home. The frame enclosing my mother's portrait I had thrust rudely with the other loose picture to the ground; and they both lay faces downward side by side. I stooped and rescued them together, and sat gazing at the mimic faces till they faded, and I saw in place of them two veritable women standing, linked together in a twilight chamber—far away. I rang the bell to order my portmanteau and an immediate meal. My plan was taken. In an hour I started for the country. Reason, impulse and passion's inciting whisper held their peace, some spirit of desolation had stilled the conflicting chorus; I heard nothing, stabbed by that appeaseless loneliness, but I saw still the stationary figures, and one beckoned; which it was I knew not, but towards it, asking not its name but craving only its compassion, in my extremity, I fled.

The journey perhaps satisfied a growing demand for motion. Rushing through the dark country towards vague and temporary consolation, I experienced a dreamy but definite delight. Perhaps I slept, certainly no sense of loss or severance disturbed me, yet it was over a deep-lying anguish that these ripples of paltry pleasure played. I roused myself reluctantly at the little wayside station, and once in the wide roadway, woke with a sudden jerk to fact. I had come to bathe in healing waters, to taste the tested streams of peace.

Truly, I was parched and sore, 'ill', said my mother on my arrival, anxious to try some innocently nauseous experiments. I laughed them and the word away. That night I courted sleep and held her for some haunted hours. A moment before waking, I lived through a vivid, frightfully actual dream.

I was a child with other children, brothers and sisters, blood companions; in waking life, unknown. We played and shouted through a labyrinth of stirring sport. Our parents often absent, were heavily existent to our sense. Present, they blessed us sombrely. One night my father brought a horror to our home. We learned he had discovered death. Shuddering, we fled the name, drowning it in noisier bursts of play. He called me, pointing upward to a high garret room. I stumbled up. The door was open, within burned a faint light. Across the floor a girl lay, prostrate, clad in a low and rich dishevelled dress. I ventured in and bent across the figure; the door closed: it was my lot to watch the dead. I fainted, sick with terror, then recovered and stationed myself dutifully by her side. Her form was beautiful, her features bore for me no individual character, they were exquisite simply as the lines of bust and shoulder; and I should as naturally have sought a smile from parted fingers as from parted lips. A reverence, not of death but beauty, barred the thought of touch, and I retreated to a corner of the dim chamber, and with my eyes fixed on the stirless figure, followed with my hand involuntarily the splendid curves in air. Eluding the shining drapery, I missed no fraction in delirious fancy of the smooth surfaces exposed to view, passing my palm aerially along the matchless line of arm and cheek, and firmer brow. I spent some countless hours, steeped in this realization of intangible delight. At length some voices intimated from a far-off passage that my task was done. They called me; I remained immovable, not to be lured from that enchanted spot. They ventured nearer, and I noted their blanched faces with a smile. Someone stole boldly in and said: 'She lives, and living, she is ours.' Then I advanced and indicated silently her icy pallor and the stiff posture of the incomparable form. They departed. I knelt down beside her, and her spirit crept towards mine. I felt life stirring slowly in her, and its current set towards me. I strove to lift her, but could not support the burden; with an effort I dragged her to a seat beneath the wall, a kind of settle, where she lay breathless but invoking breath. I stood by her panting, a small being mystically conscious of miraculous maturity, yet questioning not my mysterious self, but her.

Still pallid and still voiceless, she compelled allegiance, and my senses subtly seized a wordless whisper, 'If they know me living, I am dead. Keep this secret—I am yours and you shall learn my history.' I burned to hear it. Once again the door flew open and a crowd burst in. They clustered round me crying: 'But she lives!' A monstrous strength was given me; I clutched her softening limbs and stretched them rigid, torturing them to hideous postures, and finally, rearing myself to some gigantic stature, I stood high—a man—and flung with horrid violence the questioned corpse against the wall. It fell, answering doubt with heavy emphasis; and they fled shrieking. I leant back with savage force against the door. A glorious form confronted me, erect, instinct with life. I loosed a rapturous cry and clasped my prize. Her breath was in my ear, and the first word of her great history; then she fell backward gasping, and her features twisting, growing ghastly, shifted into a familiar face. 'Evelyn!' I cried, starting backward at the revelation — and with that cry, awoke.

It was growing light. Fragrant dawn crept to my bedside chasing the dews of sleep-bound terror, and welcoming my errant spirit back to a brighter and more actual world. I lay with shut eyes blessing the sweet ministrant until insistent daylight bade me rise. Through the window I watched the clouds, like freighted ships of storm, sailing with stately swiftness across the tranquil blue. The breeze that sped them stirred below, the fretted surface of green slopes to silvery ripples, and these wavelets laughed at the still azure of the over-hanging sea. Not far away, the veritable ocean stole the tints of sky and verdure, and blent them to a million hues, splashing mighty scorn on mockeries so impotent.

The birds about my casement hopped and twittered, till I heard the piping echo of man's petty drama in their inconsiderable fuss, and joy and jar. Nature smiled grandly on my woes, and yet she calmed them. Despair, like some thin candle flame, grew indistinguishable in her glorious light. When that died, the feeble gleam might flare anew, and add a gloom to darkness. Now, for a moment, it burned low. I went out across the shimmering fields and walking rapidly soon reached the sea. The shore was lonely. I stood high above it, gazing down, and hearkening to the magic voice below. I knew its compass, moan and threat and cruel roar, its heavy lullabies, its savage calls; no stranger had divined them listening to the wooing and enchanted song, which bade him seek oblivion on its breast. The sound was passionless and yet seductive. I recalled another voice, and half-forgotten words. 'Some contact is imperative' and laughing, I scrambled down the cliff echoing that saying gaily. Then I stripped and slid into the waiting waters: there my spirit bounded with my body, the world of mire and clay was as invisible as heaven, and it seemed more distant. I strode home soberly; this sense of calm seemed ominous; it was a veil of curious texture to hang between me and tumultuous life. I tried to shift it, even to replace it by the somberer vision of the night. But peace was obdurate and remained.

During that day, my mother handed me a letter. I read it unconcernedly, and half aloud.

'Dear lady,' it began. 'We thank you for your present. I will not pause to praise it. I have to thank you for a greater thing. It seems to me, it has always seemed, that life is long. I see it before me, like a canal that frightened me in childhood. It was in Holland. Two long lines of sombre trees stretched away into a point of distance. The dull length of water seemed interminable, and I used to dream that I was lost on it, that it bore me on and on past the dark, unvarying banks—unceasingly. It was a nightmare. There seemed no rescue, because there seemed no end. Now, too, I dream of endlessness sometimes; and sometimes it is of that which you have shown me, the changelessness of peace. I think of our long evenings on the terrace, watching the light die, of the grey mornings and the quiet days. There is no limit in my memory to that time I spent with you. In poor words again I try to thank you for it. It gleams a steady little taper that will glow I think when other lamps go out.

'We are to stay abroad some months, I think. Your thought is kind, but do not write to me. The trousseau, after which you ask, goes with us, and will be known I fancy as the better part of me.'

I folded and returned the sheet. 'When did it come?' I asked.

'A week ago; together with a note from Marcia, profusely maternal and exclamatory, from which epistle I inferred that the poor child had learned the futility of giving up before her mother's work was done.'

'The general opinion is', I said, yielding to a pursuing phrase,—'that she will "pick up" when they get away.' I looked up, and met the old lady's frankly questioning glance, answering it with cold simplicity. 'I saw her yesterday, and thought more probably that she would—die.'

'So you came down to me?'

The tale was told. 'I saw you both', I said, 'and I came down to you.'

We said no more, but later on, in the afternoon, I was summoned to my mother's room. 'You go to town tomorrow early?' she asked gently.

'Do I?' I said.

'Tomorrow, or tonight,' she urged.

'Then it had better be tonight.' I forced a smile. 'There will be festive details.' A frail hand silenced me, brushing off tears; I kissed and left it still trembling and wet.

It was past ten o'clock, and starlight when I reached town. The night was clear. I felt an uncontrollable repugnance to repose, and leaving my baggage, stepped forth in a westerly direction, careless of my road. I made a circuit of some well known thoroughfares; execrably bright they were, wide, brilliant sunforsaken places flashing their thousand shameless eyes upwards, in harsh derision at the pure pale watchers of the sky. I crossed a gaudy threshold, wondering if mean distraction might not deaden my fine sensation of unrest. I found no vulgar and substantial image could displace the lovely ghost that urged me from the world of fact towards a realm of dreary and fantastic dreams. For common drugs cannot touch torture, and this nauseous draught but lent a trivial discomfort to it, leaving hardly a taste behind. After an hour's sojourn in the wretched place, I left it, towards midnight, with the fierce need of motion still predominant:, and started on my vague journey once again. I turned southward. Lamplight played across the river, and the gloomy water paved an unwilling way for hundreds of glittering fairy feet dancing along, beneath the bridge. The moon stole from behind a cloud, and brought a troop of silver revellers to join the gold. I passed through sordid streets ill-lit, pacing on and on distractedly with even strides. Thought and motion would not link themselves together, familiar comrades though they once had been. Once or twice, I paused and fumbled at locked memory, standing still. But a long halt was physically impossible; I longed to stop and search my mind for guidance, but a despot force bade me unflaggingly proceed. And thus, through the dark night, I hastened on, and it was not permitted me to ask myself my object or my road. Once, two men pushed against me with a question. I was squared for action and dismissed them briefly. They exchanged a muttered confidence and shuffled off to an accompaniment of self-excusing oaths. A personal encounter with these vagabonds had afforded me a welcome outlet for my strange supply of vigour, and I experienced something like a muscular sensation of regret or deprivation as I heard them slip away. After a time this conscious energy diminished, my progress grew more automatic, and I felt no longer the actual relief of motion, though the incitement to it was still strong.

Some miles and hours over, I passed a huddled group of vagrants in a suburban field. One of them, a woman, moaned and wriggled in suffering or drunken sleep. I should have stayed my course enquiringly, but that all regulation of my pace had ceased then definitely to be mine: there was no choice between a slavish continuance of this even march or absolute cessation. Dawn was beginning to touch the sky. I met it in quiet meadows, turning with the thirsty grass, my face up to the dew. The birds had wakened early to some momentous day. It was a wedding morning, I remembered—their first notes proclaimed it! and it was mine to greet that opening hymn. The darkness had not questioned me where I was bound, nor did the light. Each observed my blind advancement with incurious care. I hardly noted when these watchers met, so quietly they shifted places, night yielding his post to day. I sat down, and leaned against a tree-trunk, beginning to peer vainly through the thick early mist for signs of habitation. None were visible, and I remained gazing stupidly into the white haze.

Quiescence soon summoned the banished wraiths of memory. I tried to meet them, to bridge the gap the semi-conscious night had made in my continuous and troubled thought. Unequal physically to this achievement, I leaned forward shrouding my eyes to shut out all external and confusing images; oblivion claimed me and I slept. When I awoke, stiff and weary, it was full morning, with overhead a pale and cloudless sky. Now, in the clear distance, I detected the indications of a town. My watch informed me that my breakfast hour was past; a sense of baffled hunger added confirmation, and I set out across a footpath towards the town. It proved to be a model suburb, hideously well-to-do, a place that even poverty might, and did well disdain. It seemed a spot incapable alike of greatness and of degradation, haunted by non-existent possibilities, setting forth by what it was, what it could never be. I traversed many streets of solid red-brick residences, in this paradise of self-respecting garden-fronts and immaculate window-blinds, till an hotel came into view; an unpretentious building, suggesting refuge from the smug opulence of the surrounding homes.

I walked into the coffee-room, ordered and waited breakfast. The other occupants of the room did not invite attention, but I watched them idly till the meal appeared. While I was negligently attacking it, two elderly women sauntered in, gaping some surprise at my appearance, and seated themselves at the table opposite mine.

The leading speaker wore a black ill-fitting silk gown: her voice resembled rather than a human organ, some inexpensive substitute, warranted for use and wear. 'There's something so invitin' ', she remarked, 'about a restorong, whether it's the service, or having your things so fresh and hot, I don't know, but it's always a treat to me. Do you know the Four-in-Hand?'

The passive agent in the conversation replied unnecessarily, 'No'.

'It's a big place. We dined there on our wedding-day and went to the theatre afterwards. It was the beginning of the honeymoon; I tried to disguise the fact, but we couldn't get rid of the rice anyhow, and strange enough we met two other pairs in the same state, a Mrs Phillips (you'll remember her, they were settling at Highbury). We all joined in the evening and made a matrimonial party of it, there being safety in numbers, as my husband said.'

'Rice or no rice,' was the comment, 'it's no use trying to conceal the fact. I suppose it's something in the clothes, and then the men being so extry attentive and perlite.'

My attention flagged, although this pleasing topic was enlarged upon; it had brought vividly before me an imminent ceremony in which my part had been assigned. Once or twice during the night a vague notion of my position had floated across my mind like the recurrence of an impossible, but sufficiently disturbing dream. Now I viewed the facts soberly and realized that I could never have been present. I recollected that George had not been warned of my defection, and regretted the compulsory incivility, beginning mentally to frame some plausible apology to be written when I reached town. He must have it, ere he left England, I decided; it should be sent that afternoon to Dover. I felt giddy but dismissed the weakness, and called hastily for my bill, paid it and left the place. I would set out immediately for the city I had left instinctively the night before. Several dapper, bag-carrying individuals preceded me to the station, greeting, as they neared it, other specimens of their kind. I grew indisposed to wedge myself between this mass of brisk humanity, and at length determined to take the dusty unknown road again. Time for me, that day, was practically lost; I need not nor could I count the hours; and I was dully conscious of deliverance in the fact. Hitherto I had too readily slipped past reality; I could not easily refind it. My old niche in the prosaic universe from which I was used to view surrounding life with such composed magnificence, was far to seek and high: moreover, I had climbed divergent slopes and could no longer see that ancient dwelling-place of my complacent soul. At length I ceased all effort to regain it, and yielded myself to the sensation of being a passive actor in some indefinable calamity; and of bodily fatigue. Everything during my brief journey was acutely noticeable but immeasurably distant. Some blot in space, shutting out vision, at short intervals, hovered before me as my goal. Humanity lost class and sex and even individuality, lifting towards me one wide face of woe.

Children with sharpened features swarmed: they could not move their mothers' hearts to pity, but they haunted mine. Each hopeless life looked straight at mine and claimed companionship. From happy souls, and they were few, I turned away, for they were barbarous strangers, the kindliest of whom I could not greet. The people seemed to come upon me like dark shadows, and I to dart through them, a thinner substance and a fleeter traveller than they. At length I strove to check illusions once for all, to grasp and hold reality, to seize the shape that had so long now beckoned and pursued me, that I might station it securely in some place of sanctuary, or at least of safety, out of my reach and view. My mind would call up no coherent image of it. Voice and features and more vivid postures congregated madly, but refused to group themselves in any arbitrary form. I apprehended clearly every attribute, each glance and shifting pose, and vibratory intonation, but I could not erect a personality from these consistent fragments. I was forced to yield them one by one, in solitary incompleteness; to relinquish, not in entirety but in confusion, with disparted pangs, the being I could, and yet could not recall. She passed at my bidding out of life for ever; or so I willed she should at that exalted moment of daylight and sacrifice.

I had been walking for some hours, and at last hailed a well known landmark with relief. A great clock chimed, the sunlight hung about some gilded towers; I was tired and entered the great building which I had been about to skirt. Before I could go home, I felt, there was a heavy hour to get through; it might be possibly supported here. The sunlight slanted strongly in through the high windows: gold and crimson patches stained here and there some lofty corners, unperceivable in darker seasons. People strolled in unceremoniously to rest or worship. Two parties carrying scarlet books arrived to inspect the structure and endure the approaching office. They sat staring critically upward, obviously prepared, after a systematic investigation to be suitably impressed. I chose a seat which afforded me a glimpse of nave and choir. The ancient place was mystically still despite incessant footsteps. It owned the grand secret of impregnable intrinsic calm, that revelation of slow-speaking time which it takes him centuries to impart. As I sat there, almost as motionless as the white figures planted round me in their marble robes, and listened to the distant drone of unapprehended yet familiar words, a new tranquillity stole over me, contrasting strangely with my late stuporous state of supposititious calm. Nature had thrown my passion into momentary apathy, and now it seemed not neutralized but purged. After long wandering and concealment, I espied myself, a meaner and yet finer creature than the poor shadows hitherto impersonating it; and I breathed as one who mounts to lighter air. 'Keep innocency and do the thing that is right' piped a full treble soaring sweetly, 'and that shall bring a man peace at the last.' The far-off singer flung across to me this precious fragment of the eternal story of an evil and a good man's way. I caught it while illuminative harmonies lent the groping words a ray. 'Peace', the dim arches echoed, and the word seemed to trickle coolly on the scorched surface of my soul. I blessed the unknown power which had stayed my hand from reckless murder of that lovely thing; and as I shaded vision, two half-angel faces looked at me with sad yet unreproachful eyes.

The service ended with a pause. A vast chord rent the external silence as I walked away; it left untouched the greater quiet of my heart.

I reached my rooms soon after four o'clock. The house seemed empty and my apartments were unusually neat. No sign remained of the disorder I had left there on the previous afternoon. Something—perhaps it was my chastened spirit—clothed the place with an air of welcome and assuasive rest. I changed my clothes and sat down to concoct the note for Derriman. One or two hasty scrawls in his handwriting headed a pile of letters on the table, but that correspondence, I thought wearily, could wait. I sketched somewhat sickly but in detail an imaginary illness, adding a credible explanation of my extraordinary silence, sealed and stamped the document; but the direction of it cost me effort, and hesitating, with the blank envelope before me, I began to finger nervously the heap of letters near my hand. Three were from Derriman. I thrust aside some circulars: the next was in a hand at first unrecognizable, then poignantly familiar. I tore it open; it was dated 'Wednesday evening' and without preface it began.

'I must see you; yes I do not whisper—it has been my lot so long to be silent, I can speak above my fellows now. Forgive me if, having found utterance, I make ill use of speech. Life is so long, I find. If it were shorter heroism might be possible, but it is long; we can be martyrs only, and the worst martyrdom is not suffering but annihilation; and the deepest death is not to die, but to survive life. I heard your living music—you made me hear it—and I listen still. But the other? am I to bend my ear to that? This is an honest question. God, I suppose will answer it if you cannot. At least, let me see you, no matter how or where, but soon. I told you, long ago it seems, that I had waked and it was true: you woke me, but you bade me no "good morning". Sleep was over, I got up to life: it faced me and I found it no matter of sunsets and sonatas and emotions: it was stern, I could not shift my gaze away from it, it looked so steadily at me. In the light of our meeting this afternoon, it changes colour. I see in it other faces than yours and mine. Let me speak to you, and quickly. I stand at the top of endless stairs and slip and stretch out my hand to you. Do not think I ask you to save me, I want only guidance, I seem to be going some wrong way. If it prove right I must take it, though there be no return—and taking it, we need not meet to say "good-bye".'

I read the words. Their import scarcely reached me. I folded the sheet and put it in my pocket and went out. A purpose and no thought possessed me. I must see her: facts and possibilities escaped my mind, I was beset with one devouring need. Hailing a cab and giving a direction, I told the man to drive like hell. In a few minutes he drew up at the covered doorway. I knocked and entered. A crowd of people blocked the staircase, but I got up the first few stairs and then a voice arrested me, speaking from the floor above. 'Yes,' I heard it enunciating blandly, 'she quite alarmed me. Of course the occasion is a trying one; the poor child is delicate and naturally she felt leaving me. The ceremony quite unnerved me. I felt at any moment she might give way. In fact it was that alone that kept me up. I took restoratives to church. Now they have gone.'

I stopped to hear no more, but turned to my next neighbour. 'Is Miss Desborough upstairs?'

She reared an eyeglass. 'Mr and Mrs Derriman have started.'

'How long?'

'About five minutes. They—'

I muttered thanks and pushed back into the street. My cabman leered. I named a station and repeated laconically, 'drive like hell'.

As I dashed through the well known streets the mass of people left behind appeared to people them, conspicuously the bewildered dame whom I had questioned. An appellation reached my lips, it was unspeakable, preposterous, I dragged out the letter and read the signature, 'Evelyn Desborough'. These characters looked sane, the firm lines hid no fateful warning of sudden monstrous change. The name and date confronted me, I found these signs intelligible, all that lay between them was a void and might have been unpenned. I set my teeth and held before my eyes these symbols like a lawless banner, but my soul was guiltless, bond to a base master, and God knows a savage purpose urged me on. I emptied my pockets and chinked greedily the few gold coins in my hands, scorning in thought the petty tricks of circumstance that promised to offer check to my opposeless will.

The station gained, I enquired the next train to Dover. One started in five minutes. 'And the next?' I asked. An hour later. Suddenly I resolved to wait; my plans so far determined did not demand immediate execution, and I left the booking-office and strolled across the road into the doorway of the large hotel. Entering it, I remembered a massive balcony overlooking the platform: it opened I recollected from a public room. I went upstairs, and made my way between the white tables, out through the French casements, and stood looking down upon the dingy bustling crowd below. Engines shrieked and harassed travellers gesticulated. I surveyed eagerly the excited scene. A figure, but not that I sought, detached itself from the dark agitated mass, approaching with a leisurely familiar gait. I bent forward boldly. It was Derriman. A vague disturbance shook me: then in an instant my blood burned and froze before a revelation, horrible, undreamed of; for I stood resolved to follow to earth's end a phantom, and I could not meet—*his wife!*

He came nearer and stood looking upward, straight, it seemed, at me; but his glance showed no recognition: he took out his watch and set it by the greater face above me, then turned and walked away. I saw him fumble for a cigar-case, open it, shut it quickly, put it back. Far up the platform he proceeded and stopped at length by an open carriage door: he waited a second and then entered it. A piercing whistle sounded. The black line began to move, then twisted to a speck and disappeared. I watched it vanish like some poor shred of dwindling life. My hand unclosed and I spread out the crumpled sheet within it, on the stone ledge in front of me. I tried to scan the covered page in vain. My sight was blurred, I could not trace a line. Some scattered words stamped deep came slowly back to me; my lips began to frame them: they had been wrung from, written by another, but they formed now my own unutterable cry.

'Life is so long—we can be martyrs only—and the worst martyrdom is annihilation—and the deepest death is not to die. I stand at the top of endless stairs and slip and stretch out my hand to you—'

And thus to darkness and to life's survival; as I had left her lonely, and unknowing, she left me—!

WHITE WORLD

FIRELIGHT lapped the chamber: the flames murmured feverishly, wasting like waves in futile utterance their wordless life away.

All was white outside: the sloping fields weighted with millions of torpid snowflakes bore their load with broad tranquillity, while the trees urged by intermittent gusts strove fitfully to cast off the burden pressing upon them with persistent gentleness from on high. Hedges flanked the deeply coated roadways in high blanched drifts which reared themselves slowly upwards hour by hour. These imperceptibly ascending peaks seemed striving towards the clouds that built them, seeking a stealthy union with the sullen sky. Sparse figures ploughing homeward across dreary meadows or through the clogged benighted lanes, clothed at each step more heavily, tried to shift, but vainly, to refuse with numb negation the inevitable covering of the night. These lonely or companioned wayfarers lifted no song nor spoke to one another; they plodded onwards speechless, beating off from time to time the blinding cloak of frozen mist; while that great garment hanging from the sky spread itself soundlessly upon the already shrouded earth. Descending like a pall upon red furrows and green verdure, determinedly obscuring hues once vital, it seemed to bear a part in some vast obsequy of nature, and so deeply did the genial earth lie buried, even the sanguine dawn admitted doubt that life might ever stir again in the broad and pulseless bosom of the ground.

But within the chamber firelight flickered red, and whispered inconsequently its defiant mockery of the colourless and soundless world outside. It lit and vitalized unluminous, non-living things. A row of thick crockery ranged along a crowded shelf took on an aspect of alertness and seemed almost willing to bestir itself to clinking energy at the incitement of the dancing flames. A book lying face upwards on a stool reached by the roving glare, glanced readiness to declare its contents openly: and surely a more urgent gleam had won it to pour forth illumined phrases and scatter lustrous speech into the listening air! From one—a dimmer corner of the room, a stuffed hawk peered with glassy eyes into the animate space around it, and charged alike with life, it looked a veritable bird perched high for safety, preparing to swoop promptly downwards on an appearing prey. Even the room's poor furniture was richly noticeable, and a coarsely-spun cloth upon the table, touched by the glamour of the burning fuel, showed a rare spotlessness and nicety of texture not its own. The simple place was conjured into temporary luxuriousness by the magic wand of light. And that same rod endowed it with an unwonted motion, as if the four low dappled walls had flung themselves in gay and steady insolence against the hueless and quiescent night. Indeed the room seemed planted there, a conscious protest to its cold and dumb environment, like a quick spirit in a world of death.

But if the snow had drifted in to build itself an image, force its impress on the derisive dwelling, it might well have fashioned the impassive figure which tenanted the glowing place. This being lay back, in a wide rush-bottomed chair before the hearth; a bright shawl hung round her attenuated shoulders; and across her lap, half-wound about her person, half-trailing upon the floor, was a heavy sheet which she listlessly essayed to sew. Her face alone within the vivified apartment gleamed lustreless; was wan, transparently and pitifully pale. Her lips alone were tinged; they took the colour of the dominating glow, marking a firm and faded crimson line, conspicuous among less noticeable features which it had been the task of suffering to nullify and blur. Her wasted hands clutched nervelessly the coarse and clinging fabric: and at each few stitches taken they dropped feebly down.

Now and again her head turned restlessly from side to side, as if it followed some syncopated rhythm, kept time mechanically to some inly tolling knell.

The clock ticked and the racing flakes swept wildly by the window; through some ill-fitting panes they had crept in to form a framework round the little bulging squares of glass.

A black cat spread out voluptuously upon the fox-skin by the fender, rose and bowed itself, shooting from its half-opened eyes gleams of veiled savagery upon the fire. But soon relinquishing barbaric dreams of pristine and ferocious sovereignty it stretched mildly and sheathed its claws, accepting with a half-cynical and wholly sensuous complacency the tame decrees of fate. Then with a silken condescension it sprang to the woman's knee. Holding her work aside, she bore its supple settlement compliantly, and passed the thinly covered framework of her hand slowly along the warm sleek body, in acknowledgment of the faint purr that now began to neutralize for her the intolerable ticking of the clock.

She held her fingers to the blaze, and gazed as if through distance, round the room. Her glance included every object there; effort of choice she was too weak to make, and so each trivial detail seizing its chance, became insufferably important, and with its betters teased her aching sight.

At length the maddeningly familiar place receded; she saw it mistily, herself a chained spectator, and thus viewed in dim remoteness, it seemed to be crowded with innumerable days. They entered it in seemly sequence without hurry or delay; featureless they were with regular and ordered paces filing in. Dawn followed dawn and night succeeded night, but of these spectral visitants not one departed, each remained as other dawns and nights streamed in through the for ever-opening door. The straitened space seemed framed to hold infinity, already packed with dateless hours. These congregated, swirled, like particles of dust upon a sunbeam, countless and undismissable: she watched them with a desperate intentness mentally powerless to set a limit to this ever-coming never-going time. She roused herself, fretfully weary and shifted her gaze, still feverishly earnest to actual surroundings, fixing it now on one then on another object in the room. Finally it veered between two coloured prints hung at each side the narrow window; one depicting the death of Nelson, the other, a gaudy representation of the raising of the widow's son. Often for days together she could ignore them, but eventually they resumed obtrusiveness—grew insupportably insistent—and they were importunate again tonight. Once it had been a pastime to construct in imagination the consummation of these pictured scenes, to speed the exasperating actors in them to their endings—to resuscitate the dead youth, never living, and dispatch the dying sailor, never dead. This diversion had palled and passed and now the tarnished frames enclosed for ever, in garish colours and assorted lines, a perpetual symbolical portrayal of suspense. Sitting there, facing them, alone, she sometimes half mechanically placed herself in postures similar to those confronting her of sinking and suspended life, thus tasting two eternities of ending as she identified herself with: the for ever dying and for ever dead. Indeed these haunting figures typified rudely but not inaptly the double aspect of her waning life: its protracted feebleness which death apparently disdained to terminate, and its sadder sleep of stationary existence, over which she divined some re-creating or annihilating spirit hovered, with uplifted hand, empowered yet unprepared to break. She saw distortedly the lives around her, grouped like those attendant crowds in the two prints, gazing upon the issue of her own; and did her next breath involve reanimation or extinction, it could but be provocative, she concluded, of the same faintly exclamatory sigh.

A low moan now and then escaped her, not of suffering, though it was acutely weary, a moan beseeching some immediate resolution of her undetermined fate. She waited viewing deliverance in death's creeping dews or life's enshrouded sunlight, ready to sink or spring towards it in whichever guise, to greet the first kind comer with a welcome almost said.

An audible vibration shook the silence; after some gasping hints the clock struck: her lips moved slowly to the hesitating strokes, and reassumed their firm passivity at the cessation of the sound. She closed her eyes and crossed her hands over the heaving creature on her knee: a little smile of ease relaxed her features as she became aware of its recurrent motion keeping pace with her own regularly taken breath. Its warm existence verified her own; instinctively she put a hand up to her breast—then drew it quickly back from unsought contact with a paper resting there. Her eyelids quivered in recollection and with an action drearily habitual she detached the ragged sheet and held it downwards to the light. The folded lines were interruptedly cut through, the edge bore marks of nervous handling. By the uncertain blaze she carefully deciphered the contents. Those burning phrases over-conned and over-murmured, met her gaze annulled, yet she repeated them, accustomed to their jaded emptiness, and kissed the pages with the spent fervour of a hunted passion spurred towards its worn-out joy. The words were dead under the pressure of unnatural life; unfitly slain, love-murdered things, softly and yet more tragically ended than hate's most bloodily butchered foe. She perceived suddenly the horror of their stark unburied presence and with a gesture of pathetic loathing, flung the tattered sheet to urgent flames. Then her hand sought her bosom gently and covering that robbed, forsaken nest, felt her heart beating stormy protest against the instinctive and inevitable deed. That hungry child of love surrendered now and ceasing to draw life from her, she felt a momentary ease; but loss set teeth on her as soon as its familiar lips were gone; and lest the letter's words should wholly shrivel into such smouldering oblivion as that to which she cast the written pages, she began to drag them falteringly from memory, recalling anxiously each scattered and escaping phrase. And they returned in a new garb of insignificant inflection; with tired petulance she tried to rob them of it, to reclothe them in true habits of inherent emphasis—in vain. Her eager repetition unintentionally stripped—re-dressed them, twisted them to meaningless, contorted sounds; nor could she give them simple automatic utterance and reproduce the dispassionate accuracy of the written lines. They were effectually destroyed, bereft of individual shape and import; as her miserable senses seized, they smeared them with unchosen tints and fingered them into unnatural form, till thus to keep, she found, was utterly to lose—and lost they were. She made a final effort to retain them, snatching the flyleaf from the book beside her and tracing the remembered signs with trembling care. This task completed, she reviewed it by the wavering light and it sealed failure. The words once indicative of preternatural life had already fronted her like death, but now they suffered further change, shewed putrefaction, and there as re-set forth by her own hand she saw them, shuddering at the discoloured and dismembered characters of love. Her face twitched and she made a movement to consign this page also to the fire; then she desisted, rent it into fragments and crumpling them into tiny specks, watched them flutter to the floor.

Thus the last shreds of treasured life lay round her; she put up a hand again and felt the sluggish action of unwilling animation crucifying her to life. How long, she wondered, must release still tarry? Once more she closed her eyes, but not to slumber, rather to more acute perception of the faintly broken stillness.

The latch clicked, and a woman entered, shaking off the snow that clung about her before she unfastened a sprinkled cloak and held it to the fire.

She was tall, in age about forty; her features were hardened, sternly cut: it was a curious likeness that announced her kinship with the dying girl, one not of lineament but bearing; a fine link of posture joined them and proclaimed one blood. Her hands bore evidence of toil and bled in lines cut by the frost. She dropped the cloak, left it to steam upon the fender and glanced uncritically at the apparently sleeping form.

'Has father been in?' She asked at length, but not to test her sister's assumed oblivion.

The girl kept closed eyes and offered no reply. The oppressive stillness touched at last, she half involuntarily feigned slumber to enjoy without participation in it any assuaging sound, and sensuously relieved, lay still.

The elder woman launched no further question, but stooped and picked up the scraps of paper strewing the hearth and rescued the linen sheet which had slipped down, from glowing cinders, replacing it across the arm of the low chair.

A heavy foot struck against the door; she went to open it, then closed it quietly upon the biting air. It admitted a huge white personage who seemed to take at once a vigorous possession of the frail chamber, dashing away the night that bound him with great gestures of easy power. Becoming aware of the chair's pale occupant, he modified his gigantic movements and deep vibrating voice, and asked if she were asleep. His daughter raised her eyebrows at the query, while he regarded the motionless girl with a pained and puzzled frown. His glance was impatient but solicitous; the feebleness of her attitude irked and probed him; weakness was too alien and abhorrent to his nature to induce compassion, it fretted, perplexed him like a foreign face and unfamiliar tongue. The woman standing beside him noted and diverted his troubled thought, saying: 'You'll have about forgot your supper?'

He seated himself heavily by the table, which tottered as his arm fell upon it, and stretched his gaitered legs across the hearth.

'I have about', he answered moodily, 'but that's not to be thinking of another. What's the hour?'

The clock's hand pointed some way after ten. He muttered 'Late', and plunged his hand into a deep pocket, and drew out a draggled heap of feathers, flung down a wet and huddled partridge, saying, 'Here'.

She picked up the bewildered bird now further dazed by the hypnotic light, and said, attempting pleasantry: 'It's brave work poaching a night like this—but fair game I suppose.'

'There were two of 'em', he recounted in a rumbling undertone, 'outside there in the open road at bottom of Palmer's Lane. I caught sight of a black speck at my feet and closed my fist on it, went a step on and there rose its mate—flew straight up from the snow before I'd time to know it or there'd have been a brace for you.' He leaned across and took it from her, caught its neck in a firm grip and briefly ended the creature's stupefied, dishevelled life. He threw it down and passed his foot over the damp and laid-down feathers. 'How the light scares 'em! Well the dark out there came nigh to dauntin' me. You are just in? It's late enough and time we put the night behind us. I'm for sleep.'

He bent down to unbutton his long leggings with big frozen fingers, and unlaced his clogged boots, from which the snow dropped in hard lumps that soon began to melt and make little streams along the clean brick floor.

The cat uncurled itself from slumber, crept down from its place, and casting first a furtive glance at the dead bird upon the hearth, viewed him with an apprehensive stare. Uttering a racy expression of dislike, he seized it by the tail and threw it with a certain humorous brutality over the table towards the door. It fell crouching to a dark corner and slunk off into an inner room, sending backward ere it disappeared green gleams of enmity and fear.

'Why do you let her keep the brute about her?' he demanded, rising and lifting the door that opened to the stair.

The woman followed and faced him with relenting features. 'Perhaps—because—' She paused and shivered.

'You mean', he said roughly, concluding her divined but unanticipated answer, 'because I have kept other—brutes away?'

Assenting, she pointed to her sister's hueless, inhumanly reposeful face, as it shone out now into the darkening chamber, disclosed by a spasmodic leap of flame.

He took a step forward as if to rouse her, seemed to prepare, then suddenly reject some blundering speech, finally shook his head and turned away. He laid a great hand across his eyes, and waited, his finger on the latch, then ventured doubtfully—'She'll weather it?'

His daughter took her eyes from the girl's face and passed a crooked finger up and down her tingling hand.

He grasped her violently by the shoulder. 'You think not?' he said.

She bent her head and shut the words away.

'She'll—die—then,' he persisted hoarsely, his voice regaining pitch.

A hand was lifted towards her mouth, as a whisper gave his words emphatic echo.

He clenched a tremendous fist in agony or anger, as against will, from quivering lips, his soul's belief came through. 'It's damnable—it's better so.'

A burning drop fell on his wrist and on his ears an asseveration bespeaking a more scorching woe. 'Better—I know it—I believe it too.'

He slackened his hold of her, and slid two huge fingers slowly down her arm, accepting her admission with a pacified but heavy sigh; then lifting the latch at last, he let the door swing after him; in another moment his massive tread shook the room ominously, but it soon subsided, and once more the place was still.

The woman moved about quietly, straightening the room. She reached down a cup and plate to put upon the table in preparation for a spare meal at dawn; went to the window and dislodged neatly with her maimed fingers the snow that clung about the panes; opened the casement and swept off the drifts outside. The shutters frozen to the outer wall resisted her attempts to pull them to, and so she left them, closed the casements and began to readjust the room. This done, she knelt by the hearth, beginning to rake out the dying fire.

Her sister stirred: she paused and met the languid glance that fell upon her from those half open and unslumbrous eyes. 'Oh, let that be,' the girl begged eagerly. 'I am not going up to bed. I shall stay here awhile. I'm tired of darkness—and last night our room was icy. I felt dead—knew myself laid out frozen in my grave.' The memory evoked a shudder. She went on: 'The blaze keeps off such dreams. You're tired—cold—go then, and I'll creep up when you are warmer. If you wake and miss me—if it's very late—you knock. I'll not be sleeping. Have you made fast the door?'

'It's fast enough. There'll be no soul about this cruel night.'

'None but the visitor you're looking for,' the girl mused quietly, 'and he smiles at such temperate bitterness. I can almost hear him laugh at the biting blackness of the room upstairs, although I shrink at it. He'll find me warm,' she added, smiling cheerlessly and laying a shrunken palm of ice upon her sister's cheek. 'He'll find these fingers well-nigh burning when he reaches them—so ghastly cold is he.'

'You're worse,' was the impulsive comment.

'No, I'm better, if I'm nearer rest.'

The woman with hard eyes and mouth got up and smote her hands together: twice she essayed to frame a question, but it died upon reluctant lips. At length, unwillingly, she framed it, stammering, 'If he—?'

The girl threw an arrestive arm out. 'You're wild,' she cried. 'He—he's not here. He—is forgotten. I've kept no word of his, nor touch, to take into eternity with me, and if I met him there, truly, I should not know him, such is the strangeness of his face. He's gone,' she said more soberly, 'the lover you've denied me, as surely as I'm going with the colder mate you've chosen. Tell my father this; it's well that he should know.'

She lifted inconsolate eyes to the lined, set face above her and it was gazing down, scanning her piteous glance with ruthful gravity. Her sister stood there still, solemnly conscious of her office, pledged to slay, before that appointed victim in whose destiny her own was sealed. Discerning their mutual doom, these women found each other's hands and clung together; but for a moment, then one drew hers hurriedly away and stepped quickly into the inner room to fetch some logs, which she placed carefully upon the dying fire. This done, again she hesitated, tried to speak, but failing, she turned and mounted wearily to bed. The loose latch of the stairway door slipped after her; she left it, vaguely hoping that the half-open way—the tiresome swing—of the unfastened door, might decoy upward the loth watcher, left behind.

The logs cast heaving upon the sinking fire, obscured its glow. A candle lit and left upon the table now began a fluttering contest with extinction; its flame flagged round the socket weakly, was sucked in, exhausted, and anon with feeble energy flared up again. The light glared raggedly, a struggling speck in the now sombre room.

The motionless spectator watched this spark lifting its futile protest against death, flashing its pitiably impotent and shifting eyes towards the steady gaze of conquering dark. At last the wretched gleam sprang upward with wild weakness, strove palely, dropped and died; and in that ending, she descried her own, felt the last flicker of her soul's expended light. What if the hand which lit that taper—left it burning—was once the guardian of a flame so true? That hand forsook, her heart affirmed. She moaned, threw out her arms; but space itself seemed hardly hers, she felt herself beyond it, a lost being whose whole utterance and movement could find no range or echo in the external world. This sickness frightened her, she flung it off. Had she forgotten him? It might be so, but as the soul forgets its prisoning flesh at the dread moment of their severance, shrinking with shuddering instinct from the thing it is to part from, losing all grasp and vision as it is rent away, of those lit chambers, those warm welcomes and untiring beauties of its doomed receding home.

Again the stillness became insistent, awful, isolating, like some accursed cell in which pent creatures cry and beat themselves against unechoing and non-resistant walls. She yielded, being past combat and defenceless, to the leagued powers of torture which beset her, and soon grew stuporously regardless of the unmarked hours, tasting at intervals a more assured oblivion in brief snatches of starting, restless sleep.

From one of these the clock aroused her with its laborious stroke, and stirring, she wakened to the darkness which seemed closing round her, bearing down upon her like a stealthy and surrounding foe. Her eyes were blinded by it, her arms pinioned, its murky poison clogged her throat. That soundless prison chamber then was not inviolate, for now within it, she lay captured, some grim, unseen, unheard intruder's prey.

Escape became a question and a prayer. Both were to be simply answered. Blackness, hideous and unpitying, bound her. Freedom stood—she saw it plainly—beckoning, awaiting her, outside in that vast universe of snow. She rose, swayed forward, and the sheet, her discarded work, clung round her feet entangling them; she stooped and caught it up. This too had a hue defying darkness! She wound it round her, twisting, at the instinctive action, her lips into a smile. Warily she unlatched the door to meet the night's wild greeting, her heart leapt towards that stinging welcome, flakes rushed down, melted upon her face and came again, and to these chill mysterious and persistent kisses what caress could mortal lips return? She offered none, accepting with serene delight the prodigal endearments of this chance encountered wooer, holding her frail palms outward, dallying with ere yielding to a quick desire to bare her breast. The icy air lashed it with glorious rigour; whose was this exquisitely smiting hand? Not surely his whom she had named ungently as her only and appointed fate. Could such a touch be that of death the undesired, with whom blind mortals were so unprepared to mate? She laughed incredulously at the menaces of the past night's poor masquerading traitor, here his prototype and master stood, a veritable king! She owned him, she was his exultantly, she tasted at his bidding unsurpassable and unsuspected life. She stood there awed by restoration, waiting the vision of that mighty spirit which summoned her own from non-apparent to transcendent being. This sudden strange renewal of physical and mental vigour seemed marvellously to remake or re-create her soul. Its dubious powers sprang into assertive being, its furtive impulses gathered prevailing force; it was no longer, as it once had been, a faint recipient of light; it had become itself a spark, a strong emittent ray; passive reflectiveness gave place to actual fire. Vitality astounded her as she experienced it in this stupendous, nascent self. Life held her thrall no more to its tyrannical demands, but reared itself in her a native and despotic power to which all worlds must bow. She breathed now not to meet claims but to make them, and standing there upon the threshold of new being, quiveringly omnipotent, looked forth.

Here too, the night was black, but unperceiving, she conceived its whiteness, gladdening her unseeing eyes with the imagined vista of that glistening and far-reaching tract of snow.

Slowly a consciousness of presence stole upon her quickened senses, and she waited, certainly expectant of some imminent apparition, presaged, undefined. Its herald was a far speck of light travelling low towards her, now seen, now shrouded, moving surely on. At length it showed the vague outline of an approaching figure, and her heart in one quick throb announced that indistinguishable form's identity. She waited on and tranquilly received him, withholding greeting, when as he gained her they stood face to face, sending opposing channels of warm breath into the frozen air.

A hush surrounds this meeting: muteness curtains it: in heaven when parted spirits near each other, angels still their voices, turn their dazzling looks aside, lest answering eyes be missed in radiance, answering tones in melody, and seeking souls slip past each other in the unfamiliar street.

At length she drew him in and spread from the now ignited wood a vigorous blaze about the room. As by that light his eyes beheld her his lips let loose a cry; he started and stepped forward to snatch away the cloth that wrapped her like a shroud. She stayed him, drawing it more closely round her, while from above her face looked out at him through the veil of shifting brilliance hung before it by the appearing flames; behind that pervious golden screen it shone with an unborrowed lustre, transfigured and instinct with power, bathed in the glory of her great rebirth. Towards it he raised groping eyes, and opened groping arms. Reaching out the frail structure of her hand, she caught his fingers—interlaced them in her own; swayed by that detaining touch, he shuddered, for the unsubstantially compelling contact seemed to advance no mortal claim. This man, turning a wondering glance upon the wraith of her he came to seek, was baffled and stood marvelling whither the being tangibly desired was fled; what shadow mocked its absence in the familiar stranger's form. He was as one who, dreaming, journeys forth to lop a branch off some long known and standing tree, when reaching the spot that once it tenanted, he finds only a weird shadow of its unseen boughs dancing upon the grass, cast there from whence he knows not; for these shining and victorious eyes disowned the dim and timorous light that her remembered glance had shed; nor did this unearthly but unflinching hold hint of past touches wont to impress denial and implore release.

The things and thoughts of earth attended him, assiduously aiding his bewilderment; they stood aloof from her, and almost ready for departure: she seized one ere all took irrevocable flight, putting a question to him, which he answered straightly: 'No—not—free—.'

'I'm nearer light than you,' she said with a half-jesting touch of pride, a certain scorn-tinged tenderness. 'I see no fetters, and my sight is free—no windows and no mists obstruct it—it is strong and shuns no glare.' She pushed back gently from her forehead obscuring threads of snow-wet hair and added softly: 'It's a far dawn I see, the breaking of an unmysterious day. Tonight we'll speak although we've never spoken. Smile, for it's our first meeting. Look at me.'

'Your face is strange. My God!' he cried. 'And thus it is they've saved you—how—and from what—from—Me—?'

'From life', she said, 'and I've been dying of salvation.'

'Oh, save your life,' he pleaded, stammering, astounded.

She pursued steadily: 'My life is come; it is not to be missed for ever, but time's short, and though life's here, breath's failing. See, be speedy, I am not to meet eternity unowned.'

With a gesture determinately potent he flung off this barely comprehended plea.

She did not note the deprecation, ending: 'So you have come for me.'

These words evoked a half-suppressed negation. 'I came', he said, 'because the world was white, white like the waste through which tonight I travelled—colourless—soundless—clogged; everything wore the same wan shade, voices were muffled, landmarks gone. There was but one thing audible and recognizable in the wide earth, one thing alone life-painted, speech-endowed. Dazzled, possessed and deaf, what wonder if I fled towards it—though to you.'

She passed a hand across her face and about her person still fantastically draped and said: 'This other world of yours since you forsook it, wears—look here—pale cheeks, pale lips, pale heart—the self-same hue.'

He reiterated: 'Yes, the self-same hue.'

'I have seen', she told him, 'both life's endlessness and brevity, each morning waking to a world of nothingness, it loomed before me, limitless and stationary, a cursed eternity of stagnant hours. There was no end to them; they were impassable, unpassing and unpassed. Yet I felt neither fear nor wonder, solely dull torment, when life stopped at dawn, but night revealed it visible in motion, night indeed brought terror, when rushing past my bed like spectres, lank, all of one stature, swift, unstayed, unstaying, I *saw* the days go by. A chained and doomed spectator of this alternating tragedy, I died regarding it, and waiting for dissolution—anguished—forgot you.' She paused. 'Tonight, I tasted resurrection, ere you came—now stand beyond my grave and claim you ere eternity claims me.'

Her voice was curiously clear—a cloudless voice, he thought, taking the tones of that bright distance upon which her eyes were set.

The man walked to the window, laid his head against the snow-outlined panes. He felt forsaken, helpless, even like a child who has run home for comfort and being greeted on the threshold by an alien presence, must make fitting answer to the unforeseen advances of a beautiful but fearsome guest. He had come seeking the balm of gentleness and not this smarting strength; he had meant perhaps to pray, and here confronted him in place of wavering answer, absolute demand; he had thought to slake his own poor thirst, and that but sparingly, not to quench one more urgent; he had pictured this being as he left it, clothed in a trembling body, speaking a half-learned language, halting, peering and distraught amid the windings of its unconsidered way. He found it thus, erect and stationary, illumined and articulate, standing before a path at which he shrank appalled, in proud preparedness, decisive, undismayed. He listened for remembered accents, strained his eyes for well known motions and beloved lineaments—in vain. *Was this to meet the soul?* He shrank before it, covered his eyes.

She waited patiently, sharing his conflict with an exquisite compassion, which the consciousness of its triumphant issue could not mar. She looked upon him with a regained face of childhood, sweetly troubled; maturer lines grew faint, faded as noon to twilight, till the clearness and the calm of morning reached her brow; its freshness overspread her features; its quiet mystery masked them. She diffused its cool thin air. Night hung behind her, and before her rose a new unsetting sun whose earliest rays lent her a loveliness unearthly and indeed divine.

The man stayed motionless: these two awaited like the waiting dead their summons from mortal to immortal fate.

At length his eyes unclosed and he advanced protestant. Combat was impossible, he and this being were not matched. The inspired force that fronted him challenged no meaner power. Almost disembodied now the soul before him seemed to stand; its overmastering majesty annihilated thought, and as he paused regarding it, his own flesh shrank to consciousness, seeming to fall away.

Met thus, they breathed perhaps; so spirits breathe, hardly on earth as they, panting for lighter air. He felt his manhood like a garment cling about him, shrouding but following no line of the real creature's veritable shape. And she who faced him was apparelled beautifully but unfitly (to his now piercing thought) in a too obviously distinctive human form.

It was towards no woman, rather towards his blessed doom that he at last lifted acceptant arms and uttered his assenting cry.

This was surrender: for the moment it confounded her; confusedly she claimed him; first almost as a savage beast its prey; then like an angel seizing guardianship of its appointed soul; and finally like a once imprisoned but now liberated human spirit pressing towards its inevitable mate.

The moment passed and left them in the opening arms of peace.

The lantern left on the table, by the gutted candle, had gone out. She stooped, rescued and untwisted one of the paper fragments on the hearth, slid up the glass and quietly rekindled it, saying: 'We shall need this.'

Then casting to the floor the white thing wound about her, she stepped over it and across the room to take from a peg a cloak that hung drying by the door. As she began to wrap it round her the action was arrested by a sound from the room above. She listened; it was repeated; by a quiet signal she replied, and waited, watching the stairway door. Soon a creaking descent was audible as unshod feet crept down. The door swung forward and the entry framed a half-clad and enquiring figure which cast a sleep-dazzled look around the room. It rested first on the two occupants, then travelled beyond them to the re-lit lantern which suggested even to the half-awakened thought immediately their projected flight.

The man ventured forward but a forcibly repellent gesture thrust him back. This woman would deal solely with her own, she turned towards the girl in passionate and inarticulate appeal. The women faced each other and their glances met, both unflinching, one sternly suppliant, bespeaking ruthless love; the other, undismayed, pellucid; calm with infancy's immutable repose. Wilder and stronger grew the anguished invocation and more serenely negative the answer to that prayer. Rejection bent not, broke not, nor could it touch that staunch solicitation, so emphatically speechless; warning, exhausted urgency, antagonism and illimitable tenderness alternated, met and mingled in that inalienable look. As if to quell it with an indubitable No, the girl beckoned her lover, bade him wrap the cloak about her. He obeyed, and they stood ready for departure, combating recall.

The figure in the doorway stirred, uttered a threatening moan and raised detaining arms.

A smile rebuked her, an illumined glance so radiant that she scanned vainly those transfigured features to identify them with the creature whom it was her purpose to deny. She saw this being whose first steps were measured from her arms, first slumbers taken on her breast—anew. Swiftly and magically she reviewed the subtle touches time had set upon those lineaments, figuring to herself succeeding imprints, cancelled or indelible as she had seen them vanish and appear; but never, in the face of child or maiden or in that later countenance of wan premonitory death had lurked the promise of this look.

Two disciples, she recollected, once encountering a risen Lord, had failed to greet Him: now pursuing the involuntary thought, she doubted whether, met by the wayside, this changed creature of her heart, had won 'Good-day'. The steady brilliance shed from that smile so suddenly upon her dwelt deep in memory, nor forsook it till life's end. Dazed by it now, she saw imperfectly the two dark figures move towards the outer door. Ere they gained it she had sprung towards them, and flung herself before it, resolute and cold.

The clock which had been ticking on monotonously, suddenly stopped and left the place intensely still. Speech seemed a forgotten power to the sharers of this silence; they stayed mute, as if attendant on some external mandate which should decide the issue of their fate. Its temporary arbitress, whose strong, uncovered arm was stretched across the door, grew conscious, as the minutes passed, of some constraining power, which was rendering her desperately impotent. Did this oppose, she meant to meet it, were the withstanding power divine.

She raised her eyes; they fell relentlessly upon her sister's stirless form. The girl stood upright, with her head held back resting against the window-frame, her eyelids closed. Her figure was almost in shadow, but her cheeks, fitfully outlined by the uncertain flames, showed a grey pallor, and her scarcely parted lips prefigured everlasting sleep. Wearily, as if to support or spare an overweighted body, her arms were crossed upon her breast, nervelessly clutching a fragment of her gown.

The plea of those inconscious arms, had they but dropped or shifted, must have failed, but they hung patiently as if set there for ever upon a pulseless heart. Theirs was the force intangible but strenuous that wrenched unwilling fingers from the latch, that won that unwilling warder to undo the door. It was flung wide, admitting a fierce gust of wind and snow, which awakened the quiescent prisoner. Her eyes unclosed, her breast heaved welcome to this message of deliverance: and her lover caught her as she rushed blindly forward, making for the darkness. They had crossed the threshold, when he heard a harsh recall. He turned and took the lantern from the hand that held it out to him, and then they passed into the night.

The door swung back behind them; the solitary tenant of the forsaken chamber shut and fastened it and then crept shivering to the window, passing her shaking hands along the wall and framework against which the girl had leant. Thin streams of red were trickling from the cuts on them. She smeared a finger down the tingling lines. This was shame's colour streaked upon the hands whose will it was to stay those wanderers; she noted it, remembering their white road. And through the long, cold hours till dawn, deliriously the fancy haunted her, of crimson claws fastened upon a spotless spirit which prayed and strove to go on its white way.

Within the chamber still the firelight flickered and a dying glow of warmth remained to greet the loth and tardy dawn. Without the wind blew in uncertain gusts, the snow fell steadily from an invisible and murky sky. Where long roads ended drifts were planted like rocks in high curved terraces; and over the spots where danger lay was cast the same white garb that safety wore. The ponds above their thin sheet of ice were covered, indistinguishable from surrounding meadows, and the river, surface-frozen and snow-laid, had proved that night for one unwary wayfarer a winding lane of death.

Guided by their rekindled light, the lovers took their way down a wide road flanked on one side by huge banked hedges, by sloping meadows on the other, where at long intervals, like waving sentinels the great white trees were set. Three fields below, his horse, stopped by some sturdy obstacle, had been secured and left awaiting him; it was to bear, he purposed now, the weight which even thus early had begun to press too heavily upon him; but as they reached the place of respite, it was to find the beast was loose, tracelessly gone. Nothing remained to hint the manner or direction of his going, he must have strayed or been appropriated long. The girl met this discovery with improvident indifference: to her companion it conveyed dismay, for he reviewed the exhausting journey of the earlier night, its arduous and impeded paths, its dreary distance and the hardly endurable exposure to the heat-denying air. Even now they stood in the dread grasp of the unyielding elements, the snow swirled round them, the wind cut them with its sword-like breath.

Yet, 'No way but onward' shone from the serenely steadfast face of his frail comrade, as he saw it by the faint lantern gleam, against the blanched background of a supporting tree. And to that luminous asseveration his heart against itself, cried 'Aye'.

Onward it was to be for them along the loaded and encumbered lanes, and in the teeth of the bewildering storm, which dashed across their dauntless faces pledged to stem their steps, if not their purpose, with a violent disdain.

They started forth; he strove to plough at first the obstructing mass through which they had to travel, brushing the weight from each clogged foot as he went on, but soon fatigue rendered such method of advance impossible, and every step perforce grew separate, deliberately lifted, ere it could be replunged into the snow. He held the light, while with his other arm, to which she clung, he saved her dragging progress from disaster. She propelled herself unflinchingly along, with one free arm, shielding herself from, beating off the flakes which had already closed his unprotected eyes. At intervals he opened them to scan the pathway, then stung to blindness, they shut fast again. Two hours since, body and reason had declared this madly undertaken march impossible, now at its outset, limbs and mind suspended judgement, bearing him on unquestioningly, despite the burden at his side. At first they tried to speak in short disjointed phrases, but the wild despot they defied soon interdicted speech, and they could only cling together unaware of actual contact, conscious of mutual aim. The vast unpitying loneliness of their environment, its awful, soundless desolation rendered the sense of union supreme; they were blent spirits, pressing or pressed onward to their goal. Did any eye behold them, it was solely His who set them in this waste, as the world apart from slumber-stricken and storm-frighted neighbours, to breathe, since they had summoned strength for it, that which He yielded them—the breath of life.

And finely mingled their souls drew it fully, while their panting bodies struggled with threatening extinction, and fought against the imminent advance of death. Physical sensation did but attack the outer wall of being: they, for the moment, were impervious to such onslaught, almost scornful of a power which might indeed destroy their citadel, but could not put a finger on the assured possessors of that place assailed. The present, or ultimate survival of their earthly frame claimed no regard from them while the strong sense of supernatural existence held its sway. How—hardly able to proceed himself—he dragged along his weary burden, he neither knew nor questioned, simply realizing that some force unknown had drawn them on thus far, in spite of awful obstacles and through the blinding and benumbing storm. After a time he stopped, and dumbly—for in the open path, speech was not possible—gave her the light. No longer capable of supporting with one exhausted arm, he placed both round her, half-propelling and half-bearing her along. Repeatedly she slipped, fell back against him, and mechanically he received the returning weight into his strained and failing arms. Hot, almost burning, but with frozen hands and feet, he bore her on; their pale exhausted faces resting sometimes against each other, oblivious of the contact, felt the stinging, almost lacerating hand that smote them, sending the snow into their ears to deafen, since it had already struck them blind and well-nigh dumb. Now they were forced backward by rebutting drifts, now driven on by the opposeless storm. On one wide road the wind threatened to lift and hurl them into the soft and slanting mass that formed the towering wall above them. There, cast resistlessly aside, swerved from his central course, where alone safety lay, he sank into an embedded trench—might there have lain, but that she flung herself upon her knees, tightened and gripped her hold and with a preternatural strength reclaimed him from this too early found, unchosen grave. As she leaned over him, half-prostrate, partially buried in the snow to raise him, he felt her long slurred fingers on him, somewhere tangible, and yet his flesh was numb, it was rather as if they slid across his soul.

He struggled upward, aided by her inexplicably summoned power, and saw from the white ledge above him, by the light, now set in a cleared space, and almost level with it—his one face. But wan it was, sharp, blanched; a dim receding vision; as their glances met a radiance broke across those mortal features, bringing them nearer, showing them clear, transparent and illumined as from within like the frail petals of a flower which the sunlight steeps. A peace unearthly decked and overspread them, as if from 'the land where all things are forgotten' it had been transplanted there. He seemed to join indeed no mortal comrade, when as he gained his rescuer, she sank back against him, bidding him with an exultant gesture—'On'.

With difficulty, once or twice sent staggering back, they gained the open path again, but at its end to be confronted by a barrier set impassably before them: this was a gate, through which their way now lay, blocked by a great corner drift which guarded it, denying ingress, like a mighty warder, incorruptible and grim. The upper bar alone was visible; a wind swept corner offered refuge; this they took, standing together in that overtaken haven wakened by calm to an amazement which the tempest could not stir. From a near ivy bush a startled thrush or blackbird flew off into the darkness, and this first sound, first motion, faint though it was, announced to them the hitherto unbroken stillness of their flight. They started at it, opening eyes and lips in an involuntary apprehension of external things. A questioning thought, by neither uttered, formed itself within their minds, 'Have we then hands and lips—hearts too—lost things, but ours, to be recaptured at our journey's end?'

To this vague query answer hovered distant, corporeal sense was dim. They grappled with the certainty, 'Our souls are here.'

'I cannot find myself,' he whispered, pinching his frozen features to a smile.

She met it with, 'I'm lost then; seek yourself with me.'

He turned to clasp her, but she had started forward determinedly to proceed. Baulked of the easier they made now for the open moor, but nearly beaten, with strength almost gone. A plover, somewhere disturbed, sent up a plaintive cry; a dog barked in the muffled distance. They plunged with despairing effort through the ruts unseen, treacherous and even deadly in the prevalent dark.

The small circle of light which had alone made their advancement possible could hardly guide them long. Each moment hastened its relinquishment; the falling snow had caked and frozen in the crevices of their soaked clothes and their wrists were circled by a solid band of ice. Their hands and feet were well-nigh useless, heavy, nerveless, numb. Icicles hung upon their hair, about their faces; they went decked in gemmed and glistening garments cruelly enough bestowed.

Pallid and spent, no longer conscious either of purpose or proximity, some instinct urged them forth to shelter, the first taste of which had stirred in them a hunger for it, not to be denied. Spurred by this indefinitely realized desire, they kept their course fainting and dizzy, craving but past the knowledge that they craved, relief. They stumbled insensately on, heedless of all direction, cognisant only of the few lit yards before them, and forecasting none beyond.

Now in the road again, they came upon a homestead; the gate which led to the house was open; they were hurled towards it by the wind and driven through by an imperious need of rest.

He took the light from her and weakly raised it, seeking some method of admittance. There was none. The lantern showed the broken and unshuttered windows of a deserted dwelling. Despairingly he struck the door and then fell back against it bringing down a little shower of snow. The slight concussion stimulated his confused intelligence; the hopelessness of entry soon grew obvious and he put out a hand for his companion who was clinging to a slippery trellis by the door. Together they groped round the house, leaning at each few steps against the walls.

Behind another gate showed vaguely in the blackness open. They went through it into a yard, round which the outbuildings, barely discernible in the faint light, loomed in weird masses like dense and forbidding barriers of snow. Towards one of these they staggered blindly; he tore back the sticking door and entered, giddily setting down the light. It was a large neglected building, wide, ill-roofed and high. The uneven floor was thinly powdered, bore the night's inevitable hue, the lofty beams dripped steadily melting and yet unfrozen snow, blotting in two dark lines the delicately sprinkled floor. Above the wind whizzed through the unshuttered openings, and below through many crevices blew the thin sleet into small drifts and heaps about the ground. The place was empty but for a few tattered sacks piled in one corner; these he cleared and drew her towards them, placing her gently down, then knelt supporting her, while with his almost useless fingers he tried to dislodge the snow hardening in his clogged ear. Her wet hair fell about his face and he looked down upon closed lids and frozen lashes, sending warm breath across her near blanched cheek.

Finding her stiff and icy hands he tried to chafe them, but his own were nerveless, so with poor fumbling fingers, loosening her gown, he fastened hers beneath it for the better ministry of her own faintly throbbing breast.

A blissful shadow crossed her face; all recollection of the night's wild journey had forsaken her, the sense of his beloved and everlasting presence was to be disturbed no more. She lay against him, as long ago against her lost, forgotten mother, sensible of no personality, only of safest haven and indisputable rest. The earthlier heaven of his voice and smile was merged in loftier and more massive joy.

But quickly even the dim consciousness of actual being passed: odd fancies spun around her and confused themselves with her dissolving entity, as she lay thus insentient in his arms. She felt herself borne upwards by him, piloted, sustained; they passed the clouds, she thought, leaving that whirling mass of white far far below them as they ascended to the serener realm of blue. Thus, floating on the heaven, its azure clothed them, they were one with it in hue and element; she seemed to breathe there his transmuted accents as like a whispering ether they surrounded her. Echoes of his past passion took the wind's wild sounds and rose to tempest, dropped to lullaby in this enchanted dream. The spirit's ear demands no resolution of such cadences, sung high, sung low, but bids them rather hang for ever, suspended in eternal air. As this ethereal image passed, she felt his breath recross her cheek and seemed to sway in spirit from it as if she were some soulless blossom too rudely shaken by that human breeze. Ghosts of past kisses, in this semi-consciousness, returned, and to her distempered sense, seemed to descend like blasting rain upon the petals of her fancied being, which were too frail she found, must droop beneath it, shrivel and decay. Laid prone by it, she seemed to be, as on some damp garden bed; but now this beaten flower of self was rescued by him, held in the safe keeping of his hand. Oh, might she die, in this warm refuge, nor be reset upon that swaying stalk where once she grew!

Her spark of life burned low; still in his hand she seemed to lie, still fancifully dwindled, now to no flower's likeness, but to a bird's, which captured there, beat pinions to be free. An agony of baffled flight possessed her—an instinctive need to soar—her spirit struggled with it and her eyelids quivered; she freed her prisoned hands and flung them out as if to rise.

Around her on the whitened ground were tiny creatures, truly fledged and yet more positively earthbound. Just by her feet a starling and a robin stiffly motionless, were visible, and scattered about within the lantern's glowing, and out in the darkness, their little dead companions lay.

He pointed her opened eyes towards them, but these had looked their last upon the obvious things of earth, and peered beyond, piercing the dimness to that farther dawn, the breaking of that 'unmysterious day'.

Her gaze affrighted him. She dropped her arms, shut eyes again, seeming to be, despite those lowered lids, still gazing at the persistent vision now behind the veil of sleep.

But slumber and death in this strange night were one, wearing one face, wielding one sceptre, straightening mortals to one grave: and knowing this he wrenched himself and his dear burden upwards from the beguiling ground and propping her against a supporting wall, began to kiss with frantic vehemence her eyes and lips and hair, and incoherently to frame words of awakenment and warning; but he was voiceless, smitten speechless by the strickening storm. His lips moved helplessly, no sound came from them, yet as he tortured them to utterance, he seemed to hear the shout they would have lifted striking the silence with her name, until it filled the place with strong discordance, invoking weird echoes of entreaty, which, like spirit cries, rang out from every corner of the deserted dark.

She stirred as if audibly mute, this conclamation reached her, sent from that world to which she was so near, and lifting her lids again she met his glance, stared vaguely at the contorted motions of his mouth.

Her doors of sense were just ajar, ready to shut, but swaying ere they closed.

The deadly spells of sleep must not steal over her. He snatched her from them, drawing her closely to him and dragging her with painful force up and down the long dark space. And as they staggered to and fro they smeared a jagged path of black across the fairy lawn of snow. His utmost strength was ebbing, soon his guidance failed, he swerved, sank to the ground with her and there they crouched together, he frenziedly rocking her from that importunate and fatal slumber which had crept dangerously near him too.

Each moment he grew number and more numbly conscious of their peril. Had they passed, he wondered dully, lifetimes in this benighted haven, must it prove their final home? This possibility provoked new effort; he beat off the awful languor that possessed him, forced open heavy and reluctant eyes, compelled his weighted limbs to action, cried his heart courage for a last conflict with affronted nature, strove to rise, but sick and partly stupefied, fell back again. Quite stirless his companion lay; his hand was tangled as he tried to save himself, in the damp meshes of her hair. He knelt to free it and looked down upon the face for which those tresses formed a pillow; still it wore the shadow of its first serene decision and once more nerved by this imperative resolve, this speechless statement of her undying purpose, he gained inspired strength and raised her, and with his burden reached the door.

The light gleamed in the empty place behind them, keeping the vigil of the tiny unmourned dead. The lovers left it there, bidding farewell to darkness, and went forth into the dawn.

The snow had ceased, the frost edged sharply the thin morning air. The sky above was grey, the world beneath it deeply white, the wind had mercifully fallen and they now contended only against impeded paths and the descending hand of death. That paused benignly over them, with a forbearing tenderness which they ungraciously forgot. For they were haunted by no phantoms of defeat; had thought been theirs, it must have been strung to the pitch of victory, tuned to the song of consummation: thought was not.

To her one power alone remained; a last surviving instinct urged her steps miraculously on. Lost to all sense but this one of immediate and inevitable motion, she retained it, held it as the dying hold their earnest of desired life. Desire in her had long since yielded up its breath, but the force born of it was not yet ready to succumb.

The man sustaining her might now have led her backward, borne her at will along the travelled roads; she could not halt, might not, no matter whence they went, be stayed.

Now in the glimmering dawn, despite the shrouded landmarks, the way lay clear before them, wide and unwinding beneath the slowly lightening sky. Down the long highroad, blots, now and then appeared emerging from the mist towards them, gradually growing definite as trudging figures early called to labour, who as they passed gaped curiously at this strange, staggering pair, who met their mild amazement with such drawn and ghastly faces of indifference, and seemed to greet them with the dazed and awful glances of the dead.

The wanderers neared deliverance; the end of their wild journey rose before them rearing grey towers of welcome into the grey sky.

Another farther dwelling-place there is, whither we press with failing vision and suspended breath, the way to which lies open too, in the cold twilight of the dawn. This way was theirs, but they were first to reach their nearer goal.

And it was gained. The gates of it were decked in whiteness, and the trees hung high a diamond canopy, the road was spread with hueless splendour, but for no earthly bridal and by no earthly hand. The entrance to the wide avenue was open, the birds above were waking, uttering their first sharp calls. No other living thing was stirring, the long lower windows were unshuttered but quite dark, no light gleamed from the upper range of casements, and no smoke ascended into the freezing sky.

The massive place was undisturbed and silent—a broad abode of rest.

Was it no sight for mortal eyes, this of the bridegroom bringing home his bride? At least no man beheld it, and no purer spirit veiled its face.

The spent triumphant traveller bore his burden in insensitive and anguished arms up a short winding path, no longer faltering but stepping steadily with a last energy of pain.

A little door admitted them to a dim passage; through it he went on into a vast dawn-lighted hall, round which the long low casements let in patches of the feebly approaching day. Aloft loomed a gigantic window studded with faintly luminous devices and richly tinted shields. Through one of its high open panes a bird flew in and circled bewildered round the shadowy vaulted roof above.

From the dark walls, cased in their tarnished frames, austere and passionless spectators looked sternly down upon this unanticipated entrance, questioning an alien's right to sanctuary upon their kinsman's breast. He threw a glazed but reigning glance upon their deposed arrogance, then turned his failing eyes towards the form that pressed against his hardly beating heart. She lay within his lowered arms profoundly quiet, her upturned face detaining the last flicker of a long lit smile. It paused about the rigid lids, upon her stiffening mouth, rested serenely on her pallid brow, 'No way but onward', still inscribed upon it—though she had passed him on the way.

A deadly faintness overcame him and he panted painfully for breath, gazing through gathering obscurity, striving to frame reclaiming words. They found no outlet, vainly his soul prompted utterance and he bade his lips obey.

Baulked thus, but master of a stronger speech he stooped and sought stark lips which whitened irresponsive. Aghast, he started backward, raised affrighted arms, and from that loosened grasp, she fell, her straying tresses circling round his feet. He would have rescued her, but life, and life's control were hardly his; sight had forsaken him, his limbs ignored the dazed imperfect mandate of his will.

Tottering, breathless, still he fought for speech, seeking the final succour of a cry. Denied it, as he struck in pitiful despair the obdurate portals of his lips, some compensating angel flung wide the windows of his vision, bade him see.

And he beheld, there at his feet, 'pale lips, pale cheeks, pale heart', his own white world again; and white he saw a world beyond the window, the wild and snow-clad waste, through which they came; and still beyond the winter dawn another, whiter yet, stainless, celestial, that towards which unerringly they journeyed, hers now and the next moment to be his—but one step further, almost gained—in sight.

ELINOR

MY SISTER and I were orphans and without kin. Our mother I never knew and my father I remember only faintly as stern and chill, a dread and shadowy figure moving across my childhood—a kind of visible witness to the stillness of our early life.

He died within a week of the famous victory off Trafalgar. This I remember because of my sister's saying: 'England mourns her hero—I mourn no smaller soul, although none misses him but me. You, child, never knew your father; his country scorned him, but he was great.'

After his death, the room where they had sat and studied together was never entered save by her. His books were there, ranged round the walls—a gloomy company—and as a child I thought his spirit lived there too: never at night, without a cold and clinging terror could I pass alone the door of that shut chamber. Even on summer mornings, when the birds were singing round our lonely house, it seemed to scorn their clamour and crave a quiet it could not compel.

But Elinor, as she went down in the early dawns, would always enter, to hold—I could not but believe—some strange communion with the dead. Little in life was dear to her, but that which claimed her heart was cherished with an intense and concentrated passion which found no utterance but silently possessed her soul.

She was my only teacher—as my father had been hers. From her I learned to scan the heavens and mark the courses of the stars; to reverence—above God—the earth, which was, she said, the only Deity before which man might bow. My childish eyes were dazzled with wild pictures of unknown and distant lands, peopled with savage creatures and unmolested by humanity, where nature's voice and nature's spirit might be heard and felt alone. Such scenes she chose with which to crowd my dreams; or sometimes, in the firelight, crouched beside her knee, I listened to queer goblin tales of still remoter regions, worlds which her own weird phantasy created, depicted with a marvellous and eerie power.

If ever by look or gesture I betrayed disturbance, she would pause and look with a troubled wonder into my face upturned to hers in infantine dismay. Then, taking my hand, her voice, losing the magic ring which such recitals lent it, would become compelling, while she drove determinedly away the things which most she hated—frailty and fear.

One night I vividly recall—a night of mingled rest and horror, still potent to awake sensations which have passed away.

The wind was howling round our desolate dwelling, wreathing the walls with dreary music, such as might spring from wandering forsaken spirits driven from their dark homes into a world which once they knew but now knew them no more.

I stood by the hearth of our firelit kitchen—where then we always sat—waiting for Agatha, our old and only servant, to fetch me up to bed. But she called down to me from a chamber overhead, bidding me come as it was growing late. 'Miss Jean, Miss Jean.' I heard the summons plainly and could not nerve my feet to take that solitary journey up the stair: but when my sister's voice broke in—a voice not to be disregarded—I dare not linger, so casting a wistful glance at the kind glow behind me, I crept up, shivering and fearful, planning to pass quickly and boldly my father's shut, mysterious door.

But it was open, and the moaning wind swept through. I clutched the stair-rail while my fascinated gaze was fastened on the entrance. Across the long low room beams of bright moonlight strayed. I stood before the threshold, powerless to pass it, my eyes fixed first upon the chequered floor. Travelling from thence, they were confronted by a vision—faint but awful—and I saw a figure, white and indistinct but unmistakable, stretched across my father's dimly outlined chair. A cry burst from me. I stayed, paralysed, helplessly shrieking, gazing, while the wind mingled its weary calls with my affrighted cry. A dark form suddenly sprang forth shrouding the figure in the chair, casting a shadow on the silvered floor. It came towards me and I fell half senseless—not oblivious of the horror which thrilled like a freezing current through my blood. A darkness followed; then I found myself shaking and dazed upon my sister's bed, and felt her strong, assuring hands on mine.

'What ails you, Jean?' she asked.

I told her and she listened with a sombre frown.

'The thing you saw was not your father's wraith', she said, 'only some cloth which I left in the room this morning—meaning to sew. The moonlight and your disordered fancy conjured it into shape and terror. Go down now—handle it—and see.'

Her will was stronger than my dread—her words conveyed no reassurance. I was still struck, possessed, but dare not disobey. She lifted and led me to the door, set me on the dark staircase, and I staggered down, uttering sharp, disjointed cries, feeling such throes as death cannot renew. I reached, or think I reached, the door. I knew no more. When I gained consciousness again it was past midnight, and I was in my sister's arms—a light was burning in the room. At first she soothed me with silent close caresses, but when I tasted calm, she spoke. On earth, in heaven, even in hell, she said, there dwelt no thing to merit fear. What if the spirit that I thought I saw were there—such beings, if they hovered near, came but to those they loved and not to fright us. All fearful shapes were fashioned from within and conjured by our fear. I whispered how the wind seemed full of direful voices—what were they?

'Not what you think'; she said, 'but if they were, would you not pity rather than dread their fruitless anguish? Out on the wastes tonight the leafless trees are swaying: well, if I watched them—distant in the moonlight—might I imagine them forsaken souls; but I should only long to still their wretched utterance, point them to some victorious peace. There is, my little Jean, no terror in life or death but that which lurks within the weak, unconquered soul of man. Conquer that soul and it will never mar your rest.'

I slept and woke to winter sunlight. As we went down, she took my hand and paused before the open door. We entered. 'Do you remember how we talked last night?' she asked. I said I did.

'Always remember it,' she said.

Such was my sister: and since it is her story that I tell, I need ask no indulgence for this recollection as it comes back to me.

It was a lonely life we led. Our home was situate in the midst of a wild country: no other dwelling-place stood near it, and the village lay some miles away.

We had no friends—my sister made none. I did not miss companionship; she was sufficient—all in all to me. She had one faithful and unfailing comrade—a large retriever dog called Rodney after the great commander, and this animal was dearer—nearer than any living human thing. She loved him and he understood the heart with which he had to do as I could not. Though I never doubted her affection, she appeared reticent, aloof and cold, and seemed, as I grew up, to draw from some mysterious source a life I could not share. I knew she studied, knew she thought, but what reflection filled her silent hours, what task induced her solitary vigils—that I did not know. Often at night, if I were restless, I rose and sat by my window watching the light that hers sent forth, for company; yet what, within the neighbouring room, that taper viewed, I wondered but could not divine. Sometimes it burned far on into the night; yet morning found her fresh and tranquil, with a serene though pondering brow.

When Agatha grew too old for the harder household duties, Elinor claimed them. She, too, it was who tended our scanty garden, where, in the shadow of bleak hills, few flowers would blow. She dug and planted, tending each stunted shrub, noting each puny blossom, with devoted care.

The cloud and sunshine of my sister's face, in those remembered days, painted the face of life for me.

When I was old enough to bear the long walk across the moors, Agatha begged to take me with her to the Church, where there was service once a fortnight. For my mother's sake, she urged, it was not seemly I should learn no more than heathen knew.

Elinor heard the plea; such teaching was to her poor mockery, and she disclaimed it.

'But, it was not within my power', she said to me, long afterward, 'to choose for you. All souls are free. If they make shipwreck it is upon the shifting sands of their own darkness. Many lights there are—I cannot say which you must see.'

Once, in a book of hers, I found a slip of paper covered with her cramped writing. I have it still, and shudder, as I read the lines which set so clearly forth the faith that made her earthly pilgrimage so cheerless and clothed the conflict of her death with darkness, such as few mortals know.

'Man shapes his destiny alone,' so run the characters she traced. 'No deity surveys his work. He alone sanctions his own slavery or wrests his spirit free. His only foe is weakness and his sole failure fear. His soul is bound with curious chains; they are of many fashions—finely forged—ofttimes invisible until they scar: the cruellest, pride; the subtlest, suffering, and the deadliest—that which caressing while it strangles—men call love. Surely if Satan lived, this passion were the essence of his person; so does it wreck and rend the stunted powers of mankind.'

I hoped that time would bring her gentler musings, and wondered —not I hope presumptuously—how He regarded her—that unknown Master—whose ministry she would not own. And in the winter evenings, or summer twilight, when Agatha used to make me sit beside her and read aloud stray portions of the Book, that was, she said, my father's enemy—my mother's joy, I used to watch if Elinor were listening. She sat always in the long window-seat, with Rodney by her side, quietly stroking him—knitting sometimes—his head against her knee, but never heeding the sacred words, which seemed to me too great and wonderful for any mortal to pass by.

I looked eagerly forward to those alternate Sabbaths, when the monotony of life was broken. The faces pleased me and the singing; and the stir and strangeness of the droning hours were dear to me.

When I was seventeen the Rector died. He was a frail old man, who looked as if for years he had been sleeping, forgetful of his yawning grave. Despite his reverend air and famous scholarship, he was but seldom sober, and indeed they said it was in some unholy revel that he died.

He was succeeded by a Mr Perceval, who came quite young from London to the living: a fine and handsome gentleman, and rode, they said, straighter to hounds than any in the country. Not many Sundays after his arrival, we encountered in the porch. He bowed, and asked my name and dwelling, and must come, he declared, to see us in our lonely home. He rode up often, after that, but made no way with

Elinor. She listened civilly enough to his stories of the great men and painted ladies of the Court—with which he was well acquainted—but they wearied her, delighting me. It seemed incredible, I thought, that anyone could take aught but pleasure in his gay company; yet, for what reason I did not know, at length, my sister drove him from our door.

One evening they had a contentious interview which ended in his banishment. As he went out, I heard him say: 'Yet you have sympathy with wild and wayward creatures—and they pair.'

'Yes, with their kind', she said, and added—I thought harshly, 'Here, you have no licence, and you know well enough that poachers' lives are worth wellnigh as little as those of the rabbits they would snare.'

'Must I mistake you for a woman?' he questioned in a curious tone, which I had never heard him use before.

'For what you will,' she said and shut the door.

I heard him ride away and she came in.

'Are you quite happy, Jean?' she asked, 'here in your lonely home with me?' A little wonderingly, I said I was. 'Well', she declared, 'I've quarrelled with your gallant parson. He will come here no more.' I could not forbear a sigh; he had brought some brightness into dull days. I missed him; but she was wise, I knew, and also that her will was law.

The days were darker for his absence and it was winter-time—the dullest of the year. On Sundays, I caught now and then a glance from the high pulpit which somehow made me miss him more. There was no chance of speech with him, for Agatha had long since ceased to tramp the weary miles with me. Now Elinor bore me company, saying the moors were lonely and she would wait outside under the yew for me. And she was always there.

It must have been about a month after Mr Perceval's departure, that the thing happened which was to turn strangely enough, the current of our lives. It had been a day of storm; the rain all day beating against the creaking casements: the windows rattled and the driving wind which, moaning, rose at dawn, grew wilder as the dark noon gloomed to night.

Elinor, whom the fiercest elements rather delighted than dismayed, had set out for her accustomed walk across the sodden moors, in Rodney's reluctant company, but returned early, driven back by the blinding mist which was obscuring the sparse landmarks that led to our lonely home. She entered the kitchen where I sat sewing, watching the firelight play across the barely carpeted brick floor and stood before me—a tall straight figure, finely alert, her face glowing and wet, her eyes—never matched for depth and fire—burning with half-darting and half-shrouded light.

'Well, you timorous little stay-at-home', she cried looking down amusedly at me, 'we've been through Wonderland, Rodney and I. No creature's visible in the wet veiled wastes—only the trees in fairy shrouds are swaying beneath the grimmest sky. The fields are marshes and the roads are streams, but the mist's magical! That rayless world outside has nothing earthly—it makes your firelight tawdry, Jean. Come out, if only to the door with me.'

I would not, saying, it was too dreary—chilling me, heart and frame.

'It nerves me, frame and heart,' she said, flinging back some strands of damp black hair, with a gesture of remembered joy. 'Well, we are spotting your tidy floor. Come Rod' she called to the draggled beast, stretched steaming before the hearth, 'we must mend our makes and manners for the little fine lady here.'

That evening she was gay—thrilled by the raging gusts that shook our dwelling; nor would she let me read, but sat listening—musing with smiling lips upon the storm. Now and again its violence hushed our voices—we stayed silenced; during such a pause, there came a knocking at the door.

Agatha, who had been nodding in her chair, unclosed her eyes and begged us pay no heed to it. God knew, she said, what desperate visitor we might admit; but Elinor went out with an assuring smile.

Above the wind which whistled through the passage, we heard a man's voice, mingled with Elinor's in a brief dialogue. Then the door opened and she came in, followed by the benighted traveller—a man of huge proportions and splendid carriage, with a countenance that fitly matched his form.

'Come to the fire', she said; 'you will be drenched and frozen.'

He bowed a graceful acknowledgement as I made way for him, protesting: 'It is not my wish to disturb you in this fashion, but' turning to Elinor—'this lady wills it. My intrusion I fear is fruitless, she cannot direct my way.'

'No soul could point it on such a night,' she answered him. 'Across these trackless moors, you might seek till morning and be in worse plight than before. This gentleman has travelled many aimless miles', she said, 'and lost his way.'

I noticed that her glance was fixed on him; her eyes brilliantly lit, now scanned his face and person with a distant but intent regard.

'You will', she addressed him—and a note of insistence rang dominant in the simple question—'accept our hospitality tonight and wait the favour of the morning?'

'With all my thanks, I cannot,' he replied.

'Your beast is lame', she urged, 'he may meet a worse mishap if you go further. You will scarcely reach another shelter and you can find one here.' She paused. 'I think you must,' she said.

'I thank you, but I must get on.'

She stepped forward and put a hand lightly upon his sleeve, saying: 'Be guided. Wait the morning; that is best.'

He seemed to ponder, gave her a swift straight glance and yielded with a sudden smile, which found its answer somewhere in her face.

She turned to me. 'Jean, get the lantern. You will find a shed outside', she told him; 'house the poor beast there and find us here again.'

He went protesting gratitude. As the door closed behind him, Agatha rose and tremblingly confronted Elinor, her knotted shaking hands stretched out in suppliance and fear.

'Send him away', she cried; 'there was never a man slept here since the poor master died. This is no place for him—send him away, Miss Elinor, he must not stay.'

'But I have bade him stay,' she answered quietly and took the quivering palms in hers and stroked them.

'All will be well—all shall be well,' she said. 'Jean, light a fire in my father's room.'

I started; it had not been opened since he died.

' 'Tis a grave,' said Agatha.

There was no time, I agreed, to make it habitable.

'If he must stay tonight, it had best be here.'

'Then he will have my room,' she decided. 'See to that.'

I went up wonderingly to straighten it: the boards and walls were bare in that apartment; beneath the window her books were piled in musty heaps upon the floor, and on the square oak table her last night's candle burned to its socket, bore witness to many wakeful hours.

My task completed, I went down to find the stranger in earnest talk with Elinor, who sat with a protecting hand upon the arm of Agatha's low chair. The hours drew on to midnight; Agatha retired to bed. I tended and left her sleeping: still the two sat on, oblivious of the clock's admonitory chime. They spoke of things I had no knowledge of—strange heresies, the thoughts, it seemed to me, of great but sorely disordered minds; of men whose names I did not know and books of clouded and mysterious fame.

My sister's attitude amazed me; she had met this gentleman but a few hours ago, and yet she discoursed to him with a brilliant freedom which I had never heard her use to any soul before.

As I entered the second time, he turned to me and asked: 'Does your young sister share these dreams—take part with you in the great work?'

I stared bewilderedly. She answered for me.

'Surely, no. She would not countenance them. This is the Book she cherishes'— handing him my mother's Bible which had lain that night unread upon the chair.

'I see, and this—' to me, fingering a piece of dropped embroidery, 'is yours. I have ventured to admire it in your absence. The ladies of the Court, which it is my luckless privilege to haunt, would envy you such excellence.'

I took some pleasure in this unmerited praise, and begged to hear of the gay and unfamiliar world he spoke of, for it had figured often in my dreams and now he brought it near. Discarding the dreary drivel of philosophy, he told, at my desire, tales of the grand and teeming city, picturing finely the sumptuous scene. I saw, as if indeed they passed before me, the wonderful ladies in gorgeous rustling garments, with delicate painted faces and coarse manners, fingering cards, exploiting beauty, dowered with all the historic vices and unchronicled virtues of their race. He painted the Regent too—open of countenance and elegant of limb—his evil habits, his levity and fickleness, his generous freaks and mean distortions, saying he was the finest 'whip' in England; as Mr Perceval had told us too.

We sat long listening thus to such stories as he, it seemed, took as much pleasure to tell as we to hear. At length, Elinor rose. We bade our guest Good-night. She showed him to her chamber, promising that he should be waked at dawn.

She shared my bed that night. I soon dispatched myself for rest, but she seemed disinclined for slumber and sat by the window which she opened to let the rain drip on her hands resting upon the sill.

'What of our visitor?' she questioned suddenly.

'He is handsomer than Mr Perceval', I said, 'and yet I like his features less. Despite their beauty they are somewhat harsh and cold.'

'Both men are human', she commented briefly; 'there the likeness ends. This Mr Somerset should have known my father. He comes too late.'

'It is a misfortune—since he pleases you', I said, 'that, unlike Mr Perceval, he lives so far away.'

'It is no matter', she affirmed decisively, 'for "unlike Mr Perceval", he will come again.'

Nor could I doubt it when she seemed so sure.

After awhile, she made ready for rest and I lay watching the thick dark hair that swept her splendid shoulders, framing a face which any man, I thought, might well return to see.

I had always known her beautiful; but till that night, I had never marked how beautiful. She seemed suddenly, to my eyes, arrayed in a physical glory, curiously resplendent and passing words to tell. As, half-clad in the flickering light, she moved about, I lay regarding her confronted by a revelation of new loveliness, until she turned upon me those striking eyes, which shone like dark untroubled streams, salvation in their depths and in their distance the far off dimness of the stars. Noting my gaze, she asked directly as was her manner: 'You find me handsome, Jean?'

'Not handsome—rather beautiful; and grandly beautiful, I think.'

'Did Mr Perceval think me so?' she demanded quickly, adding amazement to my surprise.

'He said you were like a queen and should have had an empire, but that your people would have killed and canonized you afterwards. "I", he said, "should have been a rebel, and you, Miss Jean, a martyr, in that kingdom", but I did not catch his meaning.'

'I do', she said; 'he must have been in a serious mood to mystify you thus.' Then—'Did you like him, Jean, that swaggering cleric?'

'I did,' I said.

She thought awhile and sighed.

Through the short hours of that night, I believe she did not sleep at all; I too was restless, and each time I woke it was to find her lying, still, indeed, but always mindful if I spoke. She rose in the chill darkness of the lulled morning to prepare the stranger's meal, and as the grey light crept into the room, I heard him slowly ride away.

The night had left no trace of weariness on my sister's features; rather a new, bright beauty, though from my broken slumbers I rose sick and heavy-eyed, viewing the incident of the past evening as though it were a distant dream. She went out early and we saw no more of her that day. She spent it roaming over the wet country, lit by a wintry sun, accompanied by the adoring brute who shared her wanderings; returning late, unwontedly gay, her presence breathing a hitherto unfelt perfume of youth and joyousness, the source of which I did not question, welcoming gladly any gleam cast from a spirit which had always seemed to shed too sombrely its light.

For over a month this mood prevailed. Twelve years my senior, alien in taste and thought, she had always seemed to stand aloof from me; but now some subtle influence drew her nearer. She sought me; opened a door in life that led me to the hidden playroom of her heart.

Then one morning there came a letter—a thrilling London-looking missive—which she read rapidly twice through.

'Mr Somerset has business in the North', she announced, 'and he is coming to us again.'

A fire was lit and burned three days in my father's neglected chamber ere he came.

This was the second of many visits; sometimes he stayed but a night, yet often longer, his presence striking me—despite the pleasure of it— as vaguely ominous and strange. We went long rambles, Rodney bounding along beside us, for he had made fast friends with Mr Somerset to Elinor's amusement and feigned dismay. When evening came, our guest would sit, a towering figure by the hearth, and talk as on the night of our first meeting. Now, in my hearing, they abandoned dull and learned themes for simple discourse, sometimes however slipping into graver thought.

One night, as he related how the old blind king, now grievously afflicted, paced restlessly through his apartments, strumming a bar of Handel or addressing in feeble accents some imaginary concourse of his ministers, she said: 'Poor wreck! what hinders it from sinking?' and he replied: 'The Tyrant of this ill-governed universe perhaps.'

She affirmed briefly: 'There is none such.'

'Yet', returned he, 'he plays a part sufficiently convincing in men's lives.'

'A phantom part,' she said. 'He being but the effigy man's weakness rears to shield and prop it.'

'Even the great Emperor', he ventured, 'though some say he has no faith, I think, holds in his way to God.'

For a moment she was silent—thinking; saying, as if to herself, at last: 'Can *no* man summon strength to stand alone!'

'It is your mission to persuade them,' he commented gravely, and she smiled. It must have been my fancy that falsely detected a lurking ring of mockery in his tone.

I had frequently wondered what was the work of which she had spoken at their first encounter to the stranger; but it had never been my way to question her: I could not take it now.

Napoleon was her hero, and they talked often earnestly of him. To me, he seemed—but I knew little—a ruthless and insatiate monster, half-god, half-demon, disastrously apparelled in the form of man. But she loved power for its majesty, careless whether it cursed or blessed mankind.

I used to watch them as they sat together in those pleasant hours and wonder if ever beings were more finely mated. She sat leaning backward in her favourite window-seat, a light flickering on the black panes behind her; her massive hands clasped loosely on her knee; her eyes, changing like strains of music, which only a soul can hear. Now and then as his glance met hers, it struck a splendid discord there, which hung irresolute suspended, till he released it with a troubled frown.

Remembering—by what freak of memory I know not—the words on that slip of paper which she had penned, the fact that they were lovers seemed at first incredible, but soon I found it one impossible to doubt.

Yet she was often harsher than her wont with him: his patience touched me. I knew little of this man, although I saw so much, and if I paint him as a shadowy, unsubstantial figure, with outward attributes alone discernible, it is because—as such perforce—he appeared to me. He took, in my humble judgment, a too great account of birth and worldly honour, and spoke of women with a lightness that displeased me, but Elinor did not combat, or seem to note these failings. It was enough for me that she approved him: to my eyes, they both seemed made to dwarf, in mind and stature, those who stood beside them, like beings of a loftier race. The future dazzled me. I saw her moving through it, like a queen; the grand Court ladies, stopped to mark her progress, whose morning beauties put their gaslit charms to shame.

And many brilliant scenes I pictured in those days; not keen enough to read my sister's destiny in her now faintly clouded brow. More sweetly than of old she smiled upon my waking and bade me kind Good-night.

Summer had come to us: the heather bloomed upon her hills: Elinor's garden beds were gay. One morning I entered with a handful of her favourite blossoms and she demanded: 'Well Jean, who is your nosegay for?'

'For your guest's room', I said; 'does he not come today?'

'Yes,' she assented sombrely. 'Edward Somerset comes this evening and tomorrow he goes early. You will miss your talk tonight: we have some matters to discuss alone.'

He came: they stayed together in my father's book-lined room where she had never taken him before. Passing the door with Agatha —who now retired early—I heard his voice raised as in supplication, and as I came down again, her accents ringing and sweet, speaking as, when I was a child and in distress, she used to speak to me.

The hours seemed long and wearisome as I remained below in the darkening kitchen watching the stars come slowly out and listening to the drone of voices from the room above.

It was late when they joined me and the lamp was lit. It shewed two pale and almost unfamiliar faces—his was distorted sadly, for I hardly recognized the cruel line his lips had taken under a lowering and darkened brow. After some forced and trivial talk he said Good-night and left us. Elinor remained with me.

'You have seen your last of Edward Somerset,' were her first words.

I started up, for the first time in all my life at issue with this woman whom I had never questioned or defied before.

'You have driven him away', I cried, 'as you drove Arthur Perceval. What have they done, these men, that you should chase them, suddenly and without reason from our door.'

'Yes, I have driven him away', she said immovably; 'but not like Mr Perceval; and Jean, I have something beside to tell you. That misused personage is coming back. I have recalled him. He wished to marry you, and I forbade it. He told me (the word has many meanings) that he loved you, child, and now, if you care to listen, he will tell the tale to you.'

My heart beat quickly with a curious joy, but now my sister's face checked any happy tumult—it looked drawn and old.

'And he loved you', I said, 'this man whom you have sent away?'

'He asked me, certainly, to be his wife.'

'What hinders happiness—what have you done?' I said.

'I cannot tell,' she murmured half-inaudibly, with an awful helpless gesture which appalled me.

'I had no choice. I should have known—perhaps I knew—there was, from the beginning, but one way. If there were such a God as you believe in, He and He only, could understand.'

'He made us and He guides,' I pleaded.

'If that were true, then He has guided. I was not made to yield to any tyrant—no, not even to the world's sublimest despot. If He made me, it is then He who made me so.'

'All souls were made for happiness,' was my last plea.

'Rather for victory,' was her reply.

I hazarded, 'Some victories are void, and some are vile.'

'All victories are great. We never speak of this again,' she said decisively at parting and kissed me, passing her fingers through my hair.

The morning brought my lover and new life for me; but since it is my sister's story that I tell, I pass on to its ending, leaving the record of my happier fate untold.

The summer passed. She watched it from afar: her eyes in those waning months grew distant and her serenity profound. My happiness was dear to her. She said one day: 'Knowledge means gentleness sometimes, and once, Jean—but I am pardoned—I was hard to you.'

Her light at nights burned longer and she spent many hours in my father's room. Rodney came in and kept her company, divining blindly that he was needed more than he used to be. But soon she was to lose this solace. Agatha's days were shortening, although she still hobbled about the house and sat mumbling pitifully in her chair. Her mind grew weak; she was beset by aged terrors which none but Elinor could pacify. The present vanished from her view; she talked often as if my father lived and our mother lay upstairs in the empty chamber, stiff and straightened for her grave. Elinor dare not leave the house; the poor old woman fretted and raved if she were absent, trembling at every footstep in the passage, crying the house was haunted—that the unburied dead walked there.

So all day long, they sat together, my sister begging hour after hour for the old tales, that if she remembered them, quieted her to tell. I could not bear this spectacle of living dissolution and shunned it, shuddering, though many times I tried to conquer the horror that my heart condemned. As she grew worse, she would not suffer Rodney in the room. He was a devil, she proclaimed; his eyes eating her life away. So he was banished to the garden, where his rattling chain irked her to frenzy, and when he was loosed, she moaned to hear him scratching for admittance at the door. Some weeks this lasted; then one morning I came down and found Elinor by the table, her head bent low upon her arm. My father's gun was laid beside it; the fire was unlit, and I felt chilled by the autumn dampness of the air.

She looked up as I entered, and rose and took my arm and led me to the garden, where her old comrade lay stretched out beside a little trickling pool of blood.

'Oh, Elinor!' I cried. 'You might have saved him; he would have found a refuge in the village, till—till Agatha was calmed—or dead.'

'He was mine; he would never have owned another master, and I would not have yielded him. He still is mine—he understands and pardons me,' she said.

She tended Agatha with still unwearying care, but sometimes listening to that babbling, incoherent speech, I saw her brow contract as if she suffered. Quickly enough, she found a means to check the pang.

My only mission was to read aloud, maintaining the old habit, for though to Agatha the import of the words was dead, she would at times sink back contentedly, soothed by the soft monotony of sound. And I remember how, one night, when Elinor had sat heedless, I thought, as usual and seemingly engaged in thought—as I came to the words: 'Thou hast not yet resisted unto blood', she started slightly, so that I paused to look at her, and saw her eyes turned to the open page that rested on my knee.

'Give me your Book,' she said that night, when I had closed it. 'It has some phrases that ring true.'

I held it out to her in silence, noting with quickened apprehension the change that a few months had wrought in her. Little by little she had grown thin; her carriage almost listless. I feared our mother's malady, but Elinor showed no sign of sickness—only a shrunken, pitiful front of pain.

I dreaded night, which brought to my ears her ceaseless pacings to and fro, and forced me to creep out and crouch on the forbidden threshold of her door; not daring to seek admission as Rodney would have done, and hardly daring to retreat. I dreaded morning, which made visible the havoc of that hidden struggle which I might not arrest or share.

As time wore on, those eyes became dim embers and her once vigorous tones like muffled bells rang slow; the tale of awful conflict was imprinted on her shadowless and joyless brow. Love, through my eyes, beheld this change with helpless awe.

My thought took shape in her remembered words: 'The soul is bound with many chains—the cruellest, pride, the subtlest, suffering, and the deadliest, that which—men call love.'

Her strength was failing by degrees, beneath this triple pressure.

Love came simply to me; my heart went gladly out to meet it; but she confronted it (this much at least was plain to me) with desperate revolt. I could not view that terrible rebellion against a power to which Nature has bade us yield, without a certain horror and dismay. It seemed, as I watched the wreck which this unnatural strife had made of her, savage and wild and wrong; and yet I could not judge her, since—as she had said—God made her so.

The wonder was that still those sleepless eyes found light enough to greet the morning; death seemed as surely set upon her features as upon those of the poor withered remnant of humanity whose life was ebbing tardily away. He seemed indeed to stand between them, gazing indifferently upon his double prey.

My lover brought a doctor from the village, a lank-haired, crooked-legged young man, whom however, it so pleased Elinor to harass with gentle raillery and mock discussions on his art, that he departed, shaking his head (whether at her condition or his own was dubious) like a bewildered sheep. When he had gone, she said to Mr Perceval: 'Dear and most officious and most reverend Sir, there is nothing amiss with me, but if there were, the ministrations of that poor youth would only make me by a smile the better, and there are things that would bring me a better smile.'

With spent and laboured breath to every anxious question, came the same reply: 'There is—nothing amiss with me.'

She gave no place to suffering, doing the tasks she had always done with flagging, slow persistence; rising haggard and grey at dawn to move with heavy steps about the household business, while in my room above I sat with folded hands sickened and helpless, powerless to protest or aid.

And since Agatha's fretful terrors required her presence indoors by day, at night she struggled forth into the solitary darkness, returning after midnight to her lonely room, where the light burned hour after hour, casting her pacing shadow on the wall.

Again the country rang with news of a great victory. England was written over with the name of Waterloo. To me it seemed almost an omen of my sister's ending, remembering how it was under the shadow of such tidings that my father died.

My lover brought us details of the Emperor's defeat, and Elinor read them with a frowning eagerness—a kind of pleased displeasure—for her nature found its element in strife.

She failed at last, and life ran stagnant in those splendid limbs. The hands whose touch had seemed of old like living rescue, now hung nerveless, as she sat painfully listening to the old woman's mumbled tales beside the fire. Two wrecks they were tossed on the same advancing waters, sinking grimly, waiting the final wave. No cry for harbour rose in them and no desire for home. I used to come upon them in the twilight, lashed together, Elinor clasping the poor demented creature, whispering weary comfort, as she gazed dimly into the dying fire.

'Write', said my lover, 'to this Edward Somerset: her strength is broken and if he comes she must yield to rescue now.'

I told him that I dared not.

'Yet you must', was his rejoinder, 'or are you ready, without an effort, to let her die?'

I wrote, saying: 'I want to see you.' For even then I could not speak for her. She was one for whom one might only act—and that with fear. 'My need is urgent: come immediately: do not delay.'

As if to mock this tardy summons, two days succeeding it, my sister sank to sudden weakness. She strove vainly to rise at daybreak and I found her leaning against the curtains of the bed. She bade me dress her and I obeyed, praying deliverance was near. She lay upon her bed, wandering in speech and thought, crying at times that Agatha would need her and she must go. At noon she rallied and staggered to the door, forced back by a feebleness that struck her with despair. She sat all evening by the window watching the darkening sky, repeating to herself at intervals: 'The work is done—the work is done.'

'What work?' I asked, trying to rouse her, and she pointed to a pile of MS in her cramped handwriting, which lay beside her on the window-seat, fingering the pages with loving care.

I stayed with her. Arthur kept watch with Agatha, who, in the room below, was rocking herself to and fro in feverish desolation, moaning incessantly for Elinor in quavering, distracted tones that reached my quickened hearing, but which my sister did not heed or hear. At eight o'clock, my lover called me from the passage and I went down, praying that Edward Somerset had come. Yet it was not his voice that greeted me, but Agatha's, wailing and distraught.

'I cannot quiet her', he said; 'she takes me for a demon who has spirited Elinor away.'

I spent some time trying to check her frenzy and at last she sank exhausted into a restless sleep.

'Stay here', I told him, 'and if she wakes, call me again.'

When I reached my sister's room, I saw amazedly that she was seated writing at the table, and as I entered she looked up with flushed and altered features. Her eyes were shining with a fierce, unnatural light.

The hearth and room were strewn with masses of charred paper and the breeze from the window which she would have always open, was sweeping the blackened fragments about the floor. I glanced hastily at the window-seat and saw that the heap of treasured papers were no longer there.

I went and stood beside her, fearing I knew not what, and let my eyes fall on the sheet of paper which lay before her; the crooked characters upon it were still wet. Only a few disjointed phrases met my view; enough to show me that the letter was addressed to Edward Somerset, and that it held confession and recall. The agony of this enforced submission had cast a dreader shadow over her face than ever resistance had laid there.

She dropped her pen and sat, both hands pressed hard against her temples, staring before her with a bitter, burning gaze. I said nothing. I could not speak, but knelt beside her, resting my head against her arm. At the touch she rose and swayed and grasped the chair.

I got up quickly to support her, and saw a change overspread her face. It grew livid—contorted. She stretched a hand out, took the page from the table and held it towards the candle's flame. It caught, but fell half-burned from her shaking fingers. The fragment fluttered to my feet. She motioned me to reach it, with a failing, insistent gesture. I put it in her hand, but she shrank back and made a sign toward the candle. I held it to the flame and won from her lips a pitiful, exultant smile. The sheet had scarcely shrivelled when I heard a heavy step upon the stair. The door sprang open. Edward Somerset stood before us in the doorway, dressed with unusual care and splendour, as if he had stepped straight from some royal audience into this unexpected ante-room of death.

Silently he confronted us, and then his eyes sought Elinor's. She met that groping glance with one of shrinking torment; but as he strode towards her, she, calling to aid some remnant of lost vigour, spread her hands out with a swift gesture of denial and dismay.

He took no note of those rejecting palms, but captured them and covered them with close caresses, while she stood passive, dazed, until he drew her into a sudden fast embrace. But for a moment, she lay there, then with a final effort, freed herself and thrust him off. Standing erect and motionless, she pressed both hands across her eyes and lifted one fierce, ringing and revulsive cry: her voice—a spark of anguish—dropped and flickered, then burst again to living flame.

'Thou hast not yet resisted—unto blood.'

It was her final utterance.

Till dawn we watched with her.

At dawn she died.

SPINE

HE saw now that they had always thought it, but it was only a year or two ago when his own crowd (he didn't count the family) had started chucking him, that that half-shaved amoeba Giles, who by the way, still owed him £15, had said to Billing that he had no spine.

It was not a fact. He had had it then. Wasn't he hawking his pen-and-inks round and getting some off at sweating prices and infernally insulted into the bargain? Hadn't he done the RA picture with Anna Baumann in it and those portraits for the Hotel Manager at Eastbourne—Self, wife and dogs?—he wanted to keep the dogs himself. And when he got the bounder's cheque hadn't he paid old Samuels three months off the year's rent owing; and £1 off the milk?

He must have been a pretty good tenant for old Samuels to have let it run on a year, and a pretty good customer to the milk people to have a bill of £6 odd. But they were neither of them pleased.

And if he had blued the rest on that little b— of a model Anna Baumann, that wasn't spending it on himself. Everyone knew she had gone straight for him (which of 'em hadn't) and he had come out of that dirty business very well. It had cost money. That was the worst of behaving decently; it always did. And nobody was pleased.

But if his work had gone to pieces he blamed old Samuels for kicking him out of the John Street rooms where he *was* working: six years and kicked out for nine months which he meant to pay. All Jews were dirt!

Then the tradespeople took old Sam's cue and behaved abominably; but the rooms had done it. No sitter would face the Studio stairs and the housekeeper was much too sweet on him. This open drain in the Caversham Road had given it the final knock. It would turn a Sargent into an Embankment screever—the wallpaper alone without the stove; the vile black tube with the vile square of red glass at the bottom.

A fire stood by you when you got home, dead sick of everything, to sit over, you and your pipe; but there was an enmity about the stove with its one red beastly eye that sucked the blood out of you, though the blighting enmity of the stove was the jocund dance to the filthy friendliness of that fungus, Mrs George; sizzling about the place like a cistern; saying everything over twice; pinching your bloaters with her poisonous thumb and coughing over everything.

She was not a liar, so from her point of view, he supposed the sheets were clean. They may have been before she started washing them — she liked them personally, as she did him; and refused to send them to the laundress because they had 'never left the house'.

That was *his* mistake. He ought to have bolted right off into another shanty and would, if it hadn't been for the job of getting one —at the price.

When he was going round for this, at one place they had offered him half a bed and said they could recommend the gentleman. He would have liked to see the gentleman—out of bed!

All said and done *he* was a gentleman: weren't half his people high up in the Services; two in the Treasury? Every starched one of them except himself battening on it, potting money out of it, having litters of jolly little kids; (there was nothing like a jolly little kid for bucking you when you were down), he used to see the kids before the whole gang cut him, the whole swanky, dreary gang absolutely stiff with spine.

If it was worth while thinking of the Almighty—no one took Him seriously nowadays—he supposed He worked that way—a few good strokes and then He biffed it: and you were the result. But you were there: you were *You*, no one else exactly like you—the same nose: they always said he had the Aston nose that shoved through things and came out smiling. What had he done with it? His mother had had it too. What had she done with it? Simply kept her head above water; that was something; with a man like the Governor any other woman would have cheerfully gone down.

He was always fond of his mother. The others had rather laughed at it, but it wasn't funny. He had always liked women with sloping shoulders and behaved well to them for that reason. Anyhow, it was a fact; there was the portrait, a genuine Lawrence to prove it, which he hadn't sold and didn't mean to sell.

His Aunt Emma had it too, the nose, and dug it gaily into all of them; but whoever drew the winning ticket no one had done more for her than he had, towing her round Galleries where he was known, telling her what to look at; driving about with her to drapers' shops and back to Hill Street to talk wash about the family—what his Mother's was and the Governor's wasn't; giving her presents at Christmas that he couldn't afford, until he saw the utter folly of it and waste of time.

It was *her* spine that was keeping her out of Kensal Green so long that they would all be past enjoying it when she got there.

Well, damn it! his had gone and he was fairly chirpy. At forty-two he wasn't looking for a new one or making any offers. He never had seen what there was in it; it merely took it out of you and didn't alter anything.

Take London, for instance; it was the same big gorgeous show whether you tossed up rotten sketches of it or not. A beautiful woman too—rather more so if you didn't. You enjoyed 'em for themselves.

It had never even mildly worried him till he met Mrs Eden. And then this insane, infernal craving had got hold of him—as bad as—well, certainly as bad as drink which for nearly a year—God only knew why or how—he'd practically chucked for it.

It was in March, at Hill Street. He remembered the dinner because he hadn't had a bad imitation of one for days and it seemed his luck to have to put it away all at one go when it would have done him comfortably for a week. He hadn't sat by her, hardly noticed her; he had rather a going bit next to him and was taken up with her. Mrs Eden only dawned on him afterwards in the drawing-room when she got up and spotted that sketch of his skyed behind the piano, which the old lady had given him ten quid for the first time Samuels threatened to sell him up.

She liked it enormously; but it wasn't that! She wasn't young or particularly good-looking; distinguished, all that: they mostly were, the old blighter's crowd; but what struck him was the way she spoke, very quietly, as if she was interested and liked you and as if you really mattered.

They went down together and she said it was much too nice a night to drive, so he walked with her from Hill Street to Wilton Street, up Piccadilly, the Park side, where the Westminster lights looked uncommonly clear and jolly.

At the door she said: 'I wonder if you would come and see me Thursdays? But then I shouldn't see you. What about Tuesday when I should?'

He couldn't place it—some silly impulse made him hesitate, but somehow she insisted without insisting.

And he had gone. They talked Art and the country; she told him they were taking a house near St Peter's, Bucks, for the summer. She thought he'd like it; there ought to be quite good sketching there.

At the end she said: 'You know, I'm coming to see your work', and then broke off, and finished with a smile that was pure sunlight when it did come out, but wasn't in a hurry to—'that is, if you'll let me?'

He went straight back and had a burst-up with Mrs George about the anointed piggishness of everything, and then knocked her clean out by telling her to take the whisky down; and next day he started to work like Hell.

Out and out he'd never done anything better, half as good—with a few more square meals and a week, say, at Boulogne or Etaples where you could get the models, he saw himself pulling off something top-hole.

Later, he didn't see Etaples or France at all; there was something else at the back of his head, and it came out one evening as he was buying violets outside the Britannia.

It was Bucks. He would go down; St Giles or St Peters; the

Worcester crockery ought to do him a week at least and a new suit. This time he would go to Hartley's tailor and strike him dead by offering to pay up and probably wouldn't have to.

It occurred to him it wasn't only the grub, the poisonous air was half the trouble; he hadn't seen or sniffed the country for over a year, or more like two. That line of the Downs in spring, the smell of the wet leaves, the damp earth, there was nothing like it; and that peculiar crispness in the air, the snap of the morning, the touch of the wind; the blue-grey haze over the hills—purple later—they go that colour—behind the black hedges blown like a flame. The bare branches of the elms, the springy turf; the sort of country he used to hunt over; half the stiff-backed dreary gang were hunting over it now.

It wasn't bad sport if you hadn't a gun, to get a dog and make him fetch the rabbits out of the brushwood; and see 'em scamper up over the dips. But it wouldn't be spring: summer: everything shimmering and humming; the sound of summer—rather blurred, nothing quite clear, no time, no beat. Chopin had done it somewhere: Vi used to play it; very badly. It made you feel you weren't in the room, a rum sort of notion—Not here—Not here!

He wondered if Mrs Eden played. Perhaps she would ask him up. It didn't matter, she would be there, somewhere about. He'd never felt anything like it before. Yes, once. The day his Mother died; they were sitting round the dining-room table after dinner, the Governor looking like a seedy goldfish, gulping down champagne and telling them all to bear up because he couldn't.

He flattered himself he had sat through the Governor in every other act, but he walked out in the middle of that one, up to his Mother's room, and turned the sheet down and looked at her and said to himself: 'Dead—by God! dead!' And—odd, that! though she was lying there so out of it, she seemed more there than usual listening to him, saying in the old way: 'I know, Stuke, I have had worries too'—as he stood there looking down at her, wondering what the Governor was alive for, and swearing he would stiffen up.

On the 24th of July he got a note from Mrs Eden asking might she come at 3.30 on the 28th? He gave Mrs George two stalls for the Bedford and washed the china over again himself. She stayed an hour. He showed her all the last things he had done and she liked them immensely and the Worcester tea-cups. She was as keen on china as he was, but didn't mind Mrs G's glass sugar basin, and thought he was rather hard on Mrs G. Next time he promised to introduce her. They kept to small things, she seemed to like it; the bother of getting a first-floor room for twopence-halfpenny, and what things cost up there and the way he'd shut his bed off; she hadn't spotted it. It didn't matter what you said or what she saw; at first as if she wasn't there and then as if you'd always known her. He asked about the house in Bucks and she said it had fallen through; they had had to take another. She didn't say where and he didn't ask; but she wanted to know where he was going and he told her possibly Boulogne. She thought it was rather sordid wasn't it? and he said: 'I don't know; it's what you see.'

They were going downstairs; there was some scent on her glove like hay-fields, and she touched his arm and said: 'I think you always see beautiful things?' He didn't answer.

As he put her into the cab she said; 'I hope we meet in the autumn. I believe we're going to have lovely weather. Rumpelmeyers.' He told the man. She and the cab had clean upset the kids in the street. She must have given the little beggars something. He stood there too—one of them piped up something at him—and saw the taxi take the corner.

It was a swinking hot summer; everyone cleared out; but there hadn't been such a circus of cockroaches in the basement within Man's memory.

He fancied he spoke to about three people besides Mrs George whom he didn't speak to. He got some picture post-cards. His brother Warrington sent him a parcel from Goldings of old shirts and a suit and a book on hygiene, which he returned to Warrington at Goldings.

He borrowed a studio and pulled the picture off. There was no mistake about it this time. Six months ago he would have envied any chap who could put his name to it; but now the only thing he felt about it was that he was rotten tired.

He didn't sleep; he missed the whisky; he hadn't been drunk since March or April; he hoped he wasn't getting fussy. It used to be enough for him if models and so on were young and larky. French women though—another story. *Il y a façon et façon* in women, in everything. God! what an age since he heard that patter: '*En voilà des phrases! Dis, donc, ça c'est des bêtises!*' Poor little Renée and the Rue Tournon and behind it all the St Sulpice bell!

Almost as queer as anything to think that at this moment while they were bawling cauliflowers down the God-forsaken road, Paris and all the rest of it was romping on.

This was November—in another month turkeys and Herald Angels would be on the job again. Next to the one when Vi was trying to smash up their engagement and finally did, he couldn't remember a stiffer year.

In the middle of December he ran up against Mrs Eden one afternoon in Dover Street, coming out of a hat shop, looking very fit. She would have passed him, hadn't recognized him, but he pulled up, or something inside him pulled up and said: 'You don't remember me?'

There was a shade of a pause, and then she said with extraordinary sweetness: 'Of course I remember you,' and she was evidently trying to get at his name. He said he was going on to his Aunt's in Hill Street; she looked relieved and said: 'Dear Miss Aston! How wonderful she is! How is she? Do look us up one day' and something about the narrowness of Dover Street and its being so badly lit. He took his hat off: there was the same scent on her gloves; and she went on up Dover Street.

He wasn't expected in Hill Street, and at first the poor old sheepbiter was rather frosty, thinking he'd come to borrow money, but thawed when he took her off the hook, and told him he was looking ill. She did hope—. He said to her; 'My good Aunt, nothing is so irrational as hope—' But she went on quite a long time about hope and the costs of his stomach. He didn't stop her; once or twice in his life he had spoken the bald truth to people and they had simply taken him for a bounder or slightly touched. He saw their point of view. He mentioned that he had just knocked up against Mrs Eden and she said; 'Oh! yes, you met her here. *He* is one of the Lincolnshire Edens; she has just brought out a book called '*Flotsam*' or '*Wreckage*'—something depressing of that kind. What can Alice Eden know about it? She lives entirely in her own world. She has just come into a second fortune.'

There was a jolly fire in the library and they sat on over it talking of Hartley's liver and whether Ada would get her divorce. What did he think? He said, as she meant to stick to India, he supposed she would still have her punkah-men to nag at if she did.

Afterwards he walked about and turned into the Pav for an hour. He thought it rather a smutty show. Going home he wished he could be as wrapped up in anything as Hartley was in his own inside.

He tried not to think of Mrs Eden. He saw that he must shake her off. She had got idiotically on his nerves. Time was when he knew scores of women—more charm, the same sort, (in the early days) better looking, much younger, much younger. What in Hell had Mrs Eden got to do with it? He tried not to think of Spine; one day he had looked it up in the dictionary and found: Spine, spin. n., a thorn; the backbone of an animal; the heart-wood of trees.

He saw now that she hadn't got it, neither had he. Charm didn't count, or work—work least of all—or whisky. It was going up, much higher—much higher; blue, wavering, cut off; the embers were smoking down below. It was there, right enough, but he was losing hold of it. He would get it again—when he was not so fagged—in the morning. It might go up, but he meant to get it. By God! he would!

He let himself in. There was no gas lit, there hardly ever was; and in the musty darkness Mrs George put her head round the kitchen stairs and wheezed out at him: 'Don't you be frightened of the 'addick, Sir, if you should go down for your kettle and see it 'anging up in the scullery. It didn't 'arf give me the jumps up there on the 'ook, looking so strange and mother-o'-pearly, with the moon shinin' on it!'

He groped upstairs and went in and lit a candle and shut the door. There was a remarkable stillness in the room; it was like a room in which some one is lying dead. He stood there a moment, listening, expecting something to happen. He remembered that she had just come into a second fortune, and slowly, in the intense quiet, it came to him that there was no Mrs Eden; there never had been; she wasn't there. He went across to the window—he didn't hear it—but he had the idea of a cab driving up. He said out loud to himself: 'Why not? Why not?' He looked out; and turned round on the room again.

There was nothing there. Not the wallpaper, not the stove; not really there; not solid, only like things that aren't; like tree-shadows, the ghosts of leaves. The sheets too—he remembered some in Brittany, at Douarnenez; he had sat up all night, what did it matter? if you slept; if you could only sleep. . . . There wasn't light enough. He lit another candle. The picture, too, not solid, quite thin, like muslin, like smoke, like vapour.

This was wrong. No one ought to feel like this, whatever they'd done or hadn't done. No beast, no animal. There was nothing there. The world was stark empty; a sort of pit; it made you giddy to look down at it; sick all over, nothing there; pure vacancy, not a living soul.

Nonsense! If you went out into the streets—the main thoroughfares, there were thousands—thousands—His eyes felt very stiff and hot: that was it; thousands of them and not one—not one! He thought suddenly of tomorrow; there was tonight too. Quite impossible, What about a drink? Why drink? He was too tired, dog-tired; better sit down, eat something; nothing but cocoa and an egg since morning. The haddock? That was (half of it) for tomorrow—tomorrow! No—no! Sometime or other you died; everyone did; his Mother had; they all would, sooner or later; a tough lot, hard to kill. This was exactly like it: like death, like life too. He was rather frightened, not of the haddock, though; he couldn't laugh. It must be pretty rank to look like that; perhaps it was swinging too—with the moon shining on it; everything else was; that dip in the Downs with the rabbits scampering over it. Rabbits, people, Warrington, Ada, Mrs Eden.

But in the midst of it all there was something quite steady and white and shining—the moon, the moon!

THE MINNOW FISHERS

'... To be calm without mental fear is the ideal of nature.' R.J.

IT WAS an after-dinner patter; someone had been generalizing on the elevating influence of Sport, of angling in particular: 'And thereby', interposed my friend, John Hilton, 'hangs a tale. It was when we lived near Maida Vale of melancholy memory; I was walking home one horribly damp afternoon by way of the canal, when suddenly out of the mist I heard a faint, rather squeaky, but quite collected exclamation, the words I didn't catch; from the events which followed they seem to have been "fetch 'im out"; but it was not repeated and I should not have noticed it but that a carpenter, who had been trudging on in front of me, pulled up and started running to the bank.

'I followed, curiously, at my leisure, and arrived at the canal; nothing more startling met my eyes than three minute and very shabby anglers, seated perilously near the edge and in a row, waiting immovably for bites.

'The puff and hurry of the carpenter behind them might have been a passing breeze; they didn't notice it, and for my part I couldn't make it out till he flung down his bag of tools and began dragging off his coat. Then I saw something, something like a piece of sacking floating idly on the stagnant yellow water some yards away from the three placid blots. It certainly, to me, resembled nothing human, just a bit of drifting stuff, but the imaginative carpenter jumped in and grabbing at it brought it eventually to the bank.

The minnow fishers, with their six small eyes fixed on three little lines, had not apparently observed the rescue, or if they had it wasn't suffered to distract them from the business in hand. I helped the carpenter to haul his burden up the bank, and from a bit of twig and twine entangled in that dripping lump I rapidly concluded that the tranquil band had previously numbered four. The rescued atom was a painful spectacle—suggestive of a crimson airball, a gruesome penny toy.

' "Been in some time", remarked the carpenter reflectively. "Thing is to hold 'im upside down to let the water out. Belongs to those blank nippers over there. Hi, there!" he shouted ineffectually.

'The nearest two were rigid, but the farther one, I thought, was moved to come to our assistance. A mistake; he was but bending dangerously forward, warily drawing up his line; it was a tremor of false hope; he let it down again, and relapsed to patient stone.

'Meanwhile we pumped and worked, how long I can't exactly say; it seemed a most unconscionable time; the carpenter humanely blasphemous, poor chap, and dripping wet.

'It seemed a hopeless job; it was decidedly exhausting; blown and gasping we kept on however. They kept on. You can't imagine anything quite so relentless and remote as the way *they* kept on, those three remorseless specks, intent, oblivious, aloof; three tiny profiles and three spindly lines as calm and obdurate as Fate. They might have stood for it; one felt at last that they were not to be disturbed; that there was something mystical, symbolic, in their complete detachment from our distant and unnecessary violence.

'But at last we brought him round, a miserable object blinking palely out again at life, laboriously restored to the damp dusk, the cheerless outlook of the dingy stretches of the bank, the stagnant water and impassive friends.

' "Must have been in a goodish time", the carpenter repeated, looking down on the wet bundle at his feet and slowly putting on his coat. "Belongs to those three limbs; they'll have to rouse theirselves and take him home. Leave that to you, Mister; I must be getting on; I'm not exactly dry." And shouldering his bag, with a polite "Good evening to you", he walked off.

'I went across and seized the first of the three fishers by the collar. "Does this small boy belong to you?" I asked severely.

'Gently, considerate of his task, he disengaged himself with a remonstrant "Hold off, Guvnor, let us be."

'With a shade more sternness I attacked the second. He also shook me off ungraciously, but pointed to the third. "Ask 'im," he added on an afterthought and with an obvious sense of treachery, "It's 'is brother."

'I proceeded to the third. On pressure, brutal and persistent, he admitted the relationship. "Well, if 'e is, *they* brought 'im out", indicating with a thumb the other two who made no sign, trusting to silence and the claims of blood to rid them of annoyance.

'Dislodging the reluctant and resentful relative, I gave the tottering victim to his care and pushed them off, following distrustfully for some distance in their wake.

'Before he turned to leave the bank, the injured relative bestowed on his betrayer a vindictive cuff, which met with no response. While we moved off, the two remaining minnow fishers sat serenely on.

'For them Peace had resumed her reign, Silence her smile; composure wrapped them and the incident was closed.'

AGLAË

'Il est bon d'attendre en repos la délivrance de l'Éternel.'

AS TANTE AGLAË sat slowly dying, she could see from her window, across, the *arrière-port*, with its gently swaying masts where the brown nets were drying, green and buff and pink hooded carts going over the bridge, with all the moving figures of the market, black against the brighter colours of the other quayside. The gay striped awnings of the *cafés*, the tall white houses rising from the grey arcades, the red-tiled *mansarde* roofs where here and there yellow wall-flowers had niched themselves: and beyond all that the lace-work tower and slated belfry of St Jacques, blue-grey against any sky and at all times stiller than the stillness of the sunshine.

She could hear over there, the rumble of cart-wheels, the shunting trains, the steamer hoots, the fish 'auction' bell tinkling faintly across the water, the big bell of St Jacques throbbing every hour after the thinner clock chimes, and just below, on the nearer quay, the children's voices, the trill of Mère Foliot's canary, the bark of Catouche the *épicier's* dog: a shout now and then from the sailors in the port mending the nets or painting the boats: and at noon and again at seven and on the nightfall the '*Tantôts*' called out to Madame Bertrand's good-night and the beat of the *sabots* on the stones as by twos and threes the men clattered out of the *café*.

But all these were a great way off, the sounds and colours of a world not here, a faintly humming and shining world which she had already left.

She was thinking now of the narrow door, under the window at which she sat, the door through which she should go only once again, and although at the moment nothing was, everything that had been or yet might be seemed to gather round it.

It was exactly two feet wide, the door, with three semi-circular worn stone steps leading up to it and for close upon fifty years every one of those she had known and cared for had gone in and out by it.

First, the grandparents and not long afterwards the parents, stricken together by a disease which had swept the town, had been carried through it, along the quay and up the cemetery hill.

And then, for a year Germaine, nearly nineteen, and Aglaë nearly twenty-four had lived on alone in the old yellow house with the red gabled roof, at this sunny corner of the *arrière-port* backing on to the

Impasse de Ravelin, that place of dirty flag-stones and zigzag window slits which never sees the sun.

The parents had left it to them with the savings from the shop, the drapery and lingerie, in the rue Larissonière on the other side of the town, where they spent their days, coming back to sleep at the house, for three generations in the family, who had owned it first when the street, now given over to the fisherfolk, was well inhabited. Naturally, the parents had said, if the house had not belonged to one, one would not have chosen it, but there they had lived, on friendly terms, though not familiar with the neighbours, highly respected and lifted by the profits of the shop and the small *propriété* above the anxieties and poverty of the quarter.

After their death the business passed into other hands and with a joint income of some 500fr. Aglaë had worked at home, as hard as ever on the lacework and fine sewing while Germaine had gone daily across the bridge to help the *modiste* at the Nouvelles Galleries then not so spacious, but newly opened, at the foot of the *grand'rue*, now much extended and stretching round with handsome plate glass windows, to the end of the arcades, taking in the entire corner of the quay.

It remained a mystery to the personnel of the Nouvelles Galleries how Germaine, with her opportunities at the Nouvelles Galleries, her beauty and the modest *rente* behind could sacrifice all these to a common fisherman, but not to anyone concerned; and it was a great thing for the house when she brought Raymond into it: to Aglaë the big bell of St Jacques seemed to swing and throb for them all through that day, and as she lay awake in the little room next theirs, through the long night too.

Germaine used to say of Raymond when he had vexed her in some little matter—it vexed to have him come striding in in his wet clothes, when he should have hung them up outside on the hook by the door—that he was simply a tiresome child and as one green pea to another, like other men.

But to Aglaë from the first he had seemed unlike them.

His eyes were very blue and clear like a child's with sweeping black lashes; and more than most men in many things he had the ways of a child. If anything pleased him—it may [might] have been a good catch, or once he had bought a lottery ticket for a franc and drawn a prize of 100 fr. with it—he would seize Germaine by the waist, kissing her half a dozen times, waltzing her round the room, and afterward come up behind Aglaë's chair, to kiss her too, once, perhaps, on the hair, on the forehead, until one day she had shrunk back [away] and he had laughed and said—'*Ben*, it is kept then for that other, the preferred one—*pas vrai*?' and she had laughed too but she had never married and he had forgotten and done the same thing more than once again.

It was even a greater day, it seemed to Aglaë when Odette was born.

Raymond was out with the boat that night and Aglaë had left the door open, creeping down from time to time to look out for him along the deserted quay.

He came in about three o'clock when the grey light was beginning to fill the room, wanting to go up to Germaine at once. But Aglaë had held him back, and they two had stood for a while at the door together, watching the masts grow clearer against the dawn: and then suddenly he had caught her hands, looking down at her with his intensely blue child's eyes, and as if it had been Our Blessed Lady Herself with whom he pleaded saying over and over again, in a voice which had too a childlike terror in it—*'Faut sauver Germaine, faut sauver Germaine'*. And they had saved her. But for some weeks afterwards she was too ill to nurse the child, or take much notice of it, ailing too, and from this first it had attached itself to Aglaë. When no one else could quiet it, it would go off quickly to sleep in her arms, getting restless if taken out of them, so that, at last, for peace sake it shared her bed.

And as Odette grew older that went on. It was always Tante Aglaë whom the shy, pale child ran after about the house all morning, and sat by, breaking the cotton off, threading the needles for the fine sewing, in winter-time beside the window and in the doorway through the long summer afternoons.

Germaine said sometimes, rather bitterly, that the child seemed scarcely hers, but in fact Raymond was everything to her and she was more jealous of his affection, and the time he spent playing with the little one than of its odd [curious] passion for the older woman.

Odette was just six when her Father died from a fall from the mast coming into harbour, a common accident enough, but rarely fatal. Half a dozen men of the quarter had had the same mishap, losing a limb and stumping about for a lifetime not much the worse for it; but Raymond in falling had struck his head, and better than having him crazed, on the women's hands, his comrades said, bringing him in, that it should be so quickly over.

He looked as few do, older in death than life, with the eyes which had given his face its extraordinary youth and gaiety closed down. Germaine cried out that they should never have let her see it: it was not the same. It was not the same, but Aglaë was not sorry to have seen it so, with something that was not suffering or sadness, but a shadow of them both cast over it: with the old young, careless look it would have been harder to let him go.

He was buried in the new Cemetery on the first day of the *semaine sainte* and on the evening of the *vendredi saint,* at eight o'clock Aglaë went alone across the bridge to St Jacques to hear the Abbé Revault preach the sermon on the Passion.

She noticed, with regret how much stouter he had become; such extreme corpulence could only be a symptom of some malignant disease. His features had sunk much farther into the purple folds of his face; and though he stood well back in the pulpit, his large pendulous body protruded over the edge, his short arms in their lace-trimmed sleeves, flapping like clipped wings above it. But his voice, coming and going in gusts was as sonorous as ever, and he had never preached more beautifully or for so long.

The Church was already packed with old and middle-aged women, all of them in black, sitting or standing, listening attentively for the text which it was his habit to give out rapidly, almost inaudibly. For a moment it seemed as if there were not to be one. The Abbé paused and looking up first at the dark arches and then down over the black crowd below asked suddenly and loudly—'*Qui est mort?*' pausing again and bending forward, waiting, as if he expected one of them to answer. When he said again more calmly—'*Qui, donc, est mort, mes enfants? Qui pleurez-vous? Le Rédempteur du monde, Notre Seigneur Jésus-Christ*' to Aglaë it seemed untrue, or if it were true as if it did not matter: it was someone else whom she saw lying dead, changed, and older, with a scar across the forehead.

She remembered the text and the sermon which followed all her life: '*Ne crains-tu point Dieu, puisque tu es condamné au même supplice? Et pour nous, nous le sommes avec justice, car nous souffrons ce que nos crimes méritent, mais Celui-ci n'a fait aucun mal.*' He spoke first, as he had done the year before, of Youth and Spring.

'*Oh! Printemps! saison des espéances et de tous les bonheurs! Lueur rose de l'aube réflétée dans les visages souriants, la joie te berce, le mystère même le sied. Oh! Printemps, que de chants de petits oiseaux, des étoiles étincelantes, quel épanouissement de fleurs parfumées cueillies de notre sainte enfance! Oh! fleurs de jeunesse, trop tôt brisées, trop vite fanées; tapissant les bois enchantés sous les cieux veloutés—cieux tendus par les mains des anges—pavillon de bleu céleste! Oh! Jeunesse, âme de ce printemps pur et sacré, ne souille donc pas ton coeur virginal en fréquentant les scènes de débauche, en prêtant l'oreille à des propos obscènes!*'

And it was of youth and the spring gone suddenly dark in the house that she had been thinking all the week. She could never have spoken of them so beautifully, she felt now she could never speak or think of them again, but his words set before her with a new clearness the things which as she had left the house that night she had hoped for a while, in this place, which had never yet failed to bring her peace, to put away. Raymond going out to the boat in the grey early mornings, with Odette perhaps running after him a little way along the quay: their walks in the evening along the sea-front: the sky had been rose and violet all that last week above an unusually blue and quiet sea, yet one night the three had walked down the break-water—and she had watched them from the bench where she was sitting—Germaine's straight figure, slight but very graceful, her small head reaching half-way up his arm, and Raymond looking taller and broader than he did at home, with Odette perched high on his shoulder—those three, very close together, seeming for the moment far away, though they were so near, standing out sharply and darkly against the bright pink sky.

'Saison de tous les bonheurs.'—She stood—coming late she had not been able to get a chair, looking down on the rows of black-clad, old and ageing women—pressing her hands together and almost crying out aloud. *'Mon Dieu, mon Dieu!'*

It might so well have been one of them, for whom it was over—or herself.

'Ne souille, donc, pas ton coeur—des propos obscènes—.' But he was not like that. She remembered once when he had been kept indoors for some short illness, how Germaine had stood over him in bed, with a cup in her hand and he had sat up, his hair ruffled, his cheeks a little flushed and said—*'Oui, je serai sage, je boirai toute ma potion'* and how Germaine had smiled down at him and said *'Grand bébé, bois donc'*.

He was like that, like his eyes and his heart was like them.

'Celui-ci n'a fait aucun mal.'

It was terrible: she stood there listening to the story of her Saviour's Passion—the Abbé was speaking now of His sufferings on the Cross, but not distinctly, she caught a word here and there *'des pieds sanglants—le front suant—toutes les infamies—'* but she did not see Him. She saw Raymond and then just below her old Mère Jupin with her leathery, yellow skin, and red-lined eyes, upturned, watery. She was very old, hardly alive but her *saletés*, her brutalities to the little grand-child left in her charge were the talk of the quarter. Perhaps it was not her fault; the older people said of her *'c'est dans le sang'* or *'c'est par famille'*, but God could choose, He had only to lift His hand and He had taken Raymond. No, Raymond had done no evil: he had been angry, naturally, at times; during his Mother's last illness the doctor had treated the family with disrespect, saying repeatedly *'L'alcoolisme, voilà l'ennemi!'* and once, much provoked, he had knocked a man down at the *café* next door: but he had done no real evil in his life—his short life—not yet thirty, and already under the earth behind the high iron gates at the top of the long hill.

'Ne crains-tu point Dieu?—puisque tu es condamné' why were they condemned? She could think of nothing that they had done—if only death could have struck them, too,—but they would live on alone in the desolate house, and perhaps to be very old: yet it was not that which she so dreaded to go back to, not even Germaine's wild sorrow. He had looked so confidently towards the future. *'Quand elle sera grande'* he would say of Odette, and sometimes, laughing, of himself and Germaine— *'Quand nous serons vieux, nous deux—au coin de feu'* or *'quand il y aura un fils à la maison.'* Most of all he had looked forward to a son.

'Ne crains-tu point Dieu?' It came all again in a louder gust; almost like a threat, as if the penalty for not fearing Him would fall on them there, at that moment, in that solemn place.

She had always believed in Him, how could one do otherwise? without expecting to understand His will, though everything had not been easy.

Before Odette was born she would rather have gone away and lived alone, leaving those two together: and it had not been possible and she had stayed.

But this was different: coming over the bridge this evening she had seen the shop and *café* lamps twinkling across the water, the masts in the harbour swinging gently in the twilight, the dredger going out noisily with its red lights and here and there a few dark figures on the quayside leaning over the low stone parapet, and calling out to it, as it went by: she saw and heard them but they were not there; they were all dead things and at the same time horribly alive, all saying as she passed them 'we are here, we shall always be here, tomorrow—next week.' And yet they were not really there. She said again to herself—*'Mon Dieu! mon Dieu!'* and then she saw that He too was there and not there, He had changed also; He had changed her; she was not herself, or someone else, a stranger standing alone in a strange crowd, in a strange church, there and yet not there; Yes, she feared Him not now with the old fear of not honouring or trusting Him enough; she no longer believed in His justice or His love.

'Oh! Amour, amour divin de Dieu' she looked up, the Abbé seemed hot and tired, he stopped to wipe his face with his handkerchief, then pointed with it in his hand, to the big crucifix on the pillar opposite the pulpit, as he came to his last word.

'Quelque soit le malheur qui nous attend, quelque soit la fange de notre passé, pas une ombre ne passe sur nos visages flétris que Jésus-Christ ne chasse de son doux et aimable sourire; pas une larme ne coule de nos paupières crispées que Jésus-Christ ne garde pour en faire un bijou pour sa couronne d'or immortelle ou pour arroser sa couronne noire d'épines!'

And then suddenly, stinging and almost blinding her, tears came.

They made things dim but they made them clear. It was Christ whom she saw now hanging there above her, His head bent, His feet crossed with the nails through them and His hands: He would not have done it. He was not like God: He had been young and had suffered too, died and done no evil; giving back life, not taking it, healing sick people, loving children. It was He who had said—*'Laissez les petits enfants—'* and *'Elle n'est pas morte, elle dort'*. Now, for the first time in all that week she saw not Raymond, but Odette; the child was left and it was to her that she went slowly home not thinking any more, not feeling anything except that she was very tired.

Germaine was sitting where she had left her staring out at the window in the room which had grown quite dark, with the child on a stool beside her talking sleepily to itself. She had not put her to bed, she said, because she could not go past the room up there, it frightened her, and the whole house, it was horrible—horrible. Aglaë lit the lamp and as she stooped to take Odette upstairs Germaine turned round to them with her white face and half blind eyes.

'The child is like you, Aglaë,' she said, 'she feels nothing, she hasn't shed a tear.' And Aglaë answered, rather wearily, that perhaps it was well for the house, if someone could still be happy in it, telling Odette to kiss her mother good-night—and then as the child went to her, her mother seized her by the shoulders—crying out in a voice that was somehow like the red and heavy and swollen eyes.

'Don't you miss your Father, who used to play with you? Don't you miss him? It is no use repeating that he will come back. He will never come back, *jamais, entends-tu—jamais, jamais, jamais*'—breaking into violent sobs as Aglaë drew Odette gently away.

Going upstairs she asked why he would not come back and when she was told that this time it was a long, long voyage she said no more till she was tucked up and had been kissed good-night and then—*'Toi, tu ne voyages pas —tu ne voyages pas, dis—'*, she said—*'tu seras là'*, sitting up in the high wooden bed—with her Mother's feverish white face and the same look in her eyes which Aglaë remembered there had been in the Father's on the night when she was born. Aglaë kissed and tucked her up again: *'Moi? mais tu sais je ne voyage jamais, je suis là, chérie, je suis toujours là.'* But neither of them had rested much that night and Aglaë had not been able to get Germaine to bed at all.

Her grief was very passionate. At first she said she must have Odette to sleep with her and then that she could not bear the child, and must have Aglaë, and then that no one could sleep with Aglaë, it was like lying beside a stone—and yet that it was impossible to sleep alone—she would never sleep again, until at length, worn-out she slept till noon and even then it was difficult to rouse her.

In a week or two she was back at the Nouvelles Galleries, though still too tired to do anything at home; though when once or twice Aglaë had swept out the neglected room, she had taken it for a reproach.

'One is not the *bon Dieu*', she said, 'one cannot do everything, and it is not always the *Fête* at the Galleries with that camel of a Duhamel *quelle poison, cette femme-là*, and as if one's suffering was not enough!'

But if the bed was not made till afternoon Aglaë made it, and one day, early in July she found Raymond's portrait under the pillow and without looking at it put it back in its place among the ornaments on the commode.

A day or two later she found it again and put it back in the same place, but when some weeks afterwards, looking under the bed for the thimble dropped from her finger, she found the portrait there, covered with dust and fallen hair, she took it down and with her heart beating and her hand shaking, threw it quickly on the fire and watched it burn. It was taken at the shop in the Rue des Postes on the Wedding Day; it was the only one they had of him, but Germaine did not say that she had lost it, or Aglaë that it had been found.

In August they took Odette to the Fair in the Place St Jacques where last year they had gone with Raymond who had bought each of them a little pink metal pig, for luck, with the name across its back, but there had been none with Aglaë, so on hers there was Annette, and giving it to her, he said, *'C'est plus jolie, Annette, n'est-ce-pas?'* and Germaine had answered, *'Annette, c'est un nom de petite fille:—Aglaë c'est justement un nom de tante, ou de religieuse, il y en a quelque chose de triste, pas jeune—pas gai.'*

'Alors, pour la Fête, nous garderons Annette,' he said and called her by that name all day, and they had all been very happy and as gay as children, spinning round to the music on the flying pigs, so near the big church door that going through to the other door to get quickly out of the crowd one could only just squeeze by.

This year Odette went round on the flying pigs alone, while they stood watching her, not holding tightly on as Aglaë had bidden her but waving dangerously to them as she passed.

'She remembers nothing', Germaine said, looking up at her and then: *'Jolie fête pour nous, deux tristes femmes, et pas un homme, pas l'ombre d'un homme; j'en ai assez.'*

So though Odette begged hard to stay they went home quite early in the afternoon—Germaine to sit over the novel with the picture of two lovers enlaced on the cover, which she had bought on the way back, and Odette and Aglaë to play at shop on the doorstep with things, reels in the work-box and coloured pebbles from the shore. But the game had not gone on very long before Odette cried out that she was forgetting everything: '*Non, non c'est moi qui vend, et deux fois tu as oublié ton petit paquet.*' She had forgotten, overtaken by a sudden weariness, an unwillingness to think or act any more. 'If you were to play with the child for a while?' she said to Germaine going in. 'I am rather tired. I want some rest.' Germaine looked up from her book with surprise and a faint alarm.

'But you have done nothing; you are never tired, it is not an illness?' It might have been one, she could give no reason for it, this unnatural fatigue yet when she was about to lie down on her bed upstairs, she found she could not. '*C'est honteux*' she said to herself going over instead to sit by the window, with idle hands and unseeing eyes, '*C'est honteux—honteux.*' It seemed for a moment as if it were not she who sat there; this was how Germaine had sat for nearly a week after Raymond's death, always repeating if one tried to speak to her '*Laisse-moi, il m'est trop difficile de supporter la vie. Laisse-moi.*'

She got up and bathed her face, brushing the wet hair back from it and went down again to prepare the dinner and after that was cleared away took out her little book of accounts but she could not do them, she could not stay indoors tonight: for the first time in all her life the daily things which had never irked her, against which she had never before rebelled pressed like a weight on her: the quiet house, the shabby streets outside, the endless sewing, pile after pile of it, always there to do, and to take away and to bring in again. It was only once a year the Fair and wretched enough today as Germaine had said for both of them, but over there it was going on, and now, almost against her will she stole out, walking quickly over the bridge to stand for an hour in the swing and glare and noise, looking across from time to time at the still, high things beyond the row of plane trees beside the Church, the flying buttresses and the belfry roof and up again to, here and there, a patch of stars in the clouded summer night above; restless and not herself; not wishing to be herself and like her name, that 'Aglaë' in which as Germaine had said there was something sad, not young, not gay: the name of a *religieuse*—yet they had peace, it was in their faces, a tranquil brightness—not sadness or rebellion or desire for any ungiven thing; no one was like them, they were only like themselves—they had all sorts of names—a name was nothing, but standing there looking up at the tower of St Jacques very dark and square and motionless against the threatening sky, '*Annette, c'est un nom de petite fille*' and '*Alors, pour la Fête, nous garderons Annette*'—it was that she heard as if it were spoken by a living voice, as if tonight were not tonight, as if everything which had come between that day and this were the dream—the dream.

Already on the side of the *Place* by the *grand'rue* they were beginning to take down the booths and put the lights out. The flying pigs by the porch were still going round to the din of the loud harsh music, but the crowd was thinner, the place would soon be as empty and silent as it was every night of the year: there was a sadness unlike any other, she thought, about the end of a *Fête*, though a *Fête* was only a little thing in life, hardly a part of it, shorter and gayer than anything else, with this different sadness at the end. She did not know, why she had come out alone to watch it, or why she did not want to leave it [go back], as she turned slowly into the rue d'Écosse, walking away from it up the long curved street.

'Annette c'est un nom de petite fille' but it was not her name and she was not even young, she was thirty-two. The street was dark, with only a lamp or two and [or] the light from a window thrown across the road in front of her, and it seemed quite empty as she turned into it—but half-way up a man lurched out from one of the doorways, swaying and moving uncertainly towards her. She stepped aside to let him pass as he came up, and he had passed her when suddenly he wheeled round, catching her, crushing her against him; blotting out everything, seizing everything and holding it in a violent darkness.

It was all over in a moment—the strength of his arm, the closeness of his body, the heat of his breath as his lips came down on hers, burning and bruising them, and letting them go at last with something left there and something taken away as if they and she herself could never be the same again.

He loosed her quickly, as he had caught her, leaving her breathless, looking up at him by the light of the lamp above them, not able to move or speak, or to feel anything except the strangeness of his lips and hers—while he stood staring back at her, smiling stupidly.

'Faut pas être fachée', he said at length. *'T'es jolie, tu sais. On a bu. C'est la fête là-bas—'* swinging round again and unsteadily on down the bend of the half-lit street.

She stood there watching him, till he was out of sight: she had meant to go as far as the Casino, and round by the sea-front, but now she turned hastily back through the square. She did not remember what he had said, but she saw his face as she had seen it in the lamplight, a young, brown, handsome face above the blue jersey worn by the seamen on the Channel boats, the face which had somehow changed her and the look of the well-known streets as she hurried through them, afraid to stay out any longer and yet not wanting to go home.

The house was in darkness when she reached it, and she crept very softly upstairs, and past the door of Germaine's room and into bed beside Odette trying to, sleep to put away the thought of what had happened in the rue d'Ecosse but no sleep came. Only after a while her closed eyes filled with tears, burning them, lying hot upon her cheeks: Odette lay by her, sleeping soundly and very far away: she felt that she was quite alone; an immense loneliness like a wound, a throbbing [dull] pain had taken hold of her, as if her body and soul were one great ache and there was nothing left of her but that.

Outside a storm had sprung up from the sea, the wind was rising, the rain beating violently against the pane. Listening to it she seemed to see it driving up in sheets from the harbour, and down, down, not here below, on the stones of the quay, but up there in the desolate Cemetery on the hill, drenching the wooden crosses and the grass of the mound under which Raymond was lying, drenching him too as he lay there also alone, out of reach, out of call, and so changed, with a scar across his forehead, and yet still Raymond with the eyes—the eyes!

She got up, lighting a candle going over to the window to look out, when suddenly in a little mirror on the wall beside it, she saw herself, her wet, stained face and behind it another face, not Raymond's, which brought a strange voice back with it—'*T'es jolie, tu sais, t'es jolie*' and all at once her whole body was shaken with sobs, she felt that [as if] something must break within her, if she could not check them; Raymond was there in the room quite near, nearer than he had been in life, and [but] she could not speak to him, he did not belong to her. She could not ask him to go or stay, she had never asked him anything, she had never asked anything of anyone but God, and asking Him now for quietness, in time her distress died down. She crept into bed again pressing her face against the pillow, but Raymond was by her closer than the child who lay beside her and she could not touch him, she could not bear it: it had never been like this before. She did not understand it or what was happening to her tonight, perhaps only God could understand and He knew that she could not bear it for very long. She remembered the text of one of the Abbé's sermons: '*Ayez la foi en Dieu—Tout ce que vous demanderez il vous sera accordé—*' but she did not know what to ask, she could only try to lie there quietly saying over to herself, '*Ayez la foi en Dieu*' and towards morning when the wind had dropped and Raymond was gone, it came to her that if he had still been there she could have touched him; that though he might never come to her like that again he had been there; he was not dead, he was alive because she was alive, and because he had been there alive with her, it seemed for a moment as if she could never die.

After that she slept herself waking late, and coming down next morning to find Germaine on the doorstep reading a letter which the postman had just brought in. She had never herself received a letter, there was no one to write, and for Germaine there were very few [not many]. She asked her now who[m] this one was from and Germaine said, a stranger or rather a friend whom she had met lately at the

Galleries. He had come in once or twice to buy things, he was a foreman of the works on the new tramways then being laid in the *grand'rue*, *'très comme il faut'* she said, 'a poet also and almost a gentleman' and when Aglaë asked his name she looked down to the bottom of the page to find it—'Leroux' she said, 'but he writes very badly—André Leroux.'

It was not long afterwards that Leroux began to come to the house and when he came, if it was not too late, Aglaë made some excuse to take Odette out of it, although from the first he had been very amiable to both of them. His home was at Rouen where he sometimes spent a Sunday coming back by an early train to his work in the town which depressed him, he said, because he disliked the sea and could never sleep by it. So, though it was some way off, he lodged at the Inn with the *bosquets* at St Pierre l'Église, the village at the end of the wide straight road bordered on one side by beeches and poplars and on the other by the river bank along which the refuse of the town was thrown in straggling heaps, crushing down the high meadow grass and the king-cups, of which, when they had to take that road, Odette made her bouquets in spring.

'C'est plus gai', he said, *'cette petite auberge à bosquets—la mer—c'est lugubre, on dirait une femme, abandonnée, toujours plaignante—accusatoire: non merci que Dieu m'en garde!'* But Aglaë did not understand how anyone could choose to walk twice a day along such a foul-smelling road or sleep any sounder so far from the freshness of the sea and in that odour of the *abattoirs* which always hung about St Pierre.

Raymond had loved the sea: his friends had all been sailors or fishermen, broad, straight men for the most part, clear-eyed, with faces browned and roughened by the wind; unlike Leroux who was thin and a remarkable tan with a stoop in his narrow shoulders, and a face, not white but the colour of the Figure on her crucifix, though when he was tired or excited, it turned almost grey.

There was something burning about the eyes, and at these times, something like ash about the face, which though he was well to do had a wasted look like his hands which were hardly ever still, the long tobacco-stained fingers perpetually rolling cigarettes or travelling up and down his knee while he talked; and he was always talking, often of things which she could not understand as the actors had done at the Theatre in the Casino to which Germaine had taken her one summer.

Raymond's friends had had little to say and when they spoke it was chiefly of the sea: Leroux was different, different from anyone she had ever seen and while he was in the house he made it strange and unlike itself.

She did not want to sit watching him and listening to him but while he was there she could not forget him or keep her eyes on her work or her mind on the work, Odette, Germaine or the happenings of the day. He made these too unlike themselves so that if she could she found some excuse and slipped upstairs and sat alone, until she heard the door bang after him and then, at once the house and her thoughts and they, all three of them were like themselves again.

She had not said this to Germaine; she had never spoken of him to her, until one night when he had stayed very late Germaine came up to her room on the way to bed, and stood in the doorway watching her put away her work in the commode.

'You don't like André', she said suddenly and sharply. 'You don't like his coming to the house.'

And Aglaë had answered that she knew nothing of him and that the house was as much Germaine's as hers. And then Germaine had broken out that she understood nothing; she could not be expected to understand because she was born *vieille fille*.

But for those who were not there was life—life. And one must live while there was yet time; there was little enough of it *grand Dieu* and the *Sainte Vierge* herself did not suppose that one could live for ever with the dead.

She stood there, taking the pins from her dark hair, letting it fall about her shoulders, her face flushed and her brown eyes shining; she looked very young tonight and very tired.

'Si, il faut vivre', she said, *'et moi; je ne suis pas faite comme toi. Ça doit te rendre folle, et moi aussi, cette couture éternelle. Ça te donne l'air d'une figure en cire, toujours assise—toujours cousant. Ça c'est la mort mais moi je veux vivre et toi tu ne sais pas ce que c'est.'*

Aglaë shut the drawer of the commode—'Naturally, if one is only a figure in wax', she spoke quietly and without bitterness—but she thought in herself. I shall always remember this—*une figure en cire—ça, c'est la mort* and then that such figures were like neither death nor life.

She had seen some waxworks once in a tent at the Fair and she saw them now, the greasy yellow faces, the glassy eyes, the rigid forms with their nailless hands, rusty clothes; there was something more lifeless than death about them and more dreadful than anything in life. In all human faces there was good and evil and something sacred, because there was the soul; in all dead faces there was something more than death, and something lovelier than life: but these had been so horribly like life, so horribly unlike it they had almost frightened her; not dead, not living; faces and not faces, in their stiffness, and their smoothness and their stare.

'And if I did not sew', she added, 'what then could I bring to the house since it is all that I can do?'

'But one cannot speak to you', Germaine said wearily, 'if it is all to be like the word of God and as if you were a child. One is not serious; it is simply André. He tires one out and then when he is gone one cannot sleep. Always it is as if we had eaten nothing, he takes it all out of one, even the bread and the soup, and in the end he is never satisfied. One does not complain, it is not his fault—it is André, and there is no one like him, you even you must see that.'

Perhaps there was not, perhaps it was just as well, perhaps it was true that she could not understand because she was born *vieille fille*, and yet in Raymond's day she had partly understood their happiness. She remembered the wedding-night and afterwards many another—looking back it seemed as if they had all been summer nights though it could not have been so—when on the other side of the thin wall, she had heard them talking, laughing together, moving about the room. But now when once or twice a week Leroux came swinging into the house, calling for this and that, mending the latch or a broken window-pane as if he were master of it, she could not and did not wish to understand. There was no need for Germaine to say that for her there was no one like him: Aglaë knew it and of her desperate hope that one day he would marry her, though that she saw could mean only a long deception. '*Tout le temps il change de femme*', she had said, 'but then, with that, he would belong to me.'

For more than an hour after she had gone to bed Aglaë stood at the window looking down on the empty quay, quite dark below and across the water to the line of dim yellow lamps on the town side, and then from these to the crowd of stars above, brighter than usual tonight up there in the high blue stillness. Old M. Bax at the optician's used to say that they were worlds like ours with people in them, but he had also said that his God was some person called Voltaire and even in the matter of repairs his word was not reliable.

Surely the stars were God's lights in heaven, and yet looking up at them she found it difficult to pray, difficult to believe that from that great distance He could hear or care for her or even know who she was. She felt herself she was not anyone, the star-light always made her feel it, and sometimes, for one dreadful moment, as if He Himself were not: until looking down again at the familiar quayside and out to the old dark town, her self came back and God, so suddenly, as real, as near as He was at St Jacques on Sundays.

Through the long week one might grow tired with nothing changing in one's life and oneself unchanged, but at the end there was Mass and Vespers—still one must pray '*Tout ce que vous demanderez*'—it was the '*Seigneur*' who had said it and He too who had spoken gently to the woman taken in adultery and the Magdalen, looking into their hearts as He would look into hers, seeing how if it was wrong to be content that things were as they were she could not help it: if she had tried, it was not possible to pray for the marriage of Germaine and Leroux.

Tomorrow it would be just a year since Raymond died: Easter was late and only yesterday she had found grape-hyacinth and violets on the dusty roadside leaving them there, with no heart to pluck and take them home because all through the long rough winter there had been nothing like the sadness of this spring. Walking along the outlying roads, taking the work back, she had seen [watched] the poplars change from golden brown to the first young green, and behind them on the orchard slopes, the apple and pear and cherry trees whitening day by day.

Up on the *château* cliffs she and Odette had spent one afternoon gathering cowslips and making balls of them, and it was, in the sunshine, a picture, she thought, sitting there on the short bright grass—the child—her cheeks glowing, her brown hair tossed, throwing the yellow balls over and catching them back, with the gulls overhead very white against a patch of grey cloud, wheeling and sweeping down suddenly—they and their shadows, across the steep cliff-side into the sea, such a silver blue and after a spell of great winds, such a quiet sea.

On the *jeudi saint* they had gone to St Jacques for the Washing of Feet but getting there late and with the Church so full had seen nothing, except at the end, the priest who had washed them, going out in his splendid vestments, and then when the crowd had cleared away the little boys in black pinafores still on their bench below the chancel steps, with the round brown loaves on their knees or tucked under their arms while they sat there pulling their boots on. The Sacristan with the shaved black chin and little twinkling eyes, stood by, not really angry, but rapping them sharply over the shoulders for laughing and kicking their boots about in a kind of game on the pavement, after the holy office and in that sacred place. Odette laughed too and spoke to the smallest with a *brosse* of thick hair and a mole on his cheek—asking him if the water was hot or cold.

'*Sais pas*', he said, '*on vous touche seulement les pieds*' only at home, he added, they had scrubbed so hard, almost to break the skin, in order to have them clean for the ceremony. '*Veux pas qu'on me touche*' Odette had said, '*au moins des gens qu'on ne connait pas.*' '*Pourquoi*' he asked, '*et pour ça ai vous donne le pain.*' And then they had talked of going out for *crevettes* at low tide, and the crabs in the pools of the rocks and of cutting their feet there. And at the end he offered her his loaf, which Aglaë forbade her to accept and he had walked half-way home with them. It made her smile—it was like that—Odette would speak to people and they would want to give her something, and not, at all, to let her go.

That day, no doubt it was the April weather, one hour all sunshine and the next a driving rain, she had caught cold and on Easter Sunday when a little fever showed itself Aglaë stayed away from the *grand' Messe*, to be with her—and Germaine came back from it *'éreintée'*, she said, and too tired with headache to go up to the Cemetery with the new *couronne* of white, and purple beads which they had bought the night before, asking Aglaë to carry it up for her, as she did in the early afternoon, going out again between six and seven to the Sermon and Benediction at St Jacques.

Lighting her candle in the chapel of the Sacred Face [Sainte Face] she remembered how high the grass had grown above the grave, thinking to go again tomorrow to speak about it to the *gardien* who had been well paid to keep it cut: and coming out by the font someone had passed her the *eau bénite* and touched her on the arm. It was Madame Rambert who had been at school with her and now kept the bookstall at the *gare maritime*.

They walked together across the Square, Madame Rambert talking of the great number of English tourists who had come over in the last few days.

Naturally she said, that meant a good Easter. The money was always safe, it was an English quality, to pay: but for the rest, after five years at the *Gare* one understood nothing of them; the money absolutely safe but no *rapport*, no confidence.

Recommend this romance and invariably they would take that other, so that at this hour one had learned to offer precisely what one did not wish to sell. And the same thing with the commissionaires. Only that morning Jean Cotard had made the observation, the money safe but always that profound mistrust *comme si on était tous des chiens* and as if one earned one's bread by an appropriation of the *petits bagages*, and not with much patience and very hardly by the insufficient *pourboire*. And then she passed on to Germaine and the affair of Leroux now common talk she said at the Nouvelles Galleries. It was to be hoped she would not lose her place. A second marriage, if not so soon, at her age, one could understand it—. And Aglaë had replied that a marriage, even a second one, was not always a matter of half an hour.

'Ni un enfant non plus', said Madame Rambert, *'et dans une famille jusqu' là si honorable! Eh! pauv' dame, elle fait une folie, une très belle folie.'*

They parted at the end of the *grand'rue*, the dusk was already falling over the quay and Aglaë stood for a moment under the arcades from which she could see, but only dimly now across the *arrière-port*, the little yellow house with its red pointed roof and narrow door, two hundred years old, or it might be older in which she was born and was somehow sure that she should die.

A child! No she had never noticed it, never thought of it, a child to take Odette's place, growing up with her, playing about the house with her, yes, she saw it preferred before her. It could not be true, she would not think of it or what it might be like, his child, a son or daughter of André Leroux.

She had to wait, before crossing the road way for some trucks being shunted along the line: the Paris train would come through at midnight bringing Leroux who had gone there on business a week ago.

But tonight at least the house would be quiet and here in the nearing dark, it was quiet too. A great peace, from the sky to the water hung over the harbour: the boats were moored, empty and silent and without lights. It was Easter night; they would not go out till morning: the masts just stirred, they were never really still; the stillness was over the sky and the town and the harbour though there might be a breeze bearing out at sea.

She crossed the road and the bridge and turned the sharp corner of the quay with its short line of irregular houses, set far back from the edge, the stretch of rough cobble-stones between, wide and grey and dim in the twilight: there was only a child on it—running towards—'Odette, Odette' she cried out as the child came up to her catching her skirt and hiding her face in it. Over beyond, at the house, in the doorway, she saw the tall thin figure of Leroux completely filling it, standing a moment and then going in; and a light showing suddenly in the dark square of the window of her sister's room above.

She bent down quickly, feeling a chill in the air and seeing the child was shivering, shaking against her.

'*Mais qu'as-tu*', she said, '*et tu sais ce n'est pas sage, tout enrhumée comme* [*que*] *tu es, sortir comme ça. Il faut revenir: vite, vite. Donne-moi la main.*' But as she touched it so hot, so burning it closed tightly and feverishly on hers, dragging her round with all the force of the small frail body and back towards the bridge. And, fast, not seeming to see or know where she was going, still pulling with the pitiful small hand, the child had borne her on and up the steep Le Follet street, only saying each time that Aglaë tried to stop or turn her back, in a dull vague way, as if she were talking in her sleep.

'*Non, je n'peux pas. Non, je n'peux pas.*' And so they had come to the Follet cliffs, where Aglaë took off her cloak, wrapping it round her, and making her sit down in a sheltered hollow in the cliff-side out of the wind just springing up not strong but keen.

And there Odette had flung herself against the long damp grass breaking into a terrible sobbing calling out wildly '*Ah! tu es là, tu es là*' as Aglaë drew her towards her, holding her closely.

'*Si, si. Mets-toi la tête contre moi. Là, ne parle pas. Vois tu, c'est moi, c'est ma main.*' Then as suddenly as the outbreak had come it had gone, leaving the child lying spent with shut eyes and limp hands, a dead weight in her arms, while below she could hear the tide lapping against the shingle and see above, beyond the low lights of the town and the line of the harbour the dark headland of La Veullette, and the Easter moon rising out of the sea.

At last she got up, setting the child on her feet, saying gently, '*Mais il fait tard, il faut vien*—' only to hear once more, in the same dull tone '*je n'peux pas. Non, je n'peux pas*' and to repeat herself almost as helplessly.

'*Mais il faut vien—il fait tard.*' Stooping to fasten the cloak more securely round her, and standing again in the high blowing grass looking out to the headland, puzzled and troubled not knowing what more to do or say.

Bright, like a star in the clearness of the oncoming April night the yellow light on the headland flashed out and went in, the red and white light on the harbour showing much nearer but fainter: and over the sea was the same great hush which a short while since had hung over the town; a sea growing darker, not blue and not grey, moving, not moving, not calling tonight in its wonderful sleep as last week with the breakers as high as the lighthouse, and foaming and grinding below on the stones, it had seemed to do for some quieting hand and there was none. There had once been one, she remembered it now; she had heard that sermon at the Sailors' Chapel at the Follet point. He had lived by the sea and gone out in boats with fishermen, such boats it might be as these in the harbour: filling the empty nets, knowing how to speak to the wind: He had walked on the water.

She saw Him—it seemed for a moment she really saw Him, tall, very stately but standing so patiently on the darkness and loneliness and wildness of the sea, the arms held out as they are to children, the Voice—she saw Him—she did not hear it—calling St Peter to Him across the waves. She knelt down on the grass, drawing the child as near as was safe to the edge of the cliff, and tried as best she could, speaking softly, almost whispering, to make her see Him too.

'*Rassurez-vous, c'est Moi,*' He had said, '*n'ayez point peur.*' If we believed in Him, if we had only a little faith, He could make us do what by ourselves we could not do.

He was there on the sea, He was at the house '*tout à fait comme moi*', she said, '*et moi tu sais, je suis toujours là*'. He was always there, though it might not be His wish that we should always see Him, saying to each of us: '*C'est Moi, n'ayez point peur. Rassurez-vous.*'

'*Mais si je pouvais Le voir*—' Odette had said holding on to her skirt again and looking intently out to sea—and Aglaë answered, '*Chérie, c'est possible: aie seulement la foi.*'

Talking of other things, if it were better to choose the green *perroquet* her mother had promised or one of Madame Rambert's kittens, it would not be well to have them both—hand in hand they had waded through the deep grass, and come to the foot of the climbing street; and there under the lamp Odette had stopped again, looking up with a livid white face, and said quite quietly, now in her waking voice.

'Non, je ne reviens pas à la maison.'

'Mais chérie, il faut.'

'Non, non, je ne reviens pas. Plutôt je marcherai sur la mer, du loin, du loin; si, si, je peux, vois-tu, je marcherai', breaking away and running fast towards the quay.

Just at the edge a fisherman caught her, *'Faut ben garder les moiuls'*, he said to Aglaë as she ran up to them. *'A c'te heure faut ben les garder à la maison.'*

Her heart was beating, but now she spoke sternly. It was wrong to go against the *Seigneur*'s will. It was His will that she should return to the house and not that she should walk upon the sea. *'Et moi'*, she added, *'pense-tu, je serai seule sans toi, et triste, je pleurerais.'* At that Odette had turned and gone obediently on. Only when they came to the house at the steps, she had pressed both hands very tightly across her eyes, saying quietly, *'Vois-tu je n'ai point peur, mais conduis-moi.'* And that way Aglaë had led her in and across the room where Leroux was sitting smoking by the table, his long legs stretched out, his head thrown back against the wall.

Upstairs she put Odette to bed, giving her a draught which she hoped would make her sleep, meaning to call the Doctor in next day and tell him of this attack of fever and its painful outcome: and on her way down to get herself some supper, looking into Germaine's room to find that she had gone to bed with a frightful migraine, she said, only wanting to be let alone.

Leroux was sitting as she had left him: the room was thick with smoke and he did not move as she came in. Why was he there? What right had he to stay on alone, smoking and sprawling in the empty room, as if the place belonged to him [was his] and he could behave in it as he pleased. She was tired: she did not wish to disturb the two above, but she would not sit and eat with him. She went over to the shelf, cutting off a piece of bread and some cheese, putting them on a plate and turning back to take them up with her.

'Restez', he said when she was at the stairway door. His tone was insupportable; not only as if the house was his but one's body and one's soul.

'I am going up, to the child', she said. He got up taking the plate from her hand and placing it on the table, standing himself behind it, thin, very tall, his head reaching nearly to the ceiling beam, with the light of the lamp thrown up in a yellow glow on his sharp grey face.

'The child can wait', he said. 'What is the matter with the child? It is simply nervous, there is nothing wrong with it. Isn't its Mother up there—*hein?* And how it loves its Mother and how its Mother loves it! What was the husband like? Perhaps, after all it is not his child—What was he like? *Et quoi! le mari?*'

She stood quite still: she thought, if I must stand here till morning, if with his sharp grey face and his long tobacco-stained fingers he should try to kill me for it I shall not speak of Raymond to Leroux. He smiled. '*Eh! bien.* I am not interested in the husband. Probably his wife deceived him; *on fait ce qu'il faut faire*, but you—the eyes are remarkable: you have the eyes and Germaine the hair.'

It was insupportable: he was not himself: he had never behaved like this before; one could not listen to him, one could not stay. He had thrown his cigarette down on the table where it was making a little smoking hole in one of the blue squares of the cloth: and he stopped it with his thumb.

'The hair,' he went on, 'there is something strange [curious] about it—*le corps, la chair, il y en a des teints, des contours, des contacts exquis; quand même ça reste toujours quelque chose à manger, le plat du jour. Les cheveux, on les goûte seulement*, and is it not by that and the way they put their hands up to it, and how perfectly they are aware of it, that when one is sick of them, dog-sick they are sometimes able to keep one for another half an hour longer.'

Why did she answer him?

'And it [is] also that which lasts—' she remembered her Mother's hair which had never, in the end, gone grey looking in death so wonderfully brown.

'It is that which remains alive when the rest has perished.'

'*Parfaitement.*' It was as if he had seen [caught] her thought.

'The loveliest I have yet seen was at the Morgue, and there was no face with it. But even with one, it has not the call, it has not the call.'

He came round the table towards her, stopping in front of the lamp and shuttering the light off, leaving the room half dark, though his eyes had some light. They were red, like two flames, they were looking at her and making her look at him, holding there in that dark quiet room as she stood very straight, very still, with her arms hanging down and her back against the stairway door.

There [was] not a sound in the room, in the house, outside:—she was waiting for that, it might come from the street, a voice or a footstep and with courage, great courage, and fast, like a leap—it was only a step and she would be out upon the quay.

But no one could pass him or what would he do? He could do what he liked, he was dreadful, his eyes were and they could do it. His eyes had got hers, they were drawing her, forcing her, nearer, much nearer.

She thought, 'I must stand very still, I have only my eyes, they are stronger than his, I belong to myself from my head to my feet, for he is not one of us, we are clean, but his hands are all stained, he has eyes like a beast's, I belong to myself, it is all that I have. I have never been touched. No—only by Raymond, so lightly—and—here in that room, on the hair on the forehead.'

She did not belong to herself yet, not alive Raymond was real not Leroux, she looked straight in his eyes, the red eyes; he was horrible, not like a man, he would spring like a beast, she could see his brown teeth and his hands—there would be nothing left of her, nothing! She could not be touched, there was life in her, life, a great beat, very loud, very still, from her head to her feet, this was life, and great strength; he was close to her now, he was reeking of smoke—he was vile, not a man. She stood stiff like a corpse with arms hanging down her back against the stairway door. She had his eyes with hers, he could not move she knew—against her eyes. Nothing but these would hold him back. And no one could touch her, no one but Raymond. 'I belong to him. I belong to him.' Perhaps she had cried it aloud but she could not be sure. A sudden dizziness had overtaken her, bringing a blackness with it like a cloud across her eyes, and then that passed, and the room grew slowly clear again. She saw Leroux still standing there, but farther off. Her head was throbbing and the room was close, too hot, too stifling. 'Open the door', she said. Her voice seemed weak and small not like her own, it sounded too a long way off.

She could not feel her hands or anything alive about herself. All she could feel was that she must have air. Leroux turned round with a sickening oath, some frightful blasphemy, and flung himself into the chair which he had left, throwing his arms out across the table and laying his head down between his arms against the edge. She went to the door and opened it and stood looking out on the quiet quay [as quiet] that in the whiteness of the moonlight [stars] it seemed even quieter than it had been two hours since when Odette had run out there to the gloomy half-lit quay and the night air freshened her face and aching head but her head still throbbed and she would have liked to stay there longer or go [on] a little way towards the town. But she felt too tired and came into [turned] the [close hot overheated] room again, slowly and leaving the door ajar.

(The words in square brackets are alternative wordings by Charlotte Mew written in the manuscript. Words in round brackets are words which seem to have been inadvertently omitted by the author.

From here to where the story breaks off unfinished, the handwriting is extremely difficult to transcribe, and this part of the manuscript seems to represent an earlier stage in the composition than the handwritten but 'fair' copy of the preceding pages. Editor's note.)

Leroux had not moved. The lamp glowed over him as if he [he was under the lamp]. The light fell [falling] full on his head and the sleeves of his striped brown coat, his hands and the big gold signet ring on the middle finger which Germaine had given him. The plate of bread and cheese was there on the table beside him where he had laid it, the ends [edge] of his outspread fingers touched the rim. She remembered how she had meant to take it upstairs with her but this seemed hours ago [Germaine] she did not know now what kept her there [why she did not take it now] why she did not go at once to bed, but she could not. She could not leave him like this [that] she could not speak to him. (fill in) (C. Mew's note.) There was something about the outspread arms and the head so low,—for so tall a man so tall—it was such a little head—: and about the whole figure that reminded her suddenly of a woman she had seen once stretched out in a house in the rue de Matelots from whom the sea had just taken everyone [thing]: she saw again her bent figure and hidden face and disordered [damp] hair—sitting [crouching] that way over the table in the empty [desolate] room, taking no notice of the neighbours who had come in to comfort her.

But Leroux too seemed quite alone in the room as if she had already left it, and in spite of herself she went across and stood for a moment behind his chair. Looking down on him there, with the light on his small head she saw that his fine black hair was wet and the starched white collar which he wore on holidays was limp with sweat. Suddenly and very gently

(One page is missing in the manuscript here. Editor's note.)

was still there, he was standing in front of her holding her black cup.

'Encore du café?'

She made him a sign to remove the *valise* and sit down.

'C'est bon—'

'Le café', she said, *'c'est ma seule qualité.'*

'It was nearly forgotten', he said, 'the *valise*, one had only two minutes to catch the train.'

She asked if [said she supposed] it was crowded.

'Naturally on Easter Sunday—well Paris is no great journey, but tonight one might have come from the world's end one feels.' He pressed [passed] his hand across his forehead and over his hair. *'Mon di!* well—one asks to feel, one asks in fact nothing else and after all there is something—in an immense fatigue.'

He had not been to bed, so to speak, he went on, the night before—he had left St Lazaire at ten and spent some hours at Rouen with his sister *institutrice et poitrinaire, pas encore fini mais ça commence et cela l'ennuie de mourir.* He had eaten little and consequently had drunk a good deal, the machine must go.

'One feels sometimes', he said, 'like the driver of an infernal *rapide* which has never stopped and is never going to, pouf-pouf! and in this era for what? To feed some new variety of worm, but at least a more engaging variety than *le sacré patron*. It will wait till one is dead. *Plus* 15-30 per cent for *ces messieurs* with the polished finger nails and the beautiful button-holes. *Travaillez mes enfants, travaillez.*'

'It is perhaps', she said, 'that the hours for everyone are too long, and the work itself not wholesome, not like the life of the sea—one has seen the men going home in the evening—.'

He rolled a cigarette and lit it. '*Permettez?*' he said. 'The trade of the sea is no more wholesome than that of the earth—personally I detest both, but there is little to choose between one trade, and another. Nearly every man is an *originel forcé* in a [some] cell, in a [some] trap—it is merely a question of size—and I would pitch every *patron* into Hell—who is not already there and simply because by God's grace he is the owner of the smartest, but this is a paltry *bain de mer,* and the tramways—that is not unhealthy work—you see them here going home, you can [may] see them in Paris, the filth and sweat, in the dust of the *boulevards,* waiting in queues for the trams, like dirty sheep. The sheep! they have a short fat time of it—not twenty-thirty years of a seesaw, the *travaux forcés* of the factory, and the suffocating kennel at Belleville, at Asnières where for an hour or so they are permitted to sleep.

'*Les femmes aussi qui sortent le soir éreintées de couture et de lessive,* and how many already *abimées* or ready to risk a pleasant death by abortion *n'ayant rien* have actually [today] not now more francs to pay their loaf and the milk for another *gosse Heureux les travailleurs, heureux les pauvres, leur patron* extends his hands to you in his benediction from the window of his auto.—*Dormez sur vos deux oreillers—vous êtes* [*tu es*] *mes enfants, je suis ton Dieu.* And if by chance one had a soul—! There is this your sea, the ships have their dreams, *le chant des sirènes, les paysages de jeunesse*; yellow sands and the palm-trees—, flamingos flying—, green islands sleeping like lizards on the steel of the sea. *Moi je ne suis pas poète mais j'en ai fait des vers*—strange speed, and strange wares. God knows what magic! *Mais reste éternellement la femme éreintée de couture ou de lessive* [*en sortant le soir*] *ce petit appartement fétide en sortant le matin le morne enfer du bureau ou de l'usine.*

'A man's life, great God, and he has one! Men! if it is [be] permitted to think of them as men, spinning round and round among the ordure in their little cages like the trapped rat in there. One day the clean earth will be beds for them and *ainsi de suite* for the puny litters they leave behind.'

'*Encore du café?*' she asked and he held out his cup.

'*C'est bon votre café.*'

'*Le café*', she admitted, '*c'est ma seule qualité*. But here it is only the visitors the *baigneurs* from Paris that one sees, in the spring in the summer, and they have invariably the air of being extremely happy, extremely gay. One had not thought of Paris as a place of so much misery, such effort.'

He smiled at her suddenly across the table, his smile was always this sudden flash. 'You are right. No, that is not Paris: call it a spot on her face. One sees black sometimes, and with me it is that four nights out of six I do not sleep—and then [that makes] everything is sc much larger than life, and detached, the perspective is lost—. No doubt I must have been arranged for on some very sleepless night—they say my mother was a *femme du monde* and my father—*sale histoire. Dieu ces femmes, quelle boue!* But we are all animals—every one of us; why should we grin in another's face.'

'It had not occurred to me', she said, 'that one was an animal though one has sometimes wondered if an animal also, even the most useless, the most dishonoured might not have some soul of its own—some little soul. That came to me one summer when there was a large rat up there in the attic, in the gutter, the house, it is evident is very old. No doubt it was starving, it became extremely bold. It would come and stare in at us through the window and Odette would laugh back at it without any fear. It was grotesque, but we grew attached to it: we gave it food until at last [length] Germaine became aware of it and insisted one day that it was vermin and must be destroyed. We begged its life but Germaine was insistent and it was she who procured the poison from M. (*name omitted in mss.*) the chemist and laid [put] it [that] down one evening. And the earliest morning we found it [our rat] again by the window but prostrate and dying though not yet dead. Its [His] ears one saw were very delicate, brown and of a texture not the same as its [his] body, finer, and creased.—One might have said—a leaf. It lay there quietly not quite dead, it was swollen, and with something very painful in its [his] eyes, the ears too crumpled, and delicate, like a leaf. It had not done any harm, but if it had that would have only been to follow its nature: if it was starving. It was [altogether] so much smaller than we, and less instructed and thus it lay at the spot where we used to feed it, not able to speak and with that something in its eyes—looking up at us—as at the point of death some very desolate human creature might have looked up at the *bon Dieu*. It looked at one as if we were gods, so, almost as if one was the *bon Dieu* oneself, and we had killed (it), only because it was as it was made.'

'*Absolument, comme le bon Dieu. Mais vous racontez bien.*'

'Perhaps it was wrong', she went on, 'but we had become attached to it. There was no other way to comfort Odette: we buried it, laid in (a) little box, up there, in a corner of the Cemetery.'

'*Le rat assassiné en terre bénite—c'est drôle*—but why? The beasts on all fours are more distinguished if it is only in their carriage—the mind too—clean—it is the foullest [the murkiest] part of us. And the life so simple, *au fond* so tranquil, *ils vont tout droit, ils vont tout droit,* they come up with their prey and seize it and lie down satisfied. But we, we are never satisfied, we never come up with ours, we never get anything actually by the throat. Always the search, always the search *et rien trouvé et la nuit tombe toujours* and Christ, Christ perhaps, *cet intéressant perdu* was the only one of us who ever really arrived—and simply, and tranquilly—by a magnificent *dédain. Mais ces* [*les*] *bêtes, ils arrivent toujours, ils vont tout droit—tout droit,* if I, *par exemple,* could have done that—! and I should have made an admirable beast, even perhaps the Emperor of the jungle. And is there not in their eyes a profundity, an innocence not in ours—the memory in fact of a paradise for which they are not required to die. Oh! I can tell you—there are transports—there is an enchantment in the darkest parts of their forests—I know, I had once a dream, *extraordinaire, extraordinaire.*'

He reached to the end of the table for his hat. 'Your coffee is good,' he said, 'and not a means of getting rid of me. And one talks too much, one is *égoïste, cela s'est vu, maintenant absolument, il faut partir.*'

But he did not get up, he sat stroking the black ribbon round his hat with his long brown fingers, looking across at her quietly [gently], more quietly [gently] than she had yet seen him look at anyone and as if from a greater distance. At other times, whenever he was in the room he had always seemed to be very near but now sitting there on the other side of the table only a foot or two away, he seemed farther off than he had ever seemed and at the same time not far off, it was very strange—and strange too that she did not want him now to go, she would rather he stayed, she did not mind how late, talking and smoking, she wished at the moment she had had her sewing—she did not like to sit so lazily with idle hands.

'*Restez*', she said—'*à vous voulez,* it is not so late one is not really so tired, and perhaps we might hear that dream—the dream of the forest?'

He laughed. 'Oh for you it would not be interesting, but even so very improving.' He stooped down suddenly, opening the *valise* taking a photograph from it and handing it across to her. '*Ma soeur*', he said, '*la poitrinaire la seule parente qui me reste*—and marriage was the dream of *cette petite condamnée*; naturally the family of the *prétendu* would not hear of it.'

Aglaë took the photograph in her hand and after looking at it passed it back to him. 'They are charming', she said, 'the eyes and the hands and the whole figure very graceful. One finds no trace of unhappiness or disappointment on the face.'

'*C'est un esprit fort*', he said, replacing the photograph in the *valise—'mais ce mariage manqué* remains the dream. And you—what I wonder are yours—and to whom do you tell them—?'

'I sleep very hardly', he said, 'I am fortunate I have but very few in the night—for these of the day too perhaps it is only when one is young that one dreams so often. And now, there is no one, if we cared to recount them who would be interested. The priest of course, one makes one's [goes to] confession every Saturday but he is only interested in one's sins, *le rêve* [one's dreams] one's hopes are for him, very wearisome, very useless.'

'Naturellement le péché, c'est là son métier—et tou' les prêtres gourmands, avares, malpropres, but the whole world of petticoats is an unclean world and of all the creatures who wear them, the *curés* are the most *infectes, ces jolies petites amies du bon Dieu.* And how gracefully it hangs on them sometimes *la jupe. Surtout quand ils sont ventries et les plus ventries les plus estimés* [*vénérés*].'

She did not reply, or entirely understand but the disrespect was unmistakable; unhappily he had no religion—and might not know how extremely disagreeable his tone must be to one of the faith and perhaps after all it was not intentional. It was certainly true that the Abbé Revault was very stout and greatly venerated [esteemed]—. For a few moments neither of them spoke and again tonight in this pause she noticed an unusual stillness in the room. The tick of the clock was always a part of it and sitting down here late as she had done so often when the other two had gone early to bed it was sometimes startling to hear it strike. Now and then a board in the old house would creak or the faint chatter of the mice which at one time had overrun it could be heard beneath the floor. But now there was just the tick tick of the clock, within and without no other sound.

'Silence, silence', Leroux cried out sharply, suddenly breaking it, 'one of the few things I really fear. I don't understand it.'

'That is perhaps because you are not accustomed to it', she suggested smiling—'but when one is—there are voices in it—distant it may be but distinct enough, there are one's thoughts.'

'The old rat, *par exemple*, up there in the Cemetery—?'

'What one remembers of that death above all', she said, 'is that he [it the poor thing] had no voice—and but for you one might have forgotten it as entirely as some others of these are forgotten who lie under very handsome monuments—and though there are realms still living in disregard

(*The text breaks off here. Editor's note.*)

Essays

THE GOVERNESS IN FICTION

THE GOVERNESS is, or was, well known to fiction. Once a prominent figure in literature, she is now, perhaps, mainly the invaluable puppet of the penny or threepenny novelette.

Among these older and more imperishable heroines we recall a few: the sweet Miss Raby of *Dr Birch and His Young Friends*; Becky Sharp; the audacious, vivacious, melodramatic Miss Gwilt of *Armadale*; the pathetic Catherine George of *The Village on the Cliff*; Jane Eyre, and Lucy Snowe. All of the same period this little company, but what an assortment of character they present! Miss Raby is but a sketch, yet one from the pen of a master. A chance allusion, a short parenthesis, suffices to make definite that delicate outline, but from these we feel the pleasant glow of 'the little schoolroom' wherein she sits! 'She keeps the accounts, writes out the bills, superintends the linen, and sews on the general shirt-buttons. Think of having such a woman at home to sew on one's shirt-buttons!' Happy 'old pupil' to whom such happiness befell.

Of another complexion is the sensational Miss Gwilt, with her 'mocking laugh', her 'symmetrical limbs', her 'merciless tyranny' of voice and eye, a private in that regiment of governess-adventuresses of whom the immortal Becky is the chief. The resemblance between them is but a superficial one, their talents were of the same order; the difference between them, both of one calling, both bold sinners as they be, is the difference between humanity and waxwork, between a figure in the National Gallery of Portraiture and an effigy in Madame Tussaud's.

Catherine George, the poor little twenty-year-old governess of *The Village on the Cliff*, has nothing in common with these arch schemers; she is a dreamer, a hungry child, who has 'not yet outgrown the golden age when all things call and beckon, and the apples and the loaves and the cakes cry, "Come, eat us! Come, eat us!" and the children wandering in fairyland reply, "We come, we come!" '

Fairyland was not to be her heritage: the cakes and apples were for other mouths; the time came when dreams had nothing to say to her; when her young life, 'part worried, part puzzled, part sad, and part happy too', missed the scant measure of its happiness, and a mistaken marriage turned her gaze from visions to the cheerless maxim, '*Ce qui coûte le plus pour plaire, c'est de cacher que l'on s'ennuie.*' She moves through a world of bright colours and snatches of music and patches of sunlight and still shadows, real yet dreamlike—a world to which her creator only can admit us. For Miss Thackeray has lent to none her golden key.

The picture of little Catherine George contrasts oddly with her father's imposing portrait of 'Rebecca, Lady Cranley'; and beside them, in this gallery of governesses, hangs 'Jane Eyre'. While *Vanity Fair* was born a classic, the legitimacy of *Jane Eyre*'s claim to that title was to be proven. Born before its time, it had yet to win the sanction of society, which proves often to the foundling, like hope, 'a timid friend'. It is instructive to remember nowadays, when nothing, it seems, is unpermissible to youth, that to the young person of that period *Jane Eyre* was a forbidden book; we doubt, however, if it was a closed one. We suspect that many a young mentor, while zealously withholding from her pupils that too unfettered, too fervid romance, pored over it in secret, burning her candle low over its pages, weaving from them dreams that were to be the realities of the magic future—that dim, yet brilliant, and all-possible future, the saddest and the happiest fallacy of youth. How many Rochesters loomed there, as unsubstantial as that sorry hero himself, hidden only by the veil of the prosaic present, waiting to storm the easy fortress of their hearts!

Jane Eyre was a revelation, but *Villette* was yet to come, and it is to *Villette* we turn for that unique presentment of the governess in literature—Lucy Snowe. It was probably the accident of the author's own experience that determined the setting of that incomparable story, but artistically no finer or fitter environment could have been chosen for Lucy Snowe: the frame was created for the picture by the stroke of genius, or the stroke of fate. In most of those dramas in which the governess plays the role of leading lady, we look for her, by the exercise of her own ingenuity or the advent of the inevitable Prince Charming, to be delivered from her bondage in the author's own good time. But *Villette* was conceived in sterner spirit, its heroine was drawn by a stronger hand. It is in the *carré*, to the sound of the school-bell, amid all the paraphernalia of the pension in the Rue Fossette, that the drama of that strange creature of ice and fire is played out. It is in the intolerable desolation of that 'long vacation' that her inflexible spirit falls upon despair. And with the fruition of hope (how characteristic it is of Charlotte Brontë to have it so!) there is to be no putting away of tasks, no cessation of labour; it is the old atmosphere of friction and of effort, which the aroma of love is to sweeten and rarefy. In yet another sense, Lucy Snowe remains above all *the* governess of fiction, if we view her through the penetrative eyes of Madame Beck. It was from no emotional point of view that that astute lady regarded her 'English teacher'; from a professional one she apprehended that she had landed a fine fish. The English teacher was almost an ideal teacher. She would perform her duties without surveillance and with discrimination, she would endure any discipline, she would exhibit a cynical impartiality and command where she could not persuade; if she lacked sympathy, she possessed that saving grace of a humorous perception, a perception with which her race is but meagrely endowed. Her skirmishes with that exasperating butterfly Ginevra Fanshawe are, after their manner, as unique as the communings of her repressed and impassioned spirit with its fate.

Happy the critic when *Villette* was young! It will not grow old, but it has passed beyond praise and analysis to the immunity of fame.

Whether the governess is in reality as interesting a figure as she appears in imagination is a question not to be disposed of here. If we are inclined to label her rather a prosaic than romantic personage, she may point with a protesting finger to the precious volumes on our shelves, and call great names to witness that she has not been found unworthy of regard.

But her proof lies mainly in the past. She survives still in the literature of the school library, a personification of all the milder virtues, clothed in the seductive but unserviceable 'plain white gown, with a bunch of roses in her belt', and with the aid of these habiliments she still contrives to satisfy the requirements of the more unsophisticated among her public.

But 'these be toys', as Bacon saith.

Mr Kenneth Grahame, in his *Golden Age*, in the few pages headed 'Exit Tyrannus', has portrayed in his own delicate fashion the mixture of regret and bravado with which his children watch their governess depart. And it is chiefly in such slight sketches that for us our governess reappears. In fact, perhaps she has been our tyrant; in fancy assuredly she has been our friend. Is she in both, in life as in literature, becoming obsolete with the three-volume novel? If so be, so be it.

MISS BOLT

I SEE her now, seated within the charmed circle of a white drugget, in our low nursery, filling up the gaps in our pinafores and budding intelligences with melancholy impartiality as we stood round her, hanging, with childish reverence and credulity, on the words of weight that fell, like those jewels in the old fairy tale, from our poor princess's mouth. Amid the dazzling lights and colours of childhood's enchanted picture, she passes in and out, an incongruous figure, persistently monochrome, untouched by any of the bright hues surrounding her, yet assuming a strange importance in the scene.

To outsiders she was simply an unusually incompetent little needle-woman; but our estimate of her personality found no adequate expression. We called her affectionately 'Bolty', and enthroned her silently in our hearts. Twice a week and on occasions of domestic pressure or festivity, she used to mount the creaky stairs. She sat by the window in a favourite corner making pinafores and darning socks, for which she received a weekly salary, and generously loading our minds with priceless experiences, less marketable, alas! than the labours of her failing eyes and unskilful hands.

Her appearance was unprepossessing. In age she was about sixty; and in height not much over five feet. Two pale blue eyes guarded a nose, technically speaking broken, but practically almost extinct. A small allowance of faded drab hair was parted sparsely on her forehead and gathered into a net behind. Her mouth was only significant as a vehicle of speech. In describing her hastily from memory, one would be tempted to forget it altogether, but for reminders in the shape of a couple of very prominent front teeth. These served frequently as a convenient substitute for scissors, which, as she remarked with thoughtful frugality when remonstrated with on the subject, ''as to be ground'. Her complexion was of a brownish-grey hue, but served to remind her that she had had 'a fine colour as a girl'. Of that period of her life, except in this particular, she never spoke. It bore perhaps the record of a tragedy that passed and left her early the frail little ghost of living humanity we knew. For she was not unlike some skeleton leaf of a forgotten summer, which the winds have neglected to sweep away.

In conversational moods she would tell us stories of deceased relations. Her voice took a dirge-like tone in the accounts of those rare personages who had 'bin good' to her, but rose to a note of enthusiastic interest in the recitals of those who had 'tret 'er bad'. We knew each tale well enough to divert new excursions of her imagination and to prompt her and correct omissions. The chief and inexhaustible topic was—'Me-brother' and his family. They unfortunately were not defunct. We knew each member as if from long companionship, and had a prescience of what each on any given occasion would do or say.

Ernie, the youngest, a child of six, was always longing for expensive mechanisms and unattainable luxuries. He was a monument of discontent. Sometimes he cried for toys, or whined because other little boys and girls had jam on their bread and butter. 'Me-brother' and his family were the gods of this little woman's life; with the exception of 'me-sister-in-law', of whom she always remarked with ominous emphasis, 'I say nothing agen'.

Miss Bolt lived alone up some blind alley near the Westminster Bridge Road, and used to drag her stoical little body to and fro in the early wet winter mornings and late nights, rather than spend omnibus money on herself. That infinitesimal sum was merged, I am sure, in the meagre earnings of 'Annie, the heldest girl', who worked in a frilling factory, and who was individualized in our minds by the possession of a mysterious talent, known as 'keepin' 'erself to 'erself'. The merit of this endowment was inscrutable then to us. It is a secret, I now suppose, which many a London girl's good angel whispers in her ear.

In like manner everything save the barest necessities of existence was reserved for the family in Lonton Crescent. 'Me-brother' was fortunately 'jest the size' for father's left-off clothes, and always particularly in want of the precise article to spare. This fact rendered his identity difficult when we made his acquaintance later, at which time he must have shrunk to about a third of his original size. He could, said his adoring sister, 'put 'is 'and to anything'; and we had no reason to doubt it, but we learned in time not to test this adaptability too far. He was tried at book-binding, furniture mending, upholstery, carpet-beating, and a variety of other things with indifferent success. These superficial failures, however (even when he brought back our treasured fairy tales with the pages stuck together and a shifting, spotted cover), did not blind us to his real powers. We learned rather to denounce with 'Aunt' those deadly and inanimate enemies of a gifted man, such as 'bad glue' and a 'basemint to work in', which make it impossible for him to get on.

His ostensible profession was of a theatrical nature, and his sister always spoke of him as 'connected with the stage'. In pantomime seasons he was busy for a time making tinsel helmets and shields. At other periods, I believe, he occasionally condescended to assist in shifting scenery. His relation to the theatre was the occasion of many professional anecdotes more or less authentic, and our ears were sometimes assailed with tales which happily never reached our understanding, leaving nothing more than a vague breath of distaste behind. Miss Bolt had no exaggerated sense of fitness, but if over-questioned, she became impenetrable for the day.

Fred, who shared his father's fatal facility, was the eldest son, the favourite of 'me-sister-in-law'. At twenty-one he had no settled occupation, but was subject to fits, which gave him claims to distinction denied to his younger and virtuous brother Ned. We have still, put away in a portfolio, two works of his signed in laborious capitals, 'F. BOLT'. One a view of the Colosseum by moonlight (apparently a superhuman reduction of a scene painting), the other a cadaverous head in sepia, described by Bolty as a 'Patry-ark, or Noah'; alternative personages indefinitely connected in her mind with the Flood. She used to recount with mingled pride and regret, the amount of pigment required for a Roman sky.

'He don't use much water,' she would say with triumphant sadness, 'and me-brother's always nagging at 'im to make the box go further; but 'e won't put up with interference from them as knows nothink of 'is art. I tell me-brother, tooition ain't no good for geniuses, it only puts 'em back.' But 'me-brother' continued to carp, and at last refused to supply paint-boxes, and Fred took to comic-song writing and appeared on the music-hall stage. 'A talented mocker, 'e is!' said his admiring aunt, relating his gifts as a caricaturist. ' 'E might 'ave bin a hactor but 'e 'adn't the haspiration; you wouldn't credit it,' she whispered in a burst of confidence, 'I always 'ad!'

Then for a brief season we knew Fred under the mysterious appellation of 'a star'. In this hour of his success, a lady of the dramatic profession took what Bolty termed 'a fancy for 'im, making 'im stay at 'er 'ouse frequent, and permitting 'im to lie on any of the droring-room sofias whenever 'e 'ad a mind to'. Naturally a passion of such magnitude must soon abate. The history of the idyll is incomplete. But the lady's feeling at length wore away, perhaps in sympathy with her upholstery, and Fred made an exit of which I forget the details, except that it was through the back door.

Ned the virtuous was fifteen. He had fewer temptations, and a ' 'eavenly disposition' with which to meet them. He worked in a printer's office. He was the 'nicest boy as ever lived', and his favourite reading was the *Lancet*, with which ambiguous description we were not then hypercritical enough to quarrel.

'Ned's a youth as will make 'is way,' his aunt recorded. 'Very perticklar 'e is too. 'E don't at all approve of Fred's gay goings on, and 'e can't abide 'is sister Fan.' I do not doubt that today he is in a position to censure and disown them both, thanking heaven from some denominational platform that he is not as other men and women are.

These shadowy beings reappear as I used to picture them, each defined and recognizable, yet none of them I ever saw. And Miss Bolt herself has never changed. I should rise and greet her without start or wonder if today she stepped between me and the light.

I remember a birthday when I was about eight or nine. The sparrows in the square always seemed to chirp louder on such mornings and to wake one earlier. I sat up in bed and listened to them, deliriously conscious of the festal nature of the day. The first serious thought was always, 'What will Bolty bring?' For she was a religious observer of birthdays, her own included. On such occasions she made a special visit and offering, and remained to tea. She had a genius for procuring delightful farthingsworths, and it was generally these insignificant but exciting articles of which we dreamed the night before.

That morning she appeared at breakfast-time. 'A trifle for you, miss,' she said, producing with curious dignity a small bunch of varied flowers. This particular offering was indicative that Bolty was very hard up. At such times (when even farthings were unobtainable for luxuries) she rose early and walked to the flower-market, which she always designated the 'Floral-'all'. Reaching there, breakfastless because she depended on a landlady's fire, she walked up and down until she had collected enough fallen blossoms to make a small bouquet. These stray blooms were then mounted on wire and presented with due impressiveness.

'Fred's 'ad another fit', she said, biting off a thread and beginning to sew. 'I've warned me-sister-in-law to put firewood in 'is 'ands at night, but it ain't no use. Master Charles, I shall 'ave to slap you, if you try to swaller needles what don't belong to you. Ernie ain't such a naughty boy. Run along and play.'

'Did he like the horse I sent him?' said Charlie, trying to recover his position gracefully by posing as a benefactor.

' 'E didn't say much, but I dessay 'e did. 'E wants a steam-engine with three carriages and rails to wind up and run along the floor. 'E was talking to 'isself about it yesterday as I come away, and Annie said, "Lor, Aunt, I wish I 'ad a cloak or somethink to cover me up, going to and from." She's got a awful cough, I wish you could 'ear 'er; me-sister-in-law's consumptive, I always did say, and there's the moral of it. I always expect Annie'll go into a decline.'

'What is a decline?' I asked anxiously. Miss Bolt always alluded to this disease with a complacent fatalism that was very bewildering. One knew not if it were meritorious or undesirable, so ambiguous was her intonation.

'There's different kinds; them as comes by nature, and them as you may git for yourself. I knew a stout young lady, wot threw herself into one, drinking vinegar by the saucerful, and sucking lemons, even in 'er bed. She ended a corpse, very rapid. Ah! Miss Mary, if you should ever feel yourself spreading, don't you be tempted to foller 'er; for what you're made, that you'll be.'

'Me-brother's jest bin turned orf of the Pantheon Theayter,' she continued, 'last Saturday night. Mr Kirby come on the Wednesday to 'ave a look round, and seemed to think everythink most satisfactory, when up comes Miss Helen Westall, in 'er silks and satins, and pokes 'er nose between the wings and puts a jewelled 'and upon 'is arm. " 'Enery, dear", she says (the lady was then playing Juliet to her companion's Romeo). 'Enery, dear, indeed! "I never would," she says, "a perduction like this don't require near so many. I've seen it done on the Continong with 'arf." So me-brother and others was discharged; and that ain't the worst I've 'eard of 'er! Lor, there's a many I see of a evening going out from the Levity stage-door to their oyster suppers and cetera, would compare favourable with 'er!' Night after night, as she went home, Miss Bolt would wait about the stage-doors of what she termed 'a terpsichoryan 'ouse', and watch the progress of an 'episode' which interested her. It was an instinctive method of satisfying her romantic sense, since a literary outlet for it was denied her.

Even the cheap and highly-seasoned fiction which she loved was beyond her means. We used to lend her our story-books, which she returned, after a decent interval, wrapped in paper, wearing a suspiciously unread air. Nor was she eager to discuss the contents. Cook occasionally lent her novelettes, which came back much sooner and more eloquently thumbed. Mrs Wright, her landlady, the wife of a night policeman, was a voracious devourer of these periodicals, but with a refinement of heartlessness only possible to the irremediably vulgar, she didn't care to lend them, and insisted that Miss Bolt should use them unread for lighting the fire.

Pride makes its martyrs and love its saints. Miss Bolt adored her brother and his children, and looked upon charity as the last degradation of the individual. Moreover, the workhouse, though externally a noble building, is somewhat spacious for the solitary soul. She had spoken mysteriously once or twice of a possible refuge for the deserving which would 'not debase'; and that afternoon she extended her confidence a little further towards me.

I sat on the floor beside her, unobtrusively threading a few needles, for even then her sight was beginning to fail. She began to picture in a low voice the haven of her dreams.

'I never see it,' she said, 'but I've 'eard of it. Perhaps your mar would know of it, perhaps not. I b'lieve they call it the "Holcroft Institootion". You 'ave a setting-room, and bedroom, and all found, and a handsome floral garden runs round the building. Your parints must 'ave bin respectable (mine was, as you know, a-well-to-do-bookbinder-now-deceased), and you must 'ave kep' off the parish till you're sixty. Such', she added, not without a tremulous and melancholy pride, ' 'as bin my endeavour. I doubt whether you'd git in without intrest, and I don't know 'oo to enquire of, but I orfen picture what a peaceful death-bed I could enjoy there!'

'Could you have us to tea, Bolty?' asked I, anxious to divert this view of it, and imagining myself, beautifully arrayed in a stiff white piqué frock, walking up the 'floral-garden' path, the observed of an admiring crowd; or sitting at the most romantic of tiny tea-tables, in a little room with casement windows and diamond panes. Perhaps even Ernie and Fanny might be there!

'I undertake', she replied, 'you could do much wot you 'ad a mind to; you notice it's a kind of reckignition of wot you've saved the Government, and not a charity—wot me-brother says must eventually debase the huming being. I never give a tea-party now, without such a set-to with Mrs Wright, it shakes me up for the day. My word!' she concluded, a pathetic quiver running through her usually monotonous drone, 'I'd give somethink to be well-to-do, and lief to light me own grate, and call me soul me own, and snap me fingers in her aggravating face!' But this modest prosperity was never to be hers. These relinquished tea-parties, besides the set-to, entailed weeks of pinching of the severest kind. 'I went to the Crescent to tea on Sunday; it ain't orfen I can. The pinch of tea I 'ave to take is more than I make do with at 'ome—I usually warm up the leaves for a evening, but you can't at another's 'ouse, and me-sister-in-law's that disagreebel about extry plates and things, I don't care to be be'olden, though it is me-brother's 'ouse. 'Owever, I was fortunate to be there when Ned and me-brother begun to talk politics. They continue, most fluent, by the hour together. Fred and me-sister-in-law don't care for it, and does their irritatin' best to interrupt; but I could listen indefinite. I stayed long after I had ought to bin 'ome to put the children to bed. It's such a treat to me to 'ear males converse!'

Ned made the unpardonable mistake of trying to convert his aunt, and she admitted, ' 'e was never the same agin'. For her views were unflinchingly agnostic. 'I told 'im', she said, 'I 'adn't no patience with them as was always 'ollerin' "yes", and setting theirselves agin them as set jest as much store by "no". If you want 'arps and 'eaven, I said, I trust you may git 'em, but don't go poking your 'opes and hinstruments down everybody's throat, whether they arsts for 'em or no. Lor!' she murmured dreamily in conclusion, 'they must 'ave a fine time of it, to be that eager to do away with the notion of a bit of rest!'

Miss Bolt usually spent her Sunday afternoons walking about the streets with a square canvas bag, picking up odds and ends of every description, for which labour a few pence from the rag-shop amply repaid her. She took a pleasure, quite out of proportion to the profit, in this undignified employment. Tidying was a mania with her. She routed the demon of disorder forcibly and with impenetrable gloom. If by chance she was absent for a week, almost every member of the household had patiently to await her return to recover some article of which she had temporarily disposed.

She used to give us hints about her own birthday observance a month or so before the day; and when we were quite small, she seemed to us but the mouthpiece of Providence, guiding to a wise decision. Later, however, we found it wiser to disregard these supernatural utterances and to trust to our own uninspired choice.

'Ain't there something to be done to your mar's mackintosh?' she would inquire, irrelevantly. 'I fancy she mentioned it. What serviceable articles they are! I come regular drenched the other morning, and your mar says, "What, Miss Bolt, ain't you a cloak or nothink?" and I noticed a tear in 'ers as she went out at the door.' Nothing, probably, had been said on the subject. This was only her way of suggesting what might prove an acceptable present for an oncoming date. She had the mackintosh eventually, but never wore it. She arrived on wet mornings as unprotected as ever, but earlier, and by the area gate, to avoid a real encounter and less imaginary questions from mother. Doubtless Annie's lungs were weak, and it is indisputable that 'aunt's' endurance was strong.

At the age of eighteen Annie married a youth a year older than herself, and Miss Bolt's visits grew irregular. When she did come, her little economies were more pronounced than ever. She would bring a nightcap or handkerchief to wash surreptitiously, as a saving of soap, performing the operation with the utmost secrecy and despatch. She begged candle-ends from cook, which she represented were to wax her thread. Her sight was definitely failing, but she would not admit it, and brought a case profusely filled with threaded needles, relying on me for emergencies. Then, for prolonged periods, she disappeared.

Once, on being pressed as to her reasons, I remember her jumping up and down the nursery in a transport of delight (the sole departure we had ever witnessed from her habitual gloom), and crying, 'I'm extending me connection, I'm extending me connection!' Poor little soul, how plainly I see you, skipping and rubbing your hands, your dull eyes almost bright with the first and last gleam of a most desolate hope.

On further question, the 'connection' narrowed itself down to a certain ham-and-beef shop, near the Angel, kept by a Mrs White. 'Such a lovely 'ouse!' she expatiated, 'with a 'andsome droring room on the first floor. I've slep' on the velvet couch there, when kep' over the night. Mr Jeffries, the carver, 'as been perticklar perlite to me. We converse frequent on politics and other things as I go through the shop of a morning.' And many an instance of administrative depravity and official wickedness in high places did these two confirm. But Mr Jeffries' attentions did not last, and Mrs White 'took offence at somethink', and the 'connection' suddenly collapsed. I can never pass the wretched place now—a vermilion-painted, ill-smelling little shop, neither too insignificant nor too sordid to revive enthusiasm in that poor little human breast—without a pang.

Annie's baby arrived, and Miss Bolt's visits became still rarer. Mother sent postcards—for we could not bear to lose sight of her—but when, after long absence, she reappeared, we learned they had never reached her. 'I never got your mar's card', she would say, perhaps before it had been mentioned; 'it's shocking the mismanagement of the Post Office, that's what it is. They are our servants, but you can't bring it 'ome to 'em. Look at them orficers of the British Museum with their uppish, interferin' ways. It's "you mustn't touch this", and "visitors is requested not to 'andle that", when it's we 'ad ought to be ordering them. The place belongs to us, and I've 'eard 'em most impident when me-brother told 'em so!' After which outburst she would subside into an occasional murmur of 'and the Queen 'erself ain't no more right to it then we 'ave——' 'But I don't grudge it 'er——', till the train of thought was changed. The corruption of Government servants in the neighbourhood of Westminster Bridge Road at last made the medium of correspondence useless.

She came sometimes, on birthdays or in the evening, shabbier and more thinly clad than ever, but was always 'engaged' if wanted for a day's work.

The last time we saw her was one autumn evening, not long after my brother Charlie died. The baby she had known was a big boy, and had been succeeded by another, who was just beginning to talk. It was a dull afternoon. There was a grey sky overhead. Through the windows you could see the leaves swirling along the pavements, blown from the dead heaps in the square. She entered softly, as her habit was, looking very old and pinched, and bade us a spiritless 'good-evening'. She sought her favourite seat by the window and sat down listlessly, maintaining for some time a silence we knew her well enough not to break. At last she said wearily, 'And where's Master Charles?' I told her hurriedly, and bade her make acquaintance with the little girl on my knee. She looked dully into the child's smiling face, and twice repeated, 'Dead, dead, Miss Mary! Well, 'e's 'appier where 'e is!'

'What is "dead"?' lisped my little maid softly. I bent and kissed the word away. But Miss Bolt answered the question solemnly, her eyes fixed on the low fire. 'It jest means as you go out like the candle or the fire or a noo piece at the theater wot 'asn't took. It don't matter much to anybody but them as wants the fire to warm 'em, and 'im wot perduced the play. That's it, ain't it, Miss Mary?' she said, turning a dim gaze on me.

'I don't know', I answered rather shortly. There was more of severance and tragedy in the air than I could bear.

'How's Fanny?' I asked abruptly, fearing I had been unkind. Miss Bolt got up and went towards the door.

'Fanny's gone where many's gone before 'er, and where many'll go after 'er. There ain't no call for you to arst after 'er no more.'

She went out. I felt too puzzled and bewildered to recall her, but in a moment she returned, carrying something wrapped in an old silk handkerchief. It was a little old volume of Goldsmith's poems. 'I thought you might set a store by it, Miss Mary', she remarked coldly, offering it to me. It was, I suppose, the last of her treasured library, six books, carefully hoarded, of which she had been very proud.

I accepted it silently, not knowing what to say. 'I think I'll go down and 'ave a bit of supper', she said, casting a lingering glance round the room. Having neatly folded up the tattered square of silk, she disappeared. Sitting in the growing darkness, we heard her uneven steps go slowly down the stairs. We never saw her again.

A year or two afterwards I thought I recognized her in a desolate little figure huddled in the corner of a stone seat on one of the bridges. It was night, and the resemblance proved to be but a chance one. I passed on, uncertain if my feeling were one of relief or regret.

For long afterward we waited, hoping she would turn up unexpectedly, as it was her wont to do. But she never came. Perhaps Mrs Wright grew importunate; perhaps the worn-out little soul reached the haven of which she dreamed! but then I think we should have known. Perhaps she has found another refuge where parish relief is not taken into account so sternly, and to enter which 'int'rest' is of less avail. Certainly we look no more for her, but she cannot be forgotten, last relic as she is of life's most exquisite possession—youth.

Its visions, its brilliant pictures and poignant sensations, lying so far behind us, are to be recaptured only in dreams. They are as effectually destroyed as those profitless butcher's shops and unzoological animals and the battered soldiers with which we used to play. But there is an element in life quite indestructible, whether it come to us at our day's outset or its end. The spirit of goodness may meet us, bare and radiant, or shrouded in this world's dingiest garb, yet it is an eternal guest, albeit for a time we may entertain our angel unawares.

Poorly and comically clad, it greeted me in the person of that sad, neutral-tinted little workwoman, who left me, like the childhood in which I knew her, mysteriously and without farewell.

NOTES IN A BRITTANY CONVENT

OUR PARTY of six 'unmated females' included a Botanist, a Zoologist, a Bacteriologist, a Vocalist, a Humorist, and a Dilettante. We started from Southampton in a gale, relieved to find its violence was not to hinder starting, and from St Malo journeyed south, at the pace of a smart four-wheeler, to arrive at dusk, famished, dishevelled, heavy-eyed, at our next stage. Our sixteen articles of luggage confronted us upon the platform, the pyramid encircled by a group of garrulous officials. We encircled them; a crowd of clamorous owners of diminutive *voitures* encircled us. Our demand for the conveyance from the Convent was met by a row of blank official faces, and a chorus of excited *cochers*, each determined to convey us and our mountain of *impedimenta* anywhere, within or without the range of possibility. Bewilderment and twilight deepened, we had eighteen miles of unknown road before us, and now the regulations of our *asile pieux* threatened complications. 'Candles', quoted the Zoologist forlornly, 'will not be provided; lights are extinguished and *baigneurs* expected to retire at nine o'clock.' That hour drew on apace; our case was obviously desperate, and while we debated it, the most ruffianly and enterprising of the Jehus, after a wordy scuffle with his kind, removed it from the realm of speculation by shouldering our baggage, and with affable though unintelligible explanations, loading three small vehicles, drawn by three spavined nags, and hustling us, weakly compliant, into yet a fourth.

Thus were we rattled in procession through the cobbled streets of the grey, curious town like travellers in a dream, to be deposited opposite an unknown inn, in a dark street upon the outskirts, into which hostelry our Jehu disappeared to have his supper, while an accomplice piled our baggage on a horseless vehicle of prehistoric pattern, round which we hovered in inarticulate despondency, a dreary group, till the exasperated Botanist at length dashed in, and snatched the supping tyrant from his meal; with violent, if vague expostulation, she goaded him, still chewing, to the stables, stood hypnotically by while he, with hungry mutterings, put to the horses, and finally we jolted off, a huddled heap beneath a pyramid of oscillating trunks. After many stoppages, at some belated hour we drew up, got out and propped ourselves in an exhausted line against the convent wall. The great bell resounded with a startling clangour through the sleeping village. Two bright eyes and one soft voice behind a little *grille* at length examined us, and from our incoherent explanations rapidly concluded: '*Ah! les demoiselles anglaises!*' Who else, indeed, could such *drôles* be?

The heavy gates clanked open, and our weird chaise clattered in; our *cocher* stacked our baggage in the sanctum of the little portress, who directed us to burrow for our nightgowns. Then with her lantern she led us across a courtyard and a stretch of garden, on through silent corridors, and paused; '*Vos chambres*', said she, and vanished like an apparition. Whitewashed walls, a crucifix, a bed, a paradise in miniature! We staggered in, shut doors, and slept.

At six a tap awaked us, and a white-capped head appeared above a tray of rolls and coffee. '*Pas l'usage*', she explained with sweet severity, but as we were so late last night the reverend *mère* had thought they might be well received. They were. But not so we, by a distinguished party of compatriots with whom we shared the *soeurs*' refectory. A hundred gay *baigneurs, baigneuses*—French people all—dined loudly, amicably in the *grande salle*, but we, beneath a ban. Four haughty British stares and one averted glance passed comment, was it on the manner of our advent or our bold unchaperoned front? The leader of the coterie, a careful likeness of the captive Marie Antoinette (we named her the queen-mother), reigned at the head of the long table; on her left, a portly dame with two well-governed daughters acted as applausive audience to the queen-mother's flow of courtly reminiscence. On her right, she was supported by her son, known as the *petit abbé*, a slim youth, three parts priest and one part school-boy; the typical Etonian, coated with the mannerisms of an old ecclesiastic, suave and rosy-cheeked, straight of limb but slightly stooping, gliding with felt-slippered feet along the courtyards and corridors, subtilizing thought upon the cliffs, his round blue eyes upon his little book, his black skirts waving in the breeze; with the persuasive cadence, the inscrutable regard, the benedictory hand-clasp of his order. Such an odd defiance, so it seemed, of Nature's more robust intent. But the queen-mother willed it and it was. She also willed, within her sphere of influence, that we should be as though we were not, and within it thus we were. Once the *petit abbé* was seen harbouring a smile at some coarse sally of the Humorist's, till, caught by the queen-mother's eye, it stiffened on his youthful lips; once, in an oblivious moment of politeness (this was reported by the Vocalist), he murmured a benign 'good-morning' at *déjeuner*; once, at dusk, he was discovered leaning dreamily against the open window of the *salon* where the Vocalist was singing 'Night of June, oh! lovely night of June'. And once, one night (but only whisper it), he stooped and carried off a rose which she had dropped in passing, a black speck on a white square of moonlit stone. Poor little *petit abbé*, get thee to thy rosaries, bethink thee that this world is not thy garden; cling thou closer to the skirts of the queen-mother, stiffer than the robes of Mary Virgin, lest thou stumble into sin!

The graciousness of the indulgent foreigner, for all our lapses, social and grammatical, shone bright by contrast with this stately gloom. The voluble encouragement, the smile of *camaraderie*, which greeted us, was that of sunny France, and nowhere surely sunnier than in the shadows of those old grey walls. Nowhere could be laughter lighter or speech gayer, than that which echoed through the grave courtyards and in the quiet cloister, where between each ancient arch the big pink bushes of hydrangea bloom. Above them, roses climb up to the windows of the sisters' corridor, and through the open casements one gets glimpses of the faded doors where their black habits hang; and now and then a figure moves across the bare white wall. The scent of all the tangled flowers, the brilliant patches of sunlight on the red-tiled pavement and the patter of the voices down below, seem shut out from these rooms so void of colour and so full of silence, which belong to those who may not finger the bright stuff of dreams, the softest fabric of whose life, perhaps, is sleep.

Above this long uneven roof, the tower of the Abbey Church stands high and square; the cracked bell jangles from it, just above the broken balustrade which tells of storm: of such a storm as once blew down one side of the old structure. Even on summer nights the wind seems always moaning through the Convent corridors, though down there, by the brilliance of the moonlight in the garden, one notices, the branches scarcely stir.

The Church too, has its mute remembrancers of tempest, strewn as it is with all those litanies to the '*patronne des Bretons, refuge des pêcheurs, mère des veuves et arche de Noé*'. And above the white-capped heads which gather there on Sunday, like a flock of sea-birds, hang the models of the full-rigged ships, with parti-coloured sails, high in the haven of the arches. In the Chapel of St Joseph hangs another, very small and frail and all of white, a ghostly little ship of dreams—decidedly a dreamer's ship; the skipper steps aboard at night and wears—perhaps the face of Immortality? The saint from which this corner of the *presqu'île* takes its name, has his spacious tomb behind the altar: on it lies the tiny pair of crutches left there by a cripple of the village, whose *neuvaine* moved the good saint's bones to miracle. Though, in the estimation of a young world-worn American widow, who arrived early one morning and made the place, its charms and its traditions, her own before *déjeuner*, 'the relics after Ituly were vurry insipid, not to say quite pitiful', the tribute of little Théophile, his crutches, is picturesque enough, and it suits better with the spirit of the place, untouched and still remote, where the old peasant faiths and fashions still remain intact.

It was Madame la Baronne who brought the spirit of modernity, the odour and the flash of Paris into the unscented twilight of the old refectory, as suddenly one evening she swished in through the low cloister door, an apparition from the world of epigrams and toilettes and perfumes. She brought Monsieur le Baron too, a small superfluous appendage with a large gold ring. Two close-cropped little sons, with 'study' written large all over their white faces, followed. Culture, in the person of their English governess, held them in bondage; Discipline, in the person of papa, kept an unwinking eye on their deportment. They ate to study, slept to study, lived to study, and the possibility seemed not remote, must die to play—elsewhere. The eldest, a pale sprig of nine, spoke English well, and courteously instructed us in his own tongue, gravely indulgent to our errors, keeping his rare smiles for our more rare successes. One evening the small brother's place was empty, and a meal of bread and water was grimly carried off the board. Henri explained: 'It was that Adolphe had been naughty, had not in fact applied himself that afternoon.' The next night we missed Henri. 'Oh! but yes!' responded Adolphe to inquiry, with the transparent satisfaction of a pioneer, 'today the same thing had occurred with Henri'. And when a few days later the bright young governess did not appear, we hazarded that this time it must be that Mademoiselle was naughty too, but under the full glare of Discipline who sipped his coffee opposite, this conjecture was received with very nervous smiles. Mademoiselle was merely indisposed, they said, and, for 'alas' they substituted 'fortunately', she would rapidly recover.

That afternoon, for the first time, we found the two sedately playing in the courtyard under the walnut trees, a board and counters spread upon the old stone well. But now the agile figure of papa appears; papa armed with *grammaire* and *cahiers*; he trips across the grass, gesticulating, uttering a brisk—'*Allons, mes enfants*', and they promptly disappear.

'*Pauvres petits savants*', murmurs Madame, who is standing on the threshold of the *salon* in a distracting *costume de bicyclette*. She has been raining smiles and '*mots*' upon the *petit abbé*. He is now dispatched for her machine. While buttoning her glove, she turns to the queen-mother who reclines within, critically scanning a new book of Memoirs.

'But I find him altogether charming, your son—*mon amie*', she protests; 'the world will miss him. God has created him the lover', and as an afterthought, she adds, 'the husband—father. *C'est vous qui en avez fait le prêtre. C'est triste et aussi drôle*. And are there not enough of these good people here?' she asks, with an expressive gesture. 'Everywhere they swarm.'

They did. A party of them from some *séminaire* had come there to make holiday. One met them, a black file along the cliffs, in yellow basket hats tied down under their chins, their spare skirts flying; or one saw them grouped upon the ledges at the hour *du bain.* At dusk, they sat in twos and threes upon the benches, or paced up and down the *allées* of the garden with their books of meditation, not too preoccupied to note the more profound preoccupation of the newly-married pair who promenaded there, with glances locked, and arms entwined. '*Un vrai roman*', commented one French matron, but to our more exacting English eyes, the brightness of the romance was clouded by the bridegroom's linen, apparently intended to last out the honeymoon, which by this token should have waned.

It was one windy evening on the cliffs which saw our first encounter with the rubicund old priest who plotted our conversion. He came puffing up to join the party, and between the gusts, compliment and guide-book and theology proceeded from him in a turgid stream. To the Bacteriologist's inordinate desire for information on all subjects we owed his subsequent pursuit. These two conversed in gasps and in a compromise of languages on subtleties of archaeology and doctrine till we reached the little door into the garden, where they parted with an assignation for tomorrow's mass at 6 a.m. Catholicism came to be a craze with her, and she approached it in a scientific spirit, compared its fascinations to those of the study of malaria, drew analogies and formulated theories, and ceased to be companionable. This, for in her better moments she had amiable qualities, we bore. The black rotundity (to fall into the slough of metaphor) we found a sharper thorn. He rolled round unexpected corners, cropped up on lonely roads and pounced upon us from dark doorways—a veritable little priest of prey. In vain did we evade the pressure of his palms—fat, damp and fatherly—discourage his discourse with vacant smiles. His zeal was not discourageable. Nor was his, he said, the only mind on which our lost condition weighed. The room next his was occupied by a 'devout young miss', who publicly disturbed herself on our account. He heard her praying '*Tous les soirs*, for all the six!' This blameless incident, profanely handled by the Humorist under the title of the 'Listener detected, or the Maiden's Prayer', made an agreeable addition to her repertoire of recitations. But we owed more than this to the devout young miss, who was in time presented to us and who sought to lead us on by flowery ways. We owed to her our introduction to St Antoine de Padua—'what an accommodating saint was he! You went to him for little things—a fine day for an expedition, and so on; you made your own arrangements', and you paid him, so to speak, upon delivery, 'by no means of necessity before. And was it not, in fact, a nice simple little faith?' We thought it was, and with the exception of the Bacteriologist, who refused to be a party to it, opened up transactions with him privately, as thus. Four sous for fine weather in an ordinary way, and to be doubled on a *jour de fête*. The sum was small, but his benevolence was disproportionate.

'*Merci à St Antoine*', as they put up in the churches, we were singularly favoured by the sun. We grew to have quite an affection for our saint of little things: his statuette became our favourite in the churches, and we liked to see him stationed in the niche above the door through which the little orphans of the convent scuttle with their pitchers to the well.

The *orphelinat* is a large building on the east side of the courtyard, bleak-looking and grey with faded venetian shutters; it would look desolate without that brilliant strip which runs along beneath the windows, its thin line of ragged flowers. Over its other door *Notre Dame des Perpetuels Secours* keeps St Antoine company. Between these two and the good *soeurs*, those quaint and many little Bretons thrive. Some of this white-capped little company, in their long skirts and chequered shawls, are always passing to and fro across the grass or standing in the shadow of the trees to fill their pitchers. Always busy about something, always laughing, so it seems; or is it always only when they encounter those *demoiselles anglaises*, whom without doubt they find so comic? But I believe the smile is always there: one feels it shining quite far off before one hears the clatter of their shoes. Only at Mass one misses it, when, with their *robes de dimanche* they put on such solemn little faces, wearing that aspect of remoteness and reflection, that look of patience and of dreams upon the eyes which one meets often in the older Bretons. This lasts an hour, and then the sun is dancing in their eyes again. One has to keep their picture in one's mind. A sketch-book or a camera will set them flying like a flock of startled pigeons. The *religieuses* are just as slippery, but more sedate and diplomatic. At the suspicion of a portrait their steps quicken and they turn a sudden corner or seek refuge in a doorway; leave you to your patch of sunlight and an empty cloister. We ask the *Révérende Mère* at last if it were not permitted, and she, all smiles, returned discreetly, '*Mais elles ne sont pas assez belles!*'

In feature few of them indeed are beautiful or even young, but they have a serenity and sweetness which belongs perhaps to the religious life—a finer kind of beauty; coming of bourgeois or of peasant stock, their air and manner is of singular distinction. Their lot is one of poverty and labour, difficult to realize in these brighter, easier months of summer, when their houseful of visitors keeps them employed about the kitchen and garden, up and down the stairs and corridors, followed by a little *orpheline* or two, with pitchers, or armsful of beans or washing. If you stop them they are very ready with a word, a service, a direction; while the children stand apart, pretending, as the *soeur* is present, that they are not laughing at you—not at all! 'So Mademoiselle is going to the sea this morning? That is well. It is so hot here; ah! so hot, but there the breeze.' And then she hurries on without a glance at the blue strip framed in the garden doorway. It is too short for her—for all there is to do in it—your long, long, idle day. She leaves the pictures and the dreams to you, and hastens off about your business. These talkative holiday-keeping people have their uses, though, and perhaps their diversions. They make a bare existence possible; they are an interlude in the long year; the noisy music of the world mingles a moment with the quiet chant. And then succeed the months of tilling, sowing, planting; the labours of the farm and garden; the autumn apple-gathering; the winter sewing in the chill, dim rooms, where the high windows show a line of sea, or merely a grey patch of cloud cut by the cemetery crucifix, which stands out black against the sky.

This August afternoon, beyond the courtyard gate, across the road, outside the barn, one recognizes one or two of these black figures among the group of peasants, busy with their flails, threshing the corn in the hot sunshine. It makes for length of days, this arduous monotony. There is a railed off space in a green corner of the garden. On either side the strip of path are mounds with big, white, weather-beaten wooden crosses at the head, and underneath they lie, all quite old women, except one who died at twenty-two. She had her window, I suppose, above the arches of the cloister, looking down upon the climbing roses and the pink hydrangea bushes. Her black habit hung upon the faded door: '*Priez pour elle.*' The legend is the same for all of them, but she insists, somehow, upon her epitaph. As one swings back the gate one wonders idly if there was a story; if there was, no doubt she kept her counsel. It is so quiet in the garden, and these walks seem narrow, the walls high, the world too far away for twenty-two.

The little portress also will die young, whatever age they write up over her. She may be forty, but it is an ageless face which looks out through the open window by the gate, as you look in for letters. A face too thin and sensitive, but lovely, with its look of dreams dismissed, passed on the way to some divine reality. She sits framed in the slit of window, reading, the black profile of her veil, with its white rim, so still beneath the outline of the crucifix which hangs above it on the wall. As you pass, though she does not look up, you catch somehow the fragrance of that presence with its sense of benediction; know the smile which you may meet as you come back, so bright, so human, yet a little sad with all its sunshine, like a late spring day.

One evening I was reading in the dusk, alone in the deserted court-yard, when with a sense of someone coming I looked up, and over my blurred page discerned the slender figure with its springing step, making toward me, moving with that sober swiftness which they have, across the darkened grass in the vague shadows of the trees. She stopped beside the old stone well, and motioned me to shut the book, which I put down on it.

'But you will ruin the eyes', she said; 'there is not light enough.'

'They are quite strong', said I. 'Up to this moment one could see quite well.'

'Today perhaps—but later, when you are as old as I am, then, *mon enfant*!' and she made a little groping gesture.

'As old!' I echoed, laughing; 'none of us are half so young. We never shall be, I imagine. *Vous avez le secret de la jeunesse perpétuelle. N'est-ce pas la vérité.*'

'*Peut-être*', she smiled. '*C'est possible.* Truly it is the world which ages—that world out there,' she waved a hand, 'in which there is so much of sin, of suffering, of illusion. And is it not itself the Great Illusion—your sad, brilliant, rebellious world?'

'This place, too', I answered, 'seemed unreal, illusory, at times, in its serenity; one almost felt the weight of its repose. We of the world, as she would say, we sometimes wondered how it could be possible—their world—their life?'

'*Vous n'êtes pas Catholique*', she said, and then, lest I suspected some intention in the speech, she ended rapidly, 'It is the blessed, the protected life. And it is possible, in part, perhaps, because we do not question,—that is not permitted—we accept. And, for example, is it not this habit of the world to question—*questionner la vie, questionner la souffrance, questionner Dieu même, questionner tout,* which ages, brings the lines about the face, the weariness of heart? But it is so. *Cherchez-vous le secret de cette jeunesse perpétuelle, que vous dites qui est à nous; ne questionnez point, mon enfant, et vous resterez jeune.*'

The light had faded quickly, and this presence, so insistent yet remote, seemed almost spiritual in its obscurity. The figure was an outline only, the face a glimmer, and the soft voice musing on, a murmur in the twilight.

'Yes, it was quiet here. I could not but remark it, even in these busy days of summer; and the days of winter, they were still more tranquil. But to them, to the community, they made but little difference, the seasons; all seasons were the same with God. It rested with the world to love, to notice, to torment itself with change. But here one lived above the world, and change was not perceptible. One lived', she said; 'perhaps I should not call it life? "*La vie est la mort, la mort est la vie*",' she ended gently. 'Yes, the explanation of tranquillity was there.'

We walked across the courtyard in the darkness to her little door. '*Je prierai pour vous,*' she added, after her '*bon soir*'.

A few steps brought me to the *salon*: such a sudden glare of light, it seemed, and maze of faces and of voices to step into from the starlight and the outside stillness.

Every one had come back from the evening stroll; the Vocalist was ready with her song. Her mood was light tonight, a mood of flourishes, staccato passages and trills; sentiment in fancy dress and dominoes, and stepping delicately to a measure.

She ended with a little French gavotte. The audience applauded, made its compliments: then came a patter of good-nights, a rustle of departure, afterthoughts and more good-nights, and bows and final exits. The scene was very pretty, very friendly, very gay; it faded with bright figures passing from the yellow lamplight into the white moonlight, growing colourless and vanishing like rather noisy shadows into the mute brilliance of the night.

As one looks back there are so many scenes. Perhaps the most persistent is the picture of the little portress in her window, from which such very distant glimpses of the 'world' and its 'illusions' can come into view. She seems to borrow something from that stillness of the sunshine, in which, to memory, she always sits—a stillness which suspends the breath of question, like her spirit. 'And the explanation of tranquillity is there!'

THE POEMS OF EMILY BRONTË

TO THOSE who, holding dear, have formed for themselves any conception of that great genius who died 'between the finishing of labour and the award of praise' the works of Emily Brontë must be chiefly interesting as the record of a unique and in some senses, an appalling personality: and it is undeniable that to the majority of those readers to whom she is but casually known, this personality—one of the most remarkable in the history of modern literature—presents itself as repugnant and distasteful.

'Mind', says Mr Pater, 'we cannot choose but approve when we recognize it: soul may repel us and not because we misunderstand it.' But it is possible that here is a soul which has most repelled where least it has been understood.

It is mainly upon *Wuthering Heights* that Emily Brontë's reputation as a great artist and a repulsive woman has been built: her poems—which in part supply its key and commentary—are a truer revelation of her veritable self than that grim and matchless tragedy, by which she is too exclusively known and upon which, perforce, her fame must rest. The note of violence which in a measure disfigures, and yet in a measure enhances and always triumphantly fails to weaken, the passion of *Wuthering Heights* is absent from the author's poems—as it would probably have been absent from her later work. In that dreadful and incomparable story she was testing her powers, she had not altogether gauged them. They were, at the outset, perhaps too much for her, and overwhelmed a mind, which young in waking could not confine and comprehend itself. Swept forward by the oncoming and strong current of her genius, she was, in the first rush of it, somewhat borne away; so strongly that we too are borne along with it, forgiving the impetuosity and turbid tumult of that stream.

Charlotte has urged, in vindication of a violence she might not dismiss and could not altogether explain, that 'the writer who possesses the creative gift owns something of which he is not always master'. But that ultimately Emily must have been master of any gift she did possess, it is hardly possible to doubt. The evidence of her poems goes far to show that, in time, she would have discarded the unchecked vehemence of immaturity for a vigour more intrinsic and appealing. Her last lines—the dignity and grandeur of which it is hardly possible to overestimate—remind us that she was outgrowing her mighty childhood—that within sight of eternity the fruit of time was ripening fast.

It seems little matter for regret that no reliable likeness of Emily exists, that our mental presentment is not marred by any inefficient, dubious print, that we are bound to construct one for ourselves solely from the masterly notes with which Charlotte has furnished us in the prefaces to *Wuthering Heights* and the *Posthumous Poems* and from the suggestive study for which Miss Robinson is responsible.

But the true—the one original likeness, Emily herself has sketched: it is outlined in these slim pages of neglected verse. The eyes that watched unweariedly to find 'how very far the morning lies away'; the 'chainless soul', the 'quenchless will', the 'savage heart', and the 'resentful mood' are mirrored here.

Throughout her work, to those who look for them, sweeter and lighter fancies peer like stars between the masses of dark cloud from clearer rifts of sky. True, that these far-hung lights are few, but here the vault from which they gleam is loftier, and shows behind its hovering grey a promise of serener blue. It is then to these few, many of them halting and imperfect verses, that we must turn if we are to judge rightly of the writer. They are illuminative footnotes to the fragmentary history of that tragic, heroic and majestic soul, which walked unswervingly with Truth, viewed failure with sublime serenity, and tried conclusions with the mightiest powers that beset mankind.

Emily was essentially a poet, and it is by poets that she has been severally recognized, interpreted and portrayed. 'The pure note of absolutely right expression for things inexpressible in full by prose,' says Swinburne, 'Emily had for birthright', and Matthew Arnold wrote her elegy 'who sank baffled, unknown—self-consumed'.

Wuthering Heights, which is pre-eminently the achievement of a poet, has been not unfitly termed the 'nightmare of a recluse', and these poems may well be called day-dreams—wonderful, awful dreams indeed—in their simple but compelling passion, their self-reliance and restraint, their concentrated force and purity. In form and structure they are curiously deficient, lacking for the most part the instinctive grandeur and simplicity of style which marks the prose of *Wuthering Heights*; and it is evident that Emily had never set herself to master the art which would have clothed them fittingly, matching with certainty of rhythm their majesty of thought. They were written secretly—without thought of publication, not destined by their author to challenge or invite critical consideration. These strange self-communings took shape in intervals of leisure, snatched from prosaic but determined work. Perhaps in the northern twilight of the Haworth kitchen with 'Tabby' knitting by the dying fire. Perhaps in greyer, lonelier dawns, when Emily rose early to the self-appointed labours of the day. For it is notable that this woman, who owned above most women the 'inestimable gift of genius', was one who laid upon herself the simplest duties; that in that poor and Spartan country parsonage it was Emily who, when need came, rose in the bitter winter mornings to do the disabled servant's work, who conned her German across the pastry board, and cooked and cleaned 'as if', says her biographer, 'she had no other aim in view than the providing for the day's comfort. Of Emily's deeper self, her violent genius, neither friend nor neighbour dreamed in those days. And today it is only this Emily who is remembered.'

This is not, however, the place to dwell upon the homelier and lovelier side of that extraordinary character; it has been set forth elsewhere by competent and reverent hands. It is with the darker and deeper aspect of it that we have to do in dealing with these poems, with the spiritual and mysterious self, which they so prominently illumine. Over this figure—hardly human in its self-sufficiency and aloofness, and yet more than human in its compassionate gentleness for the doomed and erring—they cast an unmistakable—almost unearthly light: showing a soul which scorns the world with masterful persistence and disclaims all comradeship save that of the 'strange visitants of air', to itself so magically allied. For from the world and her fellows, Emily Brontë was perhaps one of nature's outcasts—a self-determined outlaw, whose indomitable spirit 'even despair', the possible outcome of her instinctive isolation, was 'powerless to destroy'.

The earth—her passionate and only love—was peopled for her by spirits of storm and cloud, of sun and darkness. These were the sole companions of those boding or ministering spirits within her soul. Fancy—that 'fairy love'—was her chosen playfellow and perhaps the only child she ever knew. Seldom, if ever, seeking intercourse with those around her, and impervious to the influence of other minds, she was mainly dependent on the material her own imagination could supply. Throughout these ideal and impersonal lyrics the individual note is everywhere discernible. They are melodies, rather than harmonies, many of a haunting and piercing sweetness, instinct with a sweeping and mournful music peculiarly her own.

Everywhere too, the note of pure passion is predominant, a passion untouched by mortality and unappropriated by sex—the passion of angels, of spirits, redeemed or fallen—if such there be. Rarely does any tranquil or tender human trait soften the brilliance of these strange imaginative pictures or relieve their gloom. Through the mist and sorrow of an ever-unsatisfied desire, she looked out upon the world, which the sad circumstances of her environment, together with the gloomy bias of her nature, showed so dark, with a curious indifference and mistrust.

'An interpreter', says Charlotte, 'should always have stood between her and the world'; but human intervention she would never have endured. It was rather a divine interpreter, which all through life her ardent spirit beat its wings to reach and strained its eyes to see. For the 'spirit-seer' who should make intelligible the awful chaos of existence and lighten its remorseless darkness, she had 'watched and sought' her 'life-time long'.

In the dialogue entitled 'The Philosopher' she utters the conclusive confession of her useless search:

> Had I but seen his glorious eye
>   *Once* light the clouds that wilder me;
> I ne'er had raised this coward cry
>   To cease to think, and cease to be;
> I ne'er had called oblivion blest,
>   Nor stretching eager hands to death,
> Implored to change for senseless rest
>   This sentient soul, this living breath—
> Oh, let me die—that power and will
>   Their cruel strife may close;
> And conquered good and conquering ill
>   Be lost in one repose.

This remarkable if somewhat incoherent poem is perhaps the most original, as it is certainly the finest in thought and conception of all her poems. It asks and answers most distinctly the dominant question, and reveals the intellectual tragedy of her life.

The thought of the pre-eminence of evil, of 'conquered good and conquering ill' with which it closes, is the text and motive of *Wuthering Heights*. And 'lost in one repose' she leaves the chief actors in that awful tale, awful—not so much in the consideration of the frenzied passions which it delineates, as in the general scheme which shows evil proceeding out of good as though it were indeed a natural outcome.

There, as in these verses, death is recognized as the one benignant power; the friend whose sad but unreproachable eyes greet alike kindly, good, and evil-comers—upon whose broad and pulseless breast the day of weeping ends. Edgar, the gentle, faithful husband, sleeps no more peacefully than the two wild lovers by his side. There can be—it is her final word—'no unquiet slumbers for the sleepers in that quiet earth.'

Death solves and absolves all—it is rest; and the resolution of discordance: there is no sense of the mystery beyond, of judgement to follow; it holds only—to quote a passage from that work whose horrors have been so faithfully remembered while its beauties are frequently passed by—'a repose that neither earth nor hell can break—an assurance of the endless and shadowless hereafter—where life is boundless in its duration, and love in its sympathy, and joy in its fulness.'

It brought no terror to this girl, who mused habitually upon facts and mysteries more terrible. It was no problem, because it was the end of problems; it scarcely meant obscurity to the soul thrust back relentlessly upon itself for light.

'The Prisoner', a very unequal fragment, ambitious in conception, but weak and disjointed in execution, closes with an utterance as passionate and individual as that with which 'The Philosopher' ends.

> Then dawns the Invisible; the unseen its truth reveals;
> My outward sense is gone, my inward essence feels:
> Oh! dreadful is the check—intense the agony—
> When the ear begins to hear, and the eye begins to see;
> When the pulse begins to throb, the brain to think again;
> The soul to feel the flesh, and the flesh to feel the chain.

['What irks me most is this shattered prison,' says Cathy, dying, but the speech is Emily's—'I'm tired of being enclosed here; I'm wearying to escape into that glorious world, and to be always there; not seeing it through tears, the yearning for it through the walls of an aching heart.']

> Yet I would lose no sting, would wish no torture less;
> The more that anguish racks, the earlier it will bless;
> And robed in fires of hell, or bright with heavenly shine,
> If it but herald death, the vision is divine!

The titles of these two poems are transparent pseudonyms for the author, and perhaps the sense of captivity underlies the utterances of 'The Philosopher' most definitely, while the philosophic spirit, which was notably Emily's own, finds its expression in the latter poem. Of the hymns or invocations to imagination variously styled 'To Imagination', 'Plead for Me', 'My Comforter', and 'How Clear She Shines', the last named concludes with some burning and vigorous lines, summing up Emily's estimate of life with bitter intensity.

The spectacle here presented is one of trackless starless darkness, where images of perverted truth, wisdom and virtue seem to sweep like malignant meteors across a sullen and unlifting sky. This distorted picture may well appal the reader when he remembers that to the lonely brooding girl it was an actual and familiar scene. Vividly, insistently, as these dread visions are set before us, it is difficult to realize what existence was for her to whom they were the substance from which her thought took shape. Turning in recoil from such a conception of reality, two other worlds absorbed her gaze—the very intensity of which obscured her vision; worlds both bounded by her own 'space-sweeping soul'.

From another noticeable address to imagination—headed 'My Comforter', this declaration looms out lurid and convincing:

So stood I, in Heaven's glorious sun,
And in the glare of Hell;
My spirit drank a mingled tone,
Of seraph's song, and demon's moan,
What my soul bore, my soul alone
Within itself can tell!

And of that 'mingled tone', the note of hell rang ominously clear. Such conflicting voices were always audible; she was always listening to something akin to the great Tannhäuser overture, while the mighty deities of Death and Time stood by. Watching and listening thus, her spirit undismayed maintained its steadfast struggling independence; and with the vision of the unseen ever before her, sorrow and guilt took shape—came into nearer view—'passed by and plucked the golden blossom' of earthly hope and earthly promise. 'I waited bliss', she cries, 'and cherished rest.'

The world counted for nothing; all it could offer she passed passionately yet coldly by. Riches and fame and love—such undesired futilities were things for which she watched weak mortals strive with distant pitying disdain. Hardly born for earth, she seemed to peer beyond it—craving a clearer vision than it yielded—crying for liberty as only captives cry—appealing strenuously 'from tyranny to God'.

Suffering and slavery were the great facts and despots of existence; and of suffering she had known enough, but hers was a nature which it could neither chasten nor subdue—it might but stir to rebellion one to whom submission was unknown. The only slavery known to her was a slavery to her own tameless and inexorable spirit; no alien power could have proved so obdurate and pitiless as was this being to itself.

Body and soul were fitly mated. The hand which applied the searing remedy to its own wounded flesh, and the hand which wrote these lines were truly one:

No promised heaven, these wild desires
Could all, or half fulfil;
No threatened hell, with quenchless fires,
Subdue this quenchless will!

It was with the face of a pagan warrior that she confronted life and met death. A pagan above all she was: the centuries of revelation behind her seem not to have won a glance of question or of recognition; Christianity, taking its place with 'the thousand creeds that move men's hearts', must have been found with them 'unutterably vain', nor does she even momentarily seem to turn from the sin and suffering of humanity to the picture of a suffering but sinless God. Indeed the religion of meditation and sacrament and self-surrender could never have won a possible assent from one who shunned so resolutely the common pledges and submissions of daily life. Only in her infinite forbearance with, and compassion for the victims of weakness and vanity and passion, does she touch that eternally uplifted figure which hangs between earth and heaven to link inseparably the human with the divine. We cannot but remember that it was not Charlotte, but the pagan Emily, who to the last protected and forgave the sorry wreck who, once the pride, had come to be the terror of their home. It was she who achieved his epitaph wherein we read, almost amazed, the plea for weakness penned by one who so accounted strength:

> Then 'Bless the friendly dust,' I said,
> 'That hides thy unlamented head.'
> Vain as thou wert and weak as vain,
> The slave of Falsehood, Pride and Pain—
> My heart has nought akin to thine;
> Thy soul is powerless over mine—
> But these were thoughts that vanished too;
> Unwise, unholy and untrue.

Revulsion ends in prayer and pity, and 'Kind Heaven' is to 'grant that spirit rest'.

Throughout these poems there is not one plea for joy, as there is hardly a hint that life can hold it; the sole prayer is for endurance, the sole hope lies in the mind from which it springs. Forced back upon the witness of her own soul for God, she lived and died a solitary, dauntless, sightless spirit, turning toward the day and sending forth the voice and vision of the night.

Permitted no revelation, offered no certainty, but desiring both, the mind is called upon to sanction the worship of which it is itself the deity:

> And am I wrong to worship where
> Faith cannot doubt, nor hope despair,
> Since my own soul can grant my prayer?
> Speak, God of visions, plead for me,
> And tell why I have chosen Thee!

There was for her no other choice—no alternative vision, and yet the impotence of her own mighty, but not almighty, spirit to dissipate the darkness of the disordered universe, to mitigate its pain, was ever present to her consciousness, and impotence to such a mind was a lash from which nothing could take the sting.

In 'Self-Interrogation' she thus reviews the past—questions the future:

> The vanished day? It leaves a sense
> Of labour hardly done;
> Of little gained with vast expense—
> A sense of grief alone!

Well, thou hast fought for many a year,
Hast fought thy whole life through,
Hast humbled Falsehood, trampled Fear;
What is there left to do?

The third and fourth verses of the same poem exhibit the writer's power of vivid personification:

Time stands before the door of Death,
Upbraiding bitterly;
And Conscience, with exhaustless breath,
Pours black reproach on me:

And though I've said that Conscience lies
And Time should Fate condemn;
Still, sad Repentance clouds my eyes,
And makes me yield to them!

The massive figures of Time and Death—two familiar deities—stand visibly before us, and we are confronted by a picture that Watts might well have painted: abstractions take shape and force themselves upon our vision almost before they can arrest our thought.

In the fine imagery of 'Death', this quality again is manifest.

Emily had the power of presenting images and impressions of a convincing reality with a neglect or disdain of detail, which displays the pure imaginative quality of her work. Scenes and moods and thoughts are flashed upon our consciousness, we know not how; their terror, or delicacy, or beauty, is surely indicated, yet never obviously drawn—she calls up spirits with a spirit's hand.

It is said that her genius was masculine, but surely it was purely spiritual, strangely and exquisitely severed from embodiment and freed from any accident of sex. Never perhaps has passion been portrayed as she portrayed it—wayward and wild as storm, but pure as fire, as incorruptible as life's own essence—deathless in the face of death. And nature is presented to us by the same unerring hand. Sublime, fantastic, are the scenes she puts before us, magically true—unmarred by any alien element—living as nature lives, set in no human frame.

The sense of colour too is here and there importunate.

In 'Stars' we pause arrested by the lines: 'Blood-red he rose, and, arrow-straight / His fierce beams struck my brow.' Strongly the splendour reaches us—seems unsurpassable, but turning to the page again it spreads and deepens with—

My lids closed down, yet through their veil
I saw him blazing still,
And steep in gold the misty dale,
And flash upon the hill.

The colour symbolism in 'The Philosopher' is one of subtle beauty and significance. The 'Day-dream' leads us through a maze of colour—half-earthly, half-celestial, and wholly brilliant as the tints which dart across the vividly remembered phases of a sensitive waking dream.

The following verse of the 'Death-scene' brings—and now, with scarcely one aid to actual sight—the shifting hues of luminous twilight into view:

> Paled, at length, the sweet sun setting
> Sunk to peace the twilight breeze:
> Summer dews fell softly, wetting
> Glen, and glade, and silent trees.

The music here perhaps calls up the vision, and merged, they form one of the loveliest pictures Emily has drawn, and the last three verses are among the most poignant and appealing she ever wrote.

> Then his eyes began to weary,
> Weighed beneath a mortal sleep;
> And their orbs grew strangely dreary,
> Clouded, even as they would weep.
>
> But they wept not, but they changed not,
> Never moved and never closed;
> Troubled still, and still they ranged not,
> Wandered not, nor yet reposed!
>
> So I knew that he was dying,
> Stooped, and raised his languid head;
> Felt no breath and heard no sighing,
> So I knew that he was dead.

Throughout the poems colour and thought and music move, mournfully blent, haunting the mind and leaving it at last unable to determine whether most poignantly it heard, or felt, or saw.

When first we listen to these songs, we are brought face to face with the woman who wrote them—we must remember who the singer is. When once we know them and have been haunted by their rebellious and contending music it will not be possible to forget. It will then be difficult to appraise them dispassionately, to single out here a lyric for appreciation, or there to critically discard some halting and imperfect piece. They will stand for the most part as a whole—the consistent, successive utterance of a soul whose claim to our admiration or regard we must emphatically accept or deny.

In a book of selections, such lyrics as 'Death', 'The Visionary', 'Hope', and the exquisite 'Remembrance' would properly find their place, but to meet them isolated thus for the first time would be to miss their real significance. To come upon such a poem as 'Remembrance', without the knowledge that its author knew absolutely nothing of the passion which breathes and burns in every line, would be to lose the apprehension of the artistic power of a writer who touched the unknown with such an unfaltering hand. Here Emily sounds, for the first and last time, the depths of human anguish; painting, with a profound and poignant power, the picture of surviving life stationed stern and unswaying before the spectacle of murdered joy.

The two most prominent women poets of the century, Mrs Browning and Christina Rossetti, among whose writings passion, exotic or mystical, plays so conspicuous a part, have never surpassed, if they have ever equalled, this love-song of a woman who never loved.

It is Emily's only recognition of that feeling which, for most women, colours and transfigures and embraces life. We feel that she alone could have thus presented it, while yet remembering how elsewhere with her own severe and serious certainty she wrote such lines as these:

> Mirth is but a mad beguiling
> Of the golden-gifted time:
> Love—a demon-meteor, wiling
> Heedless feet to gulfs of crime.

It is interesting to contrast the restrained but burning constancy of the feeling which 'Remembrance' portrays, with that of the hero of *Wuthering Heights*. It has all the tenacity—the desperate vigour of his passion without its feverish ferocity, and suggests that Emily could, when she chose, exchange the awful for the sublime. Full of a grand and sweeping music, true to the deepest and gravest passion, it ranks among the two or three of her poems which are indubitably great.

The 'Death Scene'—despite the weakness of the opening verses—a picture of moving and pathetic beauty, is the poem which least reflects the personality of the writer. The mute protest of the dying lover, which serves to check the distracting remonstrance of the living, is a fine dramatic touch; and the last four verses invite comparison with those on a similar theme by another now unnoticed poet. Hood's 'Death-Bed' is perfect in construction and very different in conception, but in both these poems truth and pathos meet. The quietude of resignation and the more awful stillness of despair are each convincingly portrayed, but Emily's scene of human ending—in spite of its technical defects—is the one of surpassing loveliness and power.

The song beginning 'The linnet in the rocky dells'—a musical and lovely dirge—contains one characteristic verse:

> Well, let them fight for honour's breath
> Or pleasure's shade pursue—
> The dweller in the land of death
> Is changed and careless too.

Changed to all 'fleeting treacheries', careless of all the poor pursuits of earth, in that 'land where all things are forgotten', to Emily must any liberated spirit be. Nature alone might be remembered—its voice regarded—its whispering solace heard. Nature, the one subduing and consolatory power, she worshipped with all the intense and concentrated passion of her soul. It was a guardian—a lover, from which if she were wrested she must die. The 'dim moon struggling in the sky' kept welcome watch with her; the stars departing left a 'desert sky'. With them she says:

I was at peace, and drank your beams
As they were life to me;
And revelled in my changeful dreams,
Like petrel on the sea.

Thought followed thought, star followed star,
Through boundless regions, on;
While one sweet influence, near and far,
Thrilled through and proved us one!

Human sympathy she never sought, and love she 'laughed to scorn', but the 'nightly stars', the 'silent dew', the sun that 'gilds the morning'—these were the 'best beloved of years', the guardians against an ever-threatening despair. Nature under all aspects greeted her always with a face of tireless beauty, a breast of wide-sufficing rest. The motherhood of earth for her children—the love of death for its own, such communion she could taste and understand. One held the liberty for which she panted, and one the rest towards which she leaned; and both surveyed, unmoved as she, the trivial prizes for which men strive and die.

In lines which recall one of Byron's well-known stanzas, she mourns in exile the 'fields of home', as he the purity and freshness of a departed youth. The thought of the stunted heather on her beloved moors evokes this outburst:

—not the loved music, whose waking
Makes the soul of the Swiss die away,
Has a spell more adored and heart-breaking
Than, for me, in that blighted heath lay.

The spirit which bent 'neath its power
How it longed—how it burned to be free!
If I could have wept in that hour
Those tears had been heaven to me.

The first six of the posthumous poems, from one of which these verses are taken, are clumsy and youthful compositions, but through them the dominant adoration of her life finds some inadequate expression. They speak her strong and unappeasable yearning for the things which alone she loved and loved so well. 'My sister Emily', wrote Charlotte, 'loved the moors. Flowers brighter than the rose bloomed in the blackest of the heath for her; out of a sullen hollow in a livid hillside her mind could make an Eden.'

She had to admit one power before which her tameless spirit knelt in 'Fond idolatry', and so she puts this plea into the voice of the spirit of wind and sun and sky:

Few hearts to mortals given,
On earth so wildly pine,
Yet few would ask a heaven
More like this earth than thine.

This later selection notably includes the famous 'Last Lines' and the five stanzas beginning 'Often rebuked, yet always back returning', the last two of which contain the essence of her personal philosophy.

I'll walk where my own nature would be leading:
It vexes me to choose another guide:
Where the grey flocks in ferny glens are feeding:
Where the wild wind blows on the mountain side.

What have those lonely mountains worth revealing?
More glory and more grief than I can tell:
The earth that wakes *one* human heart to feeling
Can centre both the worlds of Heaven and Hell.

Of her two greatest and best-known poems—the 'Old Stoic' and 'Last Lines', it is hardly necessary to speak. They are familiar to all students of English literature, and the latter stands alone and unsurpassed for depth and gravity, for passionate and lofty strength. 'No last words', says Swinburne, 'of poet or hero, or sage or saint, were ever worthy of longer and more reverent remembrance than that appeal which is so far above and beyond a prayer to the indestructible God within herself.'

On that alone might have rested her claim to fame.

But a more blessed fate than that of fame awaited her. Death snatched her early, kindly, from a life which must have been to the end, it seems, thwarted and overcast. And in the near light of its approach, she perceived it clearly no longer as a friend to welcome, but as a last enemy to overthrow. She met its challenge, and being born for conquest, overcame. There was 'Not room for Death, Nor atom that his might could render void.'

'While physically she perished, mentally she grew stronger than we had yet known her', Charlotte affirmed, relating the details of her sister's ending, with a truth and beauty of expression which she has never reached elsewhere: 'Day by day when I saw with what a front she met suffering I looked on her with an anguish of wonder and love. I have seen nothing like it; but indeed I have never seen her parallel in anything. Stronger than a man, simpler than a child, her nature stood alone.'

Her nature stood alone. That was the awful fact—the tragedy of her life.

Alone in its negation of all that other mortals hold most dear; alone in its unwavering pity for frailty and error—no touch of which could ever mar the righteousness and vigour of this one woman's heart; alone in suffering and achievement; in the dark uncompanioned vigils of its life and the triumphant conflict of its death. It seems almost as if she must stand thus alone for ever—on that 'other side of silence'; not framed for bliss, and yet too strong for an eternity of groping torment, alien alike to spirits lost and blest. Rather, resolved into the elements she worshipped, she seems to find her immortality, transmuted, given back to earth again. Her spirit—one with the keen and searching airs that sweep wildly and sweetly over the wastes she loved—finds rest, and liberty, and wandering peace.

Strong to act and think and feel in the narrow channels prescribed for her by dreary circumstance and a despotic temperament, she was yet beset by a weakness that comes of undiverted strength. Her resolute rejection of human interest and sympathy intensified her suffering and in a measure nullified her powers. She possessed a force of passion and vision not given to any of her countrywomen who have spoken widely to the world; and yet she speaks and can speak only to a few scattered hearers—to those to whom she is, in some strange and far-off fashion, personally dear.

For few will find it in their hearts to love this passionate child of storm and cloud: hers was a nature slow to attract; swift to dismay: but those who do, will love her with something of her own intensity, her own unfitful fire, and with that constancy which, it has been pointed out, is a quality with which nearly all her characters or personifications are endowed.

'She died', it was said, 'in a time of promise'; and if she had 'only lived!' cried those who, noting the immaturities and deficiencies of her always inspired but imperfect work, imagined a glorious future for one who never let her 'spirit tire with looking for what is to be'.

But we, surveying that life 'in all things troubled and taintless', foreseeing the certain sorrow, the possible failure of its future, reviewing the defeat and anguish of its past—find the cry stifled on our lips: and silence takes the place of speech as we remember that she lived long enough to lift such a cry for liberty as few women have ever lifted: to give a brief but sufficient utterance to the soul

whose calm intensity
Glared sunless on the passion sun that blinds
Unblinded——

and to die as she had lived boldly confronting, and at the last defying, death—crying there was 'not room' for it—making no way.

Wuthering Heights, said Sydney Dobell, who was the first to claim it for immortality, displayed the 'unformed writing of a giant-hand, and the large utterance of a baby-god'. Fragments of that large utterance—imperfect characters traced by that giant-hand are set before us in these lyrics. With the exception of a few weak and early pieces, there is hardly one which does not display some sombre and startling beauty—some burning thought or delicate ray of fancy—some fine image or reflection. Unique in their originality, sincerity and force, they have rested alone and almost unnoticed in the lumber room of literature: it is time the dust was shaken from them; that they stood forth to speak for themselves and their creator in unflinching tones.

They cannot attract the casual reader; they must assuredly dispense with popularity, and possibly with widespread recognition—but they will live in the mind of that finer company with whom 'remembrance makes fame'.

THE COUNTRY SUNDAY

WHEN quite a child, I was pledged to read at night and morning a book called the *Believer's Daily Remembrancer*, and in my little sweet-smelling country chamber, painfully at night and morning, I toiled my portion through. The pages were compact of capitals and strings of long, unspellable adjectives, forming apostrophes to Deity, with exclamation marks at the end. Indeed, so full of these they were, that then the name of God, as I wrote or read it, seemed incomplete without a string of them.

But Sunday was my real Remembrancer, when, from some instinct of the day's respite and restfulness, I put the book away.

And since the Country Sunday is always to me the Sunday of my childhood, it still looks out at me through all the years with a face of permanent and lovely peace. Then only was prayer possible, relieved from ponderous and inflated ornament. Perhaps, put into words, the spirit of my petition was a sentence from the French version of the Litany, lending the plea a note of pathos which our language lacks. *'O, Seigneur, ayez pitié de nous.'*

The picture of my Country Sunday is always summer; and early summer, with the roses blooming in the fields, I see. Lovers, I used to fancy them—the pink ones maidens and the white ones men, wooing each other in the twilight of the green. The sense of twilight overhung the day, for evening was and is that day's great hour. Then the bells, together with the stillness, spoke clearer peace across the meadows, and the stars—of which they seemed the voices—came later faintly into sight, like spirits smiling when their song was sung.

It was the 'day of eyes' a blind man in the village used to say, and that was why we wore our Sunday clothes; because God and His angels (those I thought the stars) were certain to be looking down. We passed that old man on the way to evening service, and he would put his fingers to his ears and tell me those were his 'peepers', with the far-off piteous smile of one doomed to find no answer to it in the faces of his kind.

We passed, too, many people on that path; among them, the Vicar's 'young lady', who long afterwards I came to know as the poor young man's undoing, a slim, white-frocked personage, with wandering blue eyes, which led in their time, and not unwittingly, more than one honest soul astray.

And Georgiana Mitchell—a strapping maiden from the rope factory—the mainstay of the choir, who prompted the love-lorn parson audibly in his occasional lapses from the sacred text.

All these people awed me somewhat; they seemed so indifferent to the fact—with which the blind man had impressed me—of the unflinching Look which marked that day. That was the thought that claimed my childhood and, in another fashion, claims it now. 'A day of eyes', of transcendental vision, when the very roses—for there are always roses in the Sunday of my fancy—challenge the pureness of our gaze, and the grass marks the manner of our going, and the sky hangs like a gigantic curtain, veiling the Face which, watching us invisibly, we somehow fail to see. It judged in those old days my scamped and ill-done tasks. It viewed my childish cruelties and still, with wider range, it views and judges now. Here in the dingy town, a book or casual visitor can chase the sense of wrong and folly, and the soul is often stifled into sleep. The futile preacher earns his meed of critical contempt as an inane and blundering egotist, but there, so little way removed from the fresh sweetness of the fragrant dust to which he must so soon return, he remains sacred still, God's Minister,—and if, poor soul, a bad one—well then—*'Dieu aie pitié de lui.'*

It is—this Sunday of my dreams—the sweet Remembrancer of all patient and holy things; amongst them, of the quiet dead. They sleep in the country, nearer those who knew and loved them, than in the grim grave-acres of the town, lying either side the little pathway, which at morn and evening their old companions tread.

There was (strangely enough, the blind man's friend) a woman who could never go to church because she said they talked of nothing there but 'dead folk',—a scathing, though unconscious commentary on the preacher's power.

Often on moonlit nights, while from within the church the wheezy voluntary sounded, the moon, to my thought, has touched white headstones, giving them a weird and wakeful prominence—leaving the unmarked mounds bathed in a gentler, more forgetful light. Under the sward they slumbered more securely, those of whom men recorded nothing, leaving their virtues and their names with God; those whom man had remembered seeming to have missed their rest. Still I recall one puzzling line, written on a small marble slab over a child, whose short years numbered only three—'Eternity is not length of life but depth of life', and I have since many times wondered what was the history of that little child.

His might well be the motto of the Country Sunday—that long, mysterious day, holding eternity within it, hinting of no tomorrow save the one which has no ending; mocking—if such a day can mock—the transitory aims and joys of common life; lifting the soul above its body and hallowing the body to its soul.

Much has been written of the Country Sunday. Addison painted in the leisurely, ornate fashion of his age, a humorous, placid, and somewhat worldly scene.

There is, too, the cynical picture of Richard Jefferies: 'All things reposed but man,' he says, 'so busy with his vulgar aims.' Nature, he shows quite callous to each time and season, and joy and sorrow, and aspiration of mankind.

And besides this, an exquisite vignette of Miss Thackeray's plants itself in memory, where the same nature is depicted in close communion with humanity, 'lifting it' with solemn and mysterious power 'above the heat and flight and bustle of life'.

Humorous, cynical, and solemn—under all these aspects it may be viewed. And under all these aspects, I, from time to time, have viewed it; but under one only do I see it always—a summer rose-surrounded day, ending in a haze of wistful sunset, pink, and slowly shifting into grey, with bells ringing persistently the Christmas anthem; with eyes in the red, dappled hedges and in the ripples of the streams. Eyes, tender or upbraiding, smiling or sorrowful, but all divine. Nature taking her Maker's message more earnestly than upon any other day; preaching His purity, His changelessness and encircling vision, whispering everywhere His peace. And above that sunset, from under the drowsy roses, through the running water and across the breeze-blown fields, the old refrain—simple, because it is a plaint of children—solemn, because the breath of prayer—'*O Seigneur, ayez pitié de nous.*'

THE LONDON SUNDAY

'SON-DAYE' an old writer calls 'God's parle with dust'; and this quaint definition is worth the thinking on; for Sunday (especially the London Sunday) is a day of voices, the greatest of which perhaps is silence. For an invisible finger rests upon the city's mighty lip; its avaricious roar subsides; the fateful cries of this Amazon syren sound, if at all, but indistinctly—muffled—as from a distant chamber, the door of which some hand holds quietly ajar. Even the utterance of want seems stifled. Vagrants fret no more along the pavement; the licensed beggars of the Sabbath whine in daintier garments from a loftier place.

'God's parle' begins with silence; the hour of awakenment starts with determined slumber. The prologue to this drama, wherein should move 'bright shadows of true rest', is chanted before a lowered curtain; for in the homes of labour crazy blinds are drawn, and not till noon will the flutter of curl papers and shirt sleeves behind them proclaim the festal nature of the day. The dawn of it appears ungreeted, yet it is man's 'walking hour',—the cool of his short day. The echoes of his great ode to labour die away; that sombre epic gives place to lyric liberty. The issues of a wider existence are to be tried in these spare hours of tranquillity;—the worker sleeps, but soon his heart will wake to its brief taste of life, and he will rise a carpenter or sweep no longer, but the man he is, to paint in his own poor colours the clouded picture of his soul. He paints it often ill, under the eyes of the eternal taskmaster—weary of taskmaskers divine or human—athirst for freedom and repose.

The curtain rises to a sound of bells,—a significant prelude. Wedding bells, they are often enough, for those who cannot spare, even for such a ceremony, a more valuable day, and the vulgar symbol of plenty, strewn lavishly about the doorway, is a pathetic comment—when the bride and bridegroom have departed in impatient cabs—on the blessing they are never likely to enjoy. The bells tell of death too; they sing sweet reminders that rest is not unattainable, that somewhere, far off, it lurks for the weary at their day's end. Thus opening and closing life is heralded on these still mornings; though the sounds are so familiar, few pause to note the lessons of toll and chime.

Railway stations are favourite trysting-places. There 'journeys end in lovers' meetings', and these prosaic—often inarticulate—couples, whose easy manners and uncultured emotions do not meet the requirements of ideal courtship, don their embarrassing finery bravely and go duteously through their parts. They are used to witnesses. Privacy and solitude—did they know how to desire them—circumstance forbids; all they are to know of each other must be learnt in these snatched hours, when they may seize some realization of the personal value of their crowded life; the quietude of the streets, the easier passage of broad thoroughfares, is no mean measure of their opportunity. Like the risen saints of old, they rise and 'appear' to each other from the prisoning graves of toil.

In the parks groups of idlers gather round the red flag of 'liberty' and the sign of the dogmatic evangelist, which flutter side by side. Many are the friendly and menacing invitations extended to the passer-by. A gentleman (poor soul!) distributes pamphlets on a new doctrine, entitled 'Comprehensionism', of which the prevailing characteristic seems to be incomprehensibility. It is founded on an allegorical interpretation of the 'House that Jack built', and the prophet of this new gospel undertakes to regenerate humanity by means of the alphabet and numerals drawn in one continuous line, and a theory of colour in which every virtue has its distinctive hue.

A 'scripture spiritualist', stronger in faith than argument, gives way, on impertinent inquiries from the public, to material expressions of indignation. He shows a tendency to shift, rather than sift, examples, and on the betrayal of a listener's doubt as to the liberation of St Peter from prison, parries the thrust with a vigorous: 'Never mind then, 'oo rolled the stones of the sepellkur awiy?'

Leaving the open air temple,—under dingier roofs, the doctrines of the red flag and incomprehensibility are expounded by cleanlier, if less vigorous prophets; and a strange study are these 'fishers of men'. Their various baits collected in a theological shop-window would make an interesting show. A scholarly sceptic—professedly of the Established Church—is lecturing to a guild of factory girls on the 'Art of being an Angel'. 'You will all, I suppose,' he begins with weary cynicism, 'hear yourselves called one some day.' Warming to his subject and heedless of the conscious giggle his opening words excite, he paints, graphically enough, the wings which emancipation shall give them in the future. Not until their social freedom is fully consummated, he declares, need they strive or hope to soar.

Not far away a Catholic priest is exhorting some nuns, a cripple and his child, and his small red-robed acolytes to 'shun the world and the lusts thereof—and pray, my brethren, for the blessed souls in purgatory; if those for whom you intercede have already entered Paradise, your prayers and offerings will be devoted by the holy saints to less fortunate spirits.' And the unblessed souls whom he addresses, forgetting their closer purgatory, pray.

'Wot,' shouts a fervid cockney evangelist to a sprinkling of hopeless ill-clad, ill-fed labourers, 'wot is the matter with you? Discontentment; that's wot it is. You ain't satisfied that the world is round, you want it square. Are you 'appy with two 'orses to drive you? No. Wot you want is four.'

Such crumbs of instruction and comfort are scattered broadcast upon the multitudes, and others of graver import and greater futility one may stop to hear.

Are these shadowy ineffectual answers given, one wonders, to a real and vital question asked by the mute glances of thousands of wan, dissipated and indifferent faces of the passers-by? 'What shall we do to inherit eternal life?' They may deny derisively all interest in the query, but their looks belie them; some outcome indeed they seek of this world's hard demands—some assured future, if it be but one of eternal rest.

Some of us fancy the sound of children's voices tunes better to birds' music than other human cries. And here in town the sparrows twitter while the city children sing their hymns and add their shrill not unmelodious notes to the day's silent music. Cowslip fields and rose-sprinkled hedges, paths walled in by corn and poppies—these the kindly year provides for little Sabbath idlers far away. Buff and blue sunbonnets flutter sedately up a village street in sight of watchers by a cottage door.

Here—in the sombre city—too, are children playing in gardens of the dead. Grey tablets flank the cinder-walks, uprooted memories haunt the place. The thin, unchildish children spell out perhaps the grave inscriptions, making their tryst by a conspicuous stone. City babies, looking pathetically guilty of their own undesired existence, doze uncovered in the sun, while their young nurses play.

Old men and women sit on benches watching the scene with dim, indifferent eyes. They come perhaps to make acquaintance with the quiet neighbours below them whom they are so soon to join.

A small and ancient church stands in the midst of this enclosure. The open windows let through the sounds of a just ended service. Snatches of the last hymn steal out, broken by nearer voices, and reach the patient figures on the benches like music in a dream:

> Oh, how glorious and resplendent,
> Fragile body shalt thou be,
> When endued with so much beauty,
> Full of health, and glad and free;
> Full of vigour, full of pleasure——

then a shriek—a scuffle on the path before them, a squail and a confusion—'That shall last eternally.'

There are quiet unpretentious streets—restful and oldfashioned—which seem to have guarded the rare secret of repose. Something akin to peace lurks in the humble front parlours of these two-storey dwellings, where wax flowers in a glass case, embedded in a rainbow mat, stand in the window. Or there are perhaps green boxes of carefully tended crocuses on the window-sill, set like a row of fairy footlights to the human scene within.

The Sabbath fire burns brightly; the modest householder sits near the light, his newspaper spread out before him. Bells are silent for awhile—the clatter of crockery supersedes them. Lovers sit round a small table, upon which aged glances beam. The birds still twitter from a neighbouring square. The roar and rush of the weary workaday city seems far enough away. Later the lovers will be linked by a borrowed hymn-book in some Bethel near, fervently singing to each other, while the praise and prayer of hundreds of such simple people rises and dies away amid the unheeding, unanswering world around them.

The lit windows of these scattered temples send gleams into the night. Brilliant saints and martyrs too, in red and gold and blue, appear like luminous visions from statelier walls, casting downward on humanity their soulless and transparent gaze.

There are sordid, noisy thoroughfares which drown defiantly, with their own wild cries, all that would rise above them.

Youths, linked sometimes six together, push roughly up and down, shouting and leering at hatless dishevelled girls, who pass them with an inviting jeer. Squirt and flower-sellers sell popular wares. 'One penny—the lady's tormenter—all one penny.' 'Vi'lets—sweet vi'lets.' Children dart in and out shrilly screaming—in chase, one might think, of their own lost childhood—far indeed to seek.

To these, the day of speech and silence will lend never perhaps 'a clue that guides through erring hours'. They wander on—wanderers ever—making of these scant hours a muddier by-way to the broader passages of the dark week.

At length footsteps grow rarer; stray couples walk the deserted streets—the brilliant saints withdraw themselves mysteriously from view. 'See you agin, Sunday', is the refrain at platforms, as the trains puff off, and more or less gallant swains swagger homeward to shift embarrassing attire.

The day of days is over. Monday, with its folly and tyranny, its vice and its bewilderment comes on apace. Far off, across his quiet fields, the countryman scans the sky; but rain or shine, the city cares not; it ploughs and sows and reaps its human harvest whatever come.

Tomorrow the lamps of lust and labour will again be lit; the 'lamp that lights Man through his heape of dark days' is flickering to extinction now; the Voice that speaks with dust is soon to mingle its high music with man's most grovelling song.

Even now the door-keepers of the vast halls of toil and sin stir in their slumber, dreaming they hear the cry that rouses them—the immemorial, relentless cry: ' "Lift up your heads, O ye gates; and be ye lift up, ye everlasting doors——" for the Prince of this world must come in.'

MARY STUART IN FICTION

'WE HAVE already wept enough for Mary Stuart, both over prose and verse', writes Carlyle in 1824. 'Madame de Stael, we observe, is her principal admirer'(!). The incidents of her story are 'getting trite'; it has no 'moral which peculiarly recommends it'. Remove the body of Mary of Scots, he says, in fact, with that engaging finality of his, and it may well have seemed then, in view of all the Defences, Detections, Dutiful Invectives, Plays, Poems, which for three centuries she had inspired, and when Scott and Schiller were the last of the superfluous crowd, that nothing remained to be said or sung. Yet within the next eighty years how many notable historians were to find their way into the maze, while Bjornson, Swinburne, and Mr Hewlett plucked their nosegays from the garden of that great romance! Scott tells us that in his youth the Queen's guilt or innocence was commonly discussed and so passionately contested that an attack upon her character in the presence of a partisan was held to justify a challenge. Ideals are poorer ghosts today; but from the first one of those whom '*les diables et les anges se disputent furieusement*', she remains above and beyond such issues, not merely a great figure in a great age, but a personality which has wonderfully survived dissection and exploitation, an ageless mistress of hearts and conqueror of fame—the secret of whose far-reaching charm, a secret still, is the secret of her long continuance—for it is not the moral, negligible enough, nor the incidents, dramatic as they are, of Mary's tragedy which account for its sustained appeal.

Elizabeth, who moves, to say the least of it, as crookedly across the same chequered board, is as absorbing a piece in the momentous game, but her gyrations leave us critically cold, and the precise shade of her private and political delinquencies has not, for the crowd at all events, been a burning question.

Mary of England, in the tragedy of Queens, shows an infinitely more heartbreaking face than Mary of Scotland, and if we still stare in upon her wretchedness, 'Old, miserable, diseased, incapable of children', there is no magic in that 'voice of shipwreck on a shoreless sea'.

The story of Joanna of Naples is curiously similar in outline to Mary Stuart's, and who remembers her today? Another Queen of France, ill-matched, a beauty, a coquette, mistrusted and slandered, ended on the scaffold, to become the subject of prolonged debate and pity; but Marie Antoinette has passed absolved into the world of shades, while Mary Stuart still looms out from the 'haunted mists of romance' with the clear persistence of actuality. '*Cette petite Reinette écossaise*', wrote Catherine de Medici of her as a child, '*n'a qu'à sourire pour tourner toutes les têtes françaises*'; it is that same far-travelling smile, attractive or repellent, piercing the intervening dusk, which keeps her within view, and on the stage of commonplace fiction where from time to time she 'stars', like a great actress playing an incorrigibly stupid part, she invests the lifeless scenes and hackneyed speeches with an incongruous interest and vitality.

She appears first in de Boisgilbert's *Marie Stuart*, (*nouvelle historique*) published in 1675, which links the romances of Scudéry with the modern historical novel. The author claims in his preface, that it is '*une histoire très véritable dans toutes les circonstances que beaucoup de gens ignorent, puis qu'elles sont également éloignées des deux idées de Martyre et de Courtisane*', a promise of impartiality not quite realized in the text, and though Freebairn, his English translator, warns us that 'whoever peruses it will meet with a Disappointment if he is in search of those airy Amusements with which such pieces are usually stuffed', it is not without imaginative touches. That same night, he says, on which the order for Mary's assassination was dispatched to Paulet, Elizabeth and one of the maids of honour sleeping in her chamber beheld in a dream the execution at Fotheringay, where '*en suitte le même Bourreau la couppoit à sa Majesté*', who straightway, on waking, recalled the messenger and reconsidered the situation. A so-called *Secret History*, compiled from several unacknowledged sources, appeared in 1725, translated by Mrs Eliza Haywood, actress, playwright, novelist, and sometimes publisher, Pope's 'shameless scribbler' and Swift's 'stupid, infamous scribbling woman', whose public, used to the highly-seasoned dishes of the writer, must have been painfully deceived if they looked for piquancy in the dull *rechauffé*.

The Recess, one of the earliest historical novels (1785), by Sophie Lee, gives, in a series of long-winded letters, the emergence from some underground apartments, the disclosure of their royal birth, and the subsequent adventures at the English Court of twin-daughters of the Queen of Scots and the Duke of Norfolk, between whom a marriage is supposed to have taken place at Bolton Castle.

Observing that it is 'the dear-bought privilege of the unfortunate to be tedious', and not depriving her heroines of this prerogative, Miss Lee trips on past wayside politics to the emotional development of her story, which unites Matilda, the elder twin, in secret 'but half-hallowed nuptials' with the Earl of Leicester, though what, after all, she asks, 'are the ties of marriage to the invisible ligaments of the soul?' Ellinor falls into the impassioned arms of Essex, whom she meets in a pavilion, 'pale, disordered, and undrest', while both, to blind Elizabeth, to whom they became 'familiar appendages', are passing as the daughters of Lady Jane Grey. 'Shades of the honoured Howard and the amiable Mary!' as Miss Lee herself exclaims. The young ladies of Belvidere House, Bath, the academy over which this energetic novelist and dramatist resided, no doubt found it thrilling enough, and perhaps in school a line was drawn between fact and the higher flights of fancy.

Miss Emily Finch, who follows her more daring and distinguished predecessor with a novel, the *Last Days of Mary Stuart*, in 1841, introduces the unhappy Queen rather to point a moral than to adorn a tale.

> Let not [she cries] the brilliant halo, which high rank and splendid endowments threw around Mary Stuart, render us blind to the defects so conspicuous in her character. Parents, who covet for your daughters what are falsely termed the *advantages* of a French education, pause for one moment before you expose them to the debasing influence of that country in which Mary of Scotland was educated. The withering simoon is not more certain in its effects.

And so on. 'The English', says an American critic of the eighties, 'seem to address their fiction to the aesthetically idiotic'; and, if this hard saying is elsewhere questionable, it is broadly true of these earlier historical romancists, whose productions, as a rule, display merely such qualities as might be looked for from the literary ventures of an intelligent paroquet.

'Le roman historique doit ètre un roman de moeurs retrospectif', says M. Emile Faguet. And it is this preoccupation of the writer with remote conditions, unobserved and unrelated to experience, yet intimately associated with the characters of his story, which makes it at best a *genre faux* involving *'une sorte de duplicité continuelle'*.

The pictures to be restored are faded, but the passions are not extinct, and the result is, as a rule, an unnatural fusion of the past and the present, producing the effect of a masquerade, in which the artist dances, sometimes awkwardly enough, with persons of whose identity he never seems quite sure. After all, he is dancing with the Dead, and, if they will not unmask for him, is it their revenge, perhaps, for the exploitation of their souls? No 'frustrate ghost' has refused to reveal herself more resolutely than Mary Stuart, since how many of her dramatists and novelists has she really inspired? Not Schiller, not Alfieri, hardly Scott; Swinburne and Mr Hewlett, in a sense, alone. Carlyle, by his bitter abuse of Scott, whose creations he affirmed amounted to 'little more than mechanical cases, deceptively painted automatons', and whom he accused of not wishing 'the world to elevate, to amend itself, to do this or that, except simply pay him for the books he kept writing', probably helped to bring discredit on that branch of art which his great countryman made famous. 'The only genuine Romance for grown people' is, he declares, 'Reality'.

We catch a feeble echo of the Prophet's views in John Galt, *Southennan* (1830) where he remarks that 'Fiction, over the doom of Darnley and the fortunes of the Scottish Queen, acknowledges the superior wonders of truth', though this admission does not deter him from launching three interminable volumes on the subject of the Queen and Chastelard, whose suit she 'regards with a degree of intellectual compassion more withering than scorn'; truth, in this romance, presumably recognizing the superiority of fiction, since 'everything at variance with propriety' is ingeniously avoided.

Chastelard, as in *The Queen's Quair*, figures as the dupe of Rizzio, and again in an earlier tale, *Ringham Gilhaïze* (1828) Galt anticipates Mr Hewlett in bringing Knox under the Queen's spell so far that 'the winning sorceries of her exceeding beauty and blandishment worked even upon his stern honesty and enchanted his jealousy asleep'.

Knox's denunciation of the Monstrous Regiment of Women left his susceptibility to feminine influence untouched. He was twice married, and had many friends and correspondents of the incompetent sex, but he abhorred the political woman. To crown Mary of Guise, he said, was as seemly a thing as to saddle 'ane unrewly kow', and where his tenderness for her more unruly daughter is concerned who are the 'witnesses for the persecution'? 'A Pope', she said with rather pathetic irony to one of Cecil's envoys, will 'excommunicate *you*, but *I* was excommunicated by a pore minister Knokes.'

Galt's historical novels were written in professed rivalry with Scott with whom he claimed at least equality; they were not the jewels in the rubbish-heap of the 'sedate Greenock burgher' whose two or three gems of simple realism shine out brightly among the refuse of his obtuse, untidy mind; but what at best were sedate Greenock or other burghers, industrious little schoolmistresses of Bath or elsewhere, Dumas or Scott himself, to make of Mary Stuart?

That which pleased her most in life was its contending music, the clash of arms, the hum of voices and buzz of crowds, the intermezzo of the song, the lute, the dance; and loving, as Buchanan says she did, 'to handle the boisterous cables', she would not miss the wilder music of the sea. Yet among all her novelists, there is but one musician to conduct the tragic symphony, and he, as he says my Lord of Bothwell did, plays his leading instrument to death.

James Grant, G.R.P. James, and Samuel Ireland (the father of the Shakespeare forger) wrote dull and flimsy romances of the period, in which Mary is, fortunately perhaps, not conspicuous.

Whyte Melville dresses up an inane and invertebrate lady of the sixties to stand for Mary Stuart, to whose 'pliant and forgiving nature' and want of promptitude in action (!) he attributes most of her misfortunes.

Miss Yonge, in *Unknown to History*, carries us back to the schoolroom of the eighties, and the tinkle of its overworked piano. Basing her story on a tradition of the seventeenth century that Mary, during her imprisonment at Lochleven, gave birth to a daughter who was conveyed to France and became a nun at Notre Dame de Soissons, she adapts the legend, essentially romantic, as it stands, to meet the requirements of a tame, domestic tale.

A child of James Hepburn and Mary Stuart pacing a convent garden, shut in with her passions and her ghosts; here, for the poet or the novelist is the finest stuff of dreams. We are, at least, indebted to Miss Yonge for having made practically no use of it.

Nor does Harriet Martineau, who did produce one creditable historical novel, conspicuously shine, though she outshines Miss Yonge in her treatment of the Queen of Scots. In *Once a Week* for 1862, we come upon her short, conscientious serial, *The Anglers of the Dove*, illustrated by Millais, whose graceful woodcuts are perhaps its chief attraction. The scenes are laid at Tutbury, Sheffield, and Buxton, and the slight plot revolves round the Northumberland and Westmorland rising.

Mary Stuart and Bess of Hardwicke inevitably present a contrast striking enough, but the caustic and dramatic touch which their characterization demands, are wanting, and the novel has yet to be written in which these two remarkable antagonists jar and fret and finally collide. The Earl of Shrewsbury is sympathetically sketched, and with a finer brush and a few more colours in her paintbox Miss Martineau might have done more with the harassed Talbot, practically with his embarrassing charge a prisoner under his own roof, the victim of domestic and political perplexities in perpetual see-saw between a shrewish wife and an exacting sovereign.

George Talbot is but one of a great company. Other men's rest was broken, other men's heads and hearts were broken, if not for Mary, at the diplomatic game in which six times out of seven the Devil won the toss. Never perhaps before in the course of one short human history was God called upon to witness to the truth of so many sturdy lies, with the glint of steel or the distorted shadow of the cross behind them. Every one lost something—if nothing more precious than his immortal soul—and the Queen herself lost everything.

'See', cried Buchanan in a savage aside, 'how finely sche playeth hir part!'

At first, a friendless girl standing alone in the treacherous and greedy crowd, she played it with singular gaiety and tolerance, and always with courage; while to the end the instruments and victims of her tragedy make, for the most part, so mean a show.

In Mr H. C. Bailey's flattering portrait of that fascinating trimmer, the *Master of Gray*, Mary, at Tutbury and Fotheringay, is behind the scenes; James VI of Scotland, a pitiful clown, shuffles across the front; while the conspirators talk—full of French oaths and Latin quotations. The death of Lethington, the most attractive and brilliant waverer of them all, is picturesque, and the brisk, somewhat jerky tale is suggestive of the delicate webbery in that sombre stuff of tragedy to which Mary lends the golden thread. 'A lady to live and to die for: and many died'; a ruffianly and courtly crew. While she is on the stage, she overshadows them, but they had their own adventurous histories and intimate entanglements—all sorts of titles to obscurer fame.

Dumas, however, the great feuilletoniste of statesmen and adventurers, in his novel, *Marie Stuart*, has made little of them. A master of dashing portraiture and effective situation, with his strong dramatic instincts and aristocratic sympathies, he should have given us something more than a mere conversational history, in which—notably in the Lochleven incidents—he is obviously indebted to *The Abbot*. In French drama, from Montchrétien to Lebrun, the Queen of Scots is a persistently recurrent figure, but she did not inspire Dumas, and has no other place worth notice in French romance.

Of all the French tragedies, the most interesting is Montchrétien's *L'Escossaise* (1601), a touching picture of Mary's last days and death at Fotheringay, in which her waiting-maids and English statesmen act as chorus.

In England, Mary has so far fallen into the hands of only two novelists capable of presenting her, and they stand widely as the poles apart.

During the century which divides Scott, the father of the historical novel, from Mr Hewlett, the methods and ideals of fiction have suffered a momentous change. We have moved fast and far from the old traditions of the art.

Scott represents a robuster, more patient and idealistic age than ours:

> Half blind
> With intellectual light, half brutalised
> With civilisation, having caught the plague
> In silks from Tarsus, shrieking east and west
> Along a thousand railroads.

His are large patriotic canvases painted in the open air, and if we look to him in vain for the modern personal note of style, natural or selfconscious, for erudition, subtle psychological analysis and intensity of passion, above and beyond all this, when we go back to our old magician, we find a conception and execution on a grander scale, a fineness of taste in the treatment of emotion, which has long gone out of fashion, a reticence and dignity in human portraiture which is absent from the latest development of the genre. He gives us in *The Abbot*, a conventional, a classic Mary Stuart 'dressed in a deep mourning robe, and with all those charms of face, shape and manner, with which faithful tradition has made each reader familiar'—'the like of which we know not to have existed in any character moving in that class of life, where the actresses as well as the actors command general and undivided attention'.

He has here such a heroine as he delights to honour, an actress moving in the highest 'class of life', and with his characteristic regard for rank, he pays a sort of personal, unconscious homage to the royal person; clothing her instinctively with all that traditional grace and majesty of which Mr Hewlett has cynically stripped her to expose his drenched wanton naked to the storm. We are therefore confronted in these two novels with a widely divergent difference, not only of treatment, but of conception; the irreconcilable difference, where the central figure is concerned, between the greatest of great ladies and *canaille*.

Not sure of what used to be called her 'innocence', not blind to her lapses, her outbreaks of malice and passion, Scott shows her 'suddenly excited, surprised, not only beyond self-command, but beyond the verge of reason'; but in his hands—in such scenes, the essential—the latent dignity of humanity is saved. The soul is always safe with him; at its worst, too sacred for profanation; at its best, of heroic mould, sublime. Schiller produced an incredibly vulgar marionette; Scott's Mary Stuart is statuesque; cold and colourless and inanimate indeed beside the bespattered, passion-wasted figure of her last painter, not truer, not perhaps to fact so true, but still impressive; and appealing with a graver voice, a grander gesture (as sculpture—as ideal beauty does appeal), the voice and gesture of a Queen of Scotland, a Queen of Tragedy, looking down with blank chiselled eyes on the new, strange Queen of Honey and Desire.

With Scott, says Ste Beuve, '*reste le dernier mot de la postérité comme des contemporains, la conclusion de l'histoire, comme de la poésie*', writing '*finis*' after him as Carlyle wrote it after Schiller; but though almost every European poet had been attracted and uninspired by her, the end was not yet, since Swinburne and Mr Hewlett were to come, throwing stronger lights and darker shadows upon Queen Mary than ever by poet or novelist were thrown before.

The author of the Scotch Trilogy may surely claim for his lady's picture, as Rossetti did for his, that it shows

> The very sky and sea-line of her soul,
> That in all years,
> They that would look on her must come to me.

The poet, however, has this advantage over the novelist, that his triptych divides, and embraces a subject the dimensions of which are too large, the diversities too marked, to be adequately treated in a single panel. From *Chastelard*, with its repellent siren note, through *Bothwell* to the sadness and sombre majesty of *Mary Stuart*, where 'this my last tragedy', as she herself writes of her death to the Duke of Guise, is reached, is a tedious and winding road, though to find her it must be taken to the end. The novelist traverses but a part of it, and intent on his particular stretch, scarcely looking before and after, gives us but a partial portrait.

Scott, with the poetic rather than the dramatic instinct, choosing the first term of the caged life, as Schiller chose the last, in his spectacle of the winged creature lamed, with its broken song, its thwarted instinct of flight, hardly identifies the captive of Lochleven with the gallant, intrepid girl who walked the Edinburgh streets, madly gay, or rode forth on her 'determined journeys' to battle, repenting 'nothing but that she was not a man, to know what life it was to lie all night in the fields or to walk on the causeway with a jack and knapscull, a Glasgow buckler and a broadsword'. And Mr Hewlett, exclusively concerned with the day of sharp conflict and short-lived passion, believing perhaps with a great French critic, that '*Elle ne devient politique, comme cela est le propre des femmes passionnées, que dans l'intérêt de la passion même et de sa vengeance*'—fails or refuses for an instant to divine the Mary of Lochleven and Fotheringay in the Mary of Holyrood and Dunbar.

In *The Queen's Quair* we come to the first attempt in fiction at real portraiture, an ugly portrait finely painted, and with it the door shuts on the old glorified waxwork once for all. The atmosphere, the colour, the movement of a time, packed as all times are with tragic and sordid incident, crowded as all times are not with sinister and striking figures, has never in the whole of English historical fiction been matched elsewhere.

The realistic method has never perhaps in England been so closely applied to an historical subject; the historical romance has never so nearly approached the novel of observation, with the result that the artist produces an amazing effect of actuality. Here, as where Lethington passes the Queen in her extremity, with his hat drawn down over his eyes; and in the scribbling of the famous letter in the fetid bedroom; there, in the flooded path at Leith which takes the Queen into Scotland 'over a foreign road'; in the glitter on the sea for Bothwell at Carberry, everywhere, in a hundred vivid strokes, true to fact, or the finer truth of inspiration, we seem to be at last in touch with history and romance itself. Forcing themselves upon our acceptance by reason of their intense vitality, Bothwell, a 'galliard, if ever there was one', with his air of 'take me or leave me, I go my way', Darnley, 'this eagle', Moray, Lethington, 'over-driven, fragile, self-wounding wretch', French Paris, 'this jaunty dog', and the rest, ring for the moment true. But the Queen herself, wonderfully galvanized figure though she is, strikes from the first a loud, false note, which jars with increased intensity through every intricate movement to the discordant close.

Or is she after all alive? There are moments when we can hardly doubt it, so marvellous is his trick of presentment, of relief, producing the sort of effect that Wiertz produces when walking through his gallery we perceive, recoil from, question, examine, and finally reject the painted figure on the wall. For she has, in a sense, inspired him; the vehemence of our rejection proves how amazing is the momentary likeness—amazing enough to be hastily confounded with identity. But there is a secret, a strange, a divine one, of personality to which he has not found the clue. 'I say that looking with that face of yours, / None shall believe you holy', cries Darnley, in Swinburne's *Chastelard*. Swinburne has not spared Mary Stuart, but he has not defaced her. His Circe pitiful, 'As pitiful as he that's hired for death, / And loves the slaying yet better than the hire', passes, not only because he takes us on to the point where the woman survives the wanton and the Queen survives the woman, but because, marred as she is by all griefs and disgraces, his Mary Stuart is Mary Stuart still. Mr Hewlett's 'Queen of Desire', his draggled huntress, will not pass, and not only because the '*insatiable besoin d'amour*' distorts her. He speaks in a brilliant passage of fineness as her great quality, and it was not her least distinction; but if hers was not precisely that 'fineness of truth' which to Walter Pater stood for beauty, it was something more than the mere surface fineness of an incomparable courtesan. She was first and last a Queen. The child of the French Court, disposing of her small cast-off robes with touching gravity, and the broken woman of Fotheringay commending her 'poor desolate servants' to the care of each last correspondent in turn, are, for all the unlikeness between their faces of unlived and outlived passion, recognizable still. And if it was Mary who wrote to Bothwell: 'Now seeing that to obey you, my deir lufe, I spair nouther honour, conscience, hazard, nor greitness', and this is a woman's voice, it was also Mary who, under the shadow of the scaffold, in view of that magnificent opportunity in which death was to avenge the indignity of life, wrote to Elizabeth:

> Nothing is left of me now but the soul, which all your power cannot make captive; yet while abandoning this world and preparing myself for a better, I must remind you that one day you will have to answer for your charge and for all those whom you doom, and that I desire that my blood and my country may be remembered in that time.

And this, whatever the colour of the soul behind it, is the voice of a Princess.

He does not hear it.

'Neither', he seems to cry with Byron, 'will I make Ladies' books *al dilettar le femine e la plebe*.'

'A book about Queen Mary, if it be honest,' urges Mr Hewlett, 'has no business to be a genteel exercise in the romantic', and it is true enough that previous exercises have been too genteel; but neither, if he is to be credible, must the novelist of Queen Mary, painting her as the woman of one passion, mistake the passion. She had in common with her enemy, Catherine de Medici, of whom a contemporary ambassador writes, 'All her actions have ever been ruled and guided by one most powerful desire, the desire to reign, *un affetto di signoreggiare*'—the passion for sovereignty; while of Mary, the lady of lost causes, another contemporary says: 'The thing that most she thirsteth after is Victory, so that for victory's sake payne and perylls semeth pleasant unto her, and in respect of victory welthe and all thyngs semeth to her contemptuous and vile.'

With all her complexities she possessed this simplicity of greatness, and whenever she is consistent and single-hearted, it is when this passion, unobscured by any passing cloud of a baser obsession, is supreme. No one mistrusted her more profoundly, disliked her more cordially than Froude, no one has abused her more zealously than Buchanan; but Froude's 'bad woman disguised in the livery of a martyr', and Buchanan's 'outrageous hart', which 'nouther in love or in hatrit can keep any mean', the almost incredible fiend which looks out now and again, veiled or openly, from their imaginative pages, is more convincing than the erotic derelict of *The Queen's Quair*.

It is, after all, less on their adventures or achievements than on their power of personification that the survival of great personages depends. So, for all slips of theirs, their poets and their commentators, Jeanne d'Arc still stands for Inspiration, and Mary Magdalen for Devotion, and Mary Stuart for Romance.

That the only novelist who has ever really grappled with her, claiming, as Mr Hewlett does, to have 'pierced the fold of her secret', should have robbed her of this essential quality, making her sordid, almost squalid, goes some way to prove what was before suspected, that she is not a subject for the novelist at all. She calls for a larger stage: she moves reluctantly to any measure less stately or tempestuous than that of life itself. Her story has appealed to writers of every school and temperament, with its wealth of incident and passion, its rich background of whispering courts and noisy combats, and the stretches, at all junctures, of intervening sea. Its procession of kings, queens, lovers, statesmen, adventurers, prelates, preachers, gaolers, and cut-throats, marshalled more or less successfully, is always an imposing show. But the dominant, over-lit, over-twisted figure to which all points converge and round which the whole amazing tangle winds, moves in fiction for the most part mechanically, monotonously, or with a too theatrical allure across her too restricted stage. She is handled, but never really grasped; she eludes capture in this domain, as elsewhere she evades complete analysis, for none has quite caught the spirit or touched the charm.

She will destroy the most admirable picture by stepping out of it; she will spoil the most impressive speech with some chance aside, *in propria persona*, some little memorable, unpremeditated word. '*Je mieulx mourir de me faire telle*', perhaps she says, disposing with it of a hundred eloquent pages.

Even her face comes down to us in baffled portraiture; which of all these faces is Mary Stuart's face? From some, they say the 'tracked and hunted creature' looks out in the 'sidelong glance', but which touches life to the point of the gaiety, the bitterness, the beauty that were her portion? Did she miss her painter as Mona Lisa found hers, or was she too real for representation, and is she too romantic for 'romance'?

Others have passed to the immunity of fame; but Mary Stuart, rejecting failure, has not yet gone by. Losing the kingdom she so greatly coveted, she has captured another in the imagination of posterity.

A great achievement gained at the cost of a great disaster. For had she won the crown she fought for, Mary of Scotland and England, setting back the clock for Europe, must have turned to the world another face. Her small hand holding many keys would not so lightly or so magically have touched us.

As it is she holds the key of dreams, and hears through three centuries her poets singing, as of old they sang: '*Contentez-vous mes yeux, / Vous ne verrez jamais chose de plus belle.*'

MEN AND TREES

I

IT WAS a blind man in old Palestine who saw men as trees walking a year before Pilate washed his hands of the blood of a Just Person, and the other day in a London studio I met another, quite 'dark' as they say in Devonshire, who must have had some vision of men and trees. We had talked mechanically over the tea-cups: éclairs, Maeterlinck, Vesta Tilley; I would rather have asked him what he made of us from the Studio patter, how we 'saw' this or that or didn't 'see' it, our poses and our pictures, while the picture framed by the window which wasn't going to be hung anywhere made no claim. The greys and greens were deepening there; the line of lamps, just lit, cut the broken mass of trees in the gardens opposite; a light rain was beginning to freshen the dusty leaves. The London trees are all prisoners of men, some unreasonably mutilated like the lopped crowd in Greenwich Park, while, now and then, there is a wholesale massacre such as that of the seven hundred in Kensington Gardens, which took place, no one knows why, some thirty years ago, against which even the executioners protested and perhaps the homeless rooks as vainly. In my own wooded neighbourhood one after another falls; progress pulls down the old spacious shabby houses and puts up flats for the half-world; a popular draper rears a proud red monument to success; the green vanishes: even tomorrow one may miss the familiar plane of yesterday, and the birds go with the trees.

'You are looking at something', said my blind friend quietly. 'Not here', I told him. 'It was a tree outside the British Museum they were felling last week, with all the instruments of butchery, the axe and the rope and the saw, and the clearing round it like a scaffold; it went on for days and I didn't altogether care for it.' 'No,' he agreed, with sudden animation, 'I really can't bear to see a tree cut down—a big tree: it's a sort of sacrilege. I suppose we belong, of course we do—I anyhow—to the Dark Ages.' And then Beauty and Fashion broke in, frankly bored with sylvan nonsense, and I moved on to remember a passage from a French novel I had just been reading—the chance encounter of the hero of too many *bonnes infortunes* with a *petite à l'ulster* and *visage de Pierrot*:

> *Nous voilà partis tous les deux le long des boulevards morts nous contant nos mutuelles douleurs. Sa logeuse l'a chassée en lui volant trois pantalons, elle avait aussi un petit ami qui est parti*

avec une vieille dame riche, mais ce qui l'ennuie le plus est d'avoir perdu sa petite chambre d'où l'on voyait un arbre.

And then—but what miles away! Jefferies, who was only a quiet lover of trees, though 'never was such a worshipper of Earth'! 'How happy the trees must be to hear the song of the birds again in their branches. After the silence and the leaflessness to have the birds back once more—to feel them busy at the nest-building', he says somewhere. And again: 'I wish the trees, the elms would grow tall enough and thick enough to hide the steeples—in the ships men live, in the houses among the trees men live: these steeples are empty.'

And again: 'The mystery of nature and life hovers about the columned temple of the forest. The secret is always behind a tree, as of old time it was always behind the pillar of the temple—' forgetting that of old time the tree was the pillar of the temple. It is a clear echo of the earliest true cults, this, to hear—to feel—to have the birds; a return to the day when the tree was a sentient being with a soul of its own, or when later it became the abode or haunt of the spirit. The steeples are empty. Here is his inherent Paganism: ages before the steeples the primeval church was the forest, and the secret of all things was within or behind a tree.

The ancient and almost universal worship of trees, still prevalent in the religions of Africa and Southern Asia, surviving among some of the aboriginal hill-tribes of India in its crudest form, and not extinct in philosophic Buddhism, was perhaps the earliest form of divine ritual, a natural outcome of the tree's own beauty and man's first woodland life. The oldest inhabited world, as we look back on it from our cleared spaces, is a dense and infinite forest, a world of tree-haunted men and men-haunted trees.

Man himself, the early stories go, is descended from a tree, the ash and the elm, according to the Edda; Adonis is born of Myrrha, after she has been, for her sin, transformed into a tree; Daphne, pursued by Apollo, becomes the laurel; the classic tree-nymph dies with her tree; and to the tree from which all races sprang the souls of the dead return. An Indian race, the Gonds, still claim descent from trees, as did the Greek Pelopidae, and the Persian house of Achaemenidae; a tribe in South Nigeria believe that the souls of their dead return to trees, and the Warramunga of Australia that there they are waiting to be born again.

Primitive man, and civilized man till a few centuries back, owed almost everything to the tree, his fire and shelter, his gods and his devils. 'That Arch-fanatic Satan began his pranks in a tree.' The first houses of forest people were built round a tree with the roof sloping from it, such a tree-house as that in the first act of the *Walküre*, from the trunk of which Siegmund draws his sword. The old bridge was a tree-trunk, the Fire of London a forest fire. On the block of a dead tree Anne Boleyn and Charles I laid down their heads, and the order-book carried by the Misses Mould to its long home in the iron safe represents that dead tree which has become a 'property' in the last act of the human comedy.

The *Mayflower*, the pirate ships of the Elizabethan seamen, Nelson's *Victory* in Portsmouth Harbour are but trees upon the sea. Here and there is a rare one under it. Ste Geneviève, the patron saint of Paris, immortalized for us by Puvis de Chavanne's frescoes in the Panthéon, once, travelling to some Spanish port, exorcized the wrecking demon on one of these on which her own ship had nearly foundered. Commanding it to be cut down, she prayed, and 'as it began to fall, a wild head, grey and horrible, issued thereout, and never after perished ship there'. An old German belief that if a sick man was passed through a split tree which was then bound up, sympathetic relations were thereby set up between them, so that if it died he died, is carried seaward by a Rügen tradition that if the man perished and the surviving tree was cut down and used for shipbuilding, the dead man's ghost would haunt the ship. All that is a long way off; much nearer is Constable's elegant ash of Hampstead—in his own words, 'this young lady' who died of a broken heart. He made a sketch of her in full health and beauty, but 'on passing some time afterwards I saw, to my grief, that a wretched board had been nailed to her side, on which was written, "All vagrants and beggars will be dealt with according to law." The tree seemed to have felt the disgrace, for even then some of the top branches had withered.' In another year one half of her became paralysed, and 'not long after, this beautiful creature was cut down to a stump just high enough to hold the board'. In other times or in other countries her pardon would have been asked, or an offering made to her, or a solemn assurance that some one else was responsible for the outrage. In Siam, tree-felling is, or was until quite lately, reserved for hardened criminals, and no tree is today cut down by the Talein of Burmah without a prayer to the spirit who dwells within.

One may read whole libraries about the tree. Tree-myth, tree-marriage, tree-burial, tree-murder (under 'Forestry'), shelf upon shelf of books, dreams analysed and prayers dissected, millions of words strewn round it like its own dead leaves, and outside these stands the living tree, aloof, splendid; as magical as it was before one of them was written; and sometimes—there is always this about the city tree and the trees of commerce, and those forlorn ones grouped round a deserted house—something tragic and touching too.

'Every man is born a king and most men die in exile like most kings', wrote Oscar Wilde. He might as well, even better, have written it of the tree. That is the tree. A king; an exile; a victim.

And this beauty. The scientist puts it into schedules and cuts sections of it and labels specimens for museums, and while he is busy the soul of it makes a little journey and comes back when he has gone to bed. No soul can breathe buried alive beneath the weight of all these tabulated facts.

The great tropical forests are being gradually penetrated: they are not yet ours. They belong to the not quite earthly birds, the very human beasts, and the darker elemental races of men who are born and do battle and grow old and die more simply and swiftly, but moved by the same instincts, as the 'poor little street-bred people that vapour and fume and brag'.

For us there is what is left of wooded Europe, a patch of it here and there, trimmed, thinned and paper-strewn. The oaks stood thick before the Temples on the hills of Rome. France was an uncleared forest, and for men in those days the last secret of all was often enough behind a tree.

Fontainebleau may owe its ancient name, Forêt de la Bierre, to the victims of Charles the Bald's brigands, birds of the bough themselves, left under it to rot.

But even modern tourist Fontainebleau has not thrown off the forest spell. There is a village on one of the great roads where at nightfall the pigmy houses and their trivial lights are quite unreal. Nothing is real but the infinite vague road stretching away world without end between the infinite black wall of trees. More unreal than anything is Paris, so near and so remote, her picnicking *modistes* and *commis-voyageurs*, the Madeleine and the Folies Bergères. The spectre of the great Huntsman, '*fort noir et hideux*', rides upon this road. Henri IV first heard his horn; Louis XIV saw him, they say, on this same road again; in the sixties there were still old men who said they met with him on moonlight nights. It is only a matter of waiting and listening now to hear him overtake the flying wood-maiden, the wind in her scared cry and the rustling leaves of her trodden hair. Go but a short way off the track, and some at least of the tree-people are loitering, watching, whispering, within call. The wood-nymphs, gay and dangerous lovers and untired dancers; mischievous oak-housed elves, good enough if they are not vexed; malignant disease-dealing demons of the tree; and perhaps, for spirits are wandering things, the three sad poplar sisters who yoked the horses for their presumptuous brother, crying out that their shoots are torn; though not here is that acacia, in a flower of which, three thousand years ago, a man once starting on a journey left his heart.

But it must not be day. The darkness of a room is dead, the unlit night of the open moor and the seashore is a living darkness; the forest darkness, always stirred by elusive voices, is like no other—an enchanted dark.

The poet made his picture out of this:

In painting her I shrined her face
'Mid mystic trees, where light falls in
Hardly at all; a covert place
Where you may look to find a din
Of doubtful talk, and a live flame
Wandering, and many a shape whose name
Not itself knoweth; and old dew,
And your own footsteps meeting you
And all things going as they came.

It is impossible to think of trees without sooner or later remembering the opening of Hudson's *El Ombú*, perhaps the most beautiful passage in modern prose:

> They say that sorrow and at last ruin comes upon the house on whose roof the shadow of the ombú tree falls; and on that house which now is not, the shadow of this tree came every summer day when the sun was low. They say, too, that those who sit much in the ombú shade become crazed. . . . 'It is true' (says the shepherd of the Buenos Ayres pampas who tells the story) 'that evil fortune came to the old house in the end; but into every door sorrow must enter—sorrow and death that comes to all men, and every house must fall at last.'

The music—it is all pure music—ends on a note of madness which brings no harshness into the exquisite close; the red line moving across the water, the flamingos flying, 'the crazed live many years'.

I suppose there was some witchcraft in the *ombú*. Old Culpeper's astrological piety would not have allowed this slur on Nature. His trees are all good for something, (those that think otherwise are 'beside the bridge')—madness and witchcraft, as well as for the fastening of loose teeth. 'They say, if you tie a bull, be he ever so mad, to a fig-tree, he will quickly become tame and gentle.' They do not say how often it has been tried. The bay-tree is 'a tree of the sun and resisteth witchcraft very potently; neither witch nor devil will hurt a man in a place where a bay-tree is'.

Witchcraft and cattle and the tree are brought together by another seventeenth-century writer—John Aubrey—who says of the whitty or wayfaring tree: 'In Herefordshire they did plant them neer their houses, when I was a boy, as a preservative against witchcraft, and made pinnes for their yokes of it, to keep their oxen from being forespoken.'

About the same time Doctor Robert Plot, in a letter to the Dean of Christchurch, is inquiring of strange things, 'of animals, and first of strange people such as the Gubbings of Devonshire'—of stones, of accidents—and of strange trees. 'The bodies of trees that are seen to swim in a pool near Brereton in Cheshire, a certain warning to the heir of that honourable family to prepare for the next world.' It must have been a common story. John Childrey, quoting Camden, carries it on. They 'flote in Bagmere', near the family seat, 'for certain days together and may be seen of anybody, but after the heir is dead they sink. I will not undertake', says Childrey, 'to tell you the cause of the floting of these trees in Bagmere; because there are several circumstances that render it very dark.' It is also 'certain that divers ancient families in England are pre-admonished of their End by oaks bearing of strange leaves'.

Aubrey's '*remarques*' are apt to be quaintly coloured, and it is he who throws a splash of crimson across the green of a country churchyard. In Okelet, in Surrey,

> there are many Red Rose-trees planted among the graves which have been there beyond Man's Memory. The sweet-heart (Male and Female) plants Roses at the head of the Grave of the Lover deceased; a Maid that lost her Dear 20 years since, yearly hath the grave new-turf'd and continues yet unmarried.

The yew is the tree sacred to Breton cemeteries, in which there is usually but one; a root of it was supposed to shoot from the mouth of every corpse, and in the Irish story of Noise and Deirdre it was from the stakes in their bodies that the two yew-trees interlaced above their tomb were said to spring. In Galway the tradition was that the thorn grew from the dust of the dead scattered throughout the world. In Cornwall, not so long ago, you must not touch the churchyard bushes, or the fairies would be after you in the night. It is everywhere dangerous to disturb the tree-fairies; wiser to leave them and the whole wood-world alone.

By Huntly Banks, Thomas of Ereceldoune met his 'ladye gaye' at the Eildon Tree, and lived some three years in the elf-queen's country, when, to save his soul, she let him go. René de Fontainebleau, loved by the wood-maid Némorosa, forgot his human mistress in the forest, and was never after seen. *'Non, je n'irai plus au bois / Je connais trop le danger.'*

The trysting tree is always more or less enchanted. Every leaf of Hans Andersen's old oak, in its last dream, could see as if with eyes even the stars in daylight; each one a kind clear eye, reminding him of all those which had sought each other beneath his shade, the happy eyes of children and of lovers, who for three hundred years had met and parted there.

MEN AND TREES

II

LIFE and death, good and evil have always been bound up closely with the tree from the day when that desirable fatal tree was planted for the two first lovers in the midst of their lonely garden, and of the fruit of which having eaten they have surely died.

Health and healing are of the tree, but after all it is a thing of shadows; so many secrets are behind it: so many of the old happenings (not to go outside the history of Israel) have been beneath its shade, often enough under the branches of the sacred oak, the venerated tree of the Semitic and European races.

Isaiah looked forward to the time when the people of Palestine should be ashamed of the oaks which they had desired. It is not yet: they are still believed to be inhabited by spirits to whom peace-offerings of torn clothes are hung upon their boughs. But the heathen rites so long connected with them are apt to obscure their earlier and holier associations.

Jehovah first appears to Abraham at the augur's oak at Shechem; and again, under the Oak of Mamre, the most famous of Palestine's hallowed trees, in the likeness of three men, who in the original story, it is suggested, may represent the spirit of the oak in a triple form. The Angel of the Lord seated beneath the oak of Ophrah brings God's message to Gideon, who builds Him an altar there. The swing of the march in the mulberry-trees is to be the divine signal to David for battle against the Philistines; Abimelech is crowned by the oak of the pillar in Shechem when Jotham recites the oldest and loveliest of fables, the going forth of the trees to anoint a king over themselves. Deborah's nurse is buried under the oak of Bethel, thenceforward called the oak of weeping. They are all consecrated trees.

And then a cloud gathers above the oaks, incense, an acrid smoke begins to hang about 'the tree-tops tipped with fire'. God's people pass into the forest, '*monstrueuse et fauve cathédrale*'. The high passionate voice of the prophet rises, itself a threatening flame:

> The sin of Judah is written with a pen of iron, and with the point of a diamond; whilst their children remember their altars and their groves by the green trees. . . . Also upon thy palms is found the blood of the souls of the innocent poor—upon every oak. . . . Are ye not a seed of falsehood, enflaming yourselves among the oaks, slaying the children in the valleys?

No doubt the children sacrificed to Moloch, whose blood was seemingly smeared upon or otherwise offered to the sacred trees.

The Druids, who Evelyn says probably derived their oak-theology from the Grove Mamre, have a similar red record, not shirked by Borlase in his *Antiquities of Cornwall.* Every tree of the Druidical Grove at Marseilles is said to have been washed with human blood, and Frazer mentions the yearly sacrifice of a girl by a tribe in the Punjab to an old cedar-tree. These, of course, are the darker superstitions; civilization, brightly conscious of having abolished the devils with the gods, and replaced them all by the Culte du Moi, murmurs 'shocking!' and hurries on; but there is not much doubt that human sacrifices are still being offered by American and European syndicates to the sacred tree of civilization, the rubber-tree. Civilization demands speed, speed demands rubber, and rubber, coated with blood and slime, turns quickly into gold. We have almost forgotten the Congo, and the whole story of the unique and more hideous abominations of the Putumayo is not yet and probably never will be told. So far we know that within ten years the greater part of a gay, intelligent native race has been monstrously exploited and destroyed.

From impressive prospectuses and cheerful paragraphs in the financial papers—'Rubber Notes, Rubber Market Topics'—one would not suspect it; but so, changed and modernized, 'tree-worship' persists, and in the whispering hells of those inland forests there are no illusions about the white man's sacred tree. Behind the ghastliness of the ancient immolation there was the immemorial belief that life must be taken to save or transmit life; or the idea was to offer the costliest gift to the deity: a son or daughter, most frequently the first-born. This also was God's idea. Isaac was not actually sacrificed 'on the altar upon the wood', but there is blood on the Redeemer's Tree.

The difference between the old idolatry and the new is that while the old counted its victims by tens, the new can count them by hundreds or thousands: there used to be ideals; today there are dividends, very lively realities against dead dreams!

Real and pleasanter survivals of the old tree cults are scattered over Europe in fêtes and customs growing sparse towards our shores. In Cornwall, a farmer in the eighties records that in some places a procession of villagers visits the chief orchards of the parish, and choosing in each a representative tree addresses a long incantation to it, after which the tree is sprinkled with cider and the incantation repeated, while the parishioners dance round it. At one time sugared cakes were hung upon the branches. As time goes on the solemn incantation dwindles to a jolly couplet: 'Hail to thee, good apple-tree, / Pocketfuls, hatfuls, peckfuls, bushel-bagfuls'. And so the old rites of sacrifice and propitiation of the tree-spirit are unconsciously preserved and finally disappear. Throughout England we still have the Christmas-tree. Tennyson's once popular and parodied poem has gone the way of the May-queen herself. As a child I remember seeing a very shabby and rakish Jack-in-the-green in a London street. Now and then one comes across an unconscious personal echo of the outworn faith, half or wholly serious, in a lecture by Constable, an essay of Jefferies, or in Yoshio Markino's just-published *Memoirs*, in which he says of himself, as a child: 'Then the birds seemed as if they were calling me. Even branches of the trees looked as if they were beckoning me. And I went deeply into the Nature as if I were one of them. When I leaned against a tree, I felt I was a tree.'

Religion is like music, one must have an ear for it; some people have none at all; but given the ear it is all significant and wonderful, from the old plain-song to a rhapsodie of Brahms. The form changes with our shifting emotions and ideas; here and there a tune gets lost, or goes out of fashion. 'Melodies die out like the Pipe of Pan with the ears that love them and listen for them.' I do not know what has happened to the Pipe of Pan, but the trees are taller than the reeds; the birds' song is sweeter than any pipe; the birds are divine; the tree is immortal, they do not die. Paganism and the medieval Christianity grafted on to it is dying hard in Celtic Brittany; but no one who within the last ten years has seen only the fires on St John's Eve at Guingamp will say that it is dead. The bonfires at each corner of the triangular place, lit by the priests without enthusiasm, are built round high poles, each crowned with a garland of flowers. In the glare, as the flames mount and spread, the old houses round, losing actuality and substance, look like painted scenery, and the pilgrims below, who have come from all parts of the countryside, for the Fête of Notre Dame de Bon Secours, like a stage crowd. Ten years ago one or two of them snatched a *tison* from the fire; later I did not see this done. These were treasured, says Souvestre (in 1854) as charms against thunder, and the scorched garlands as talismans against sickness and sorrow (*peines de l'âme*). The fires are relics of sun-worship, but the masts and garlands distinctly suggest the tree.

The Celts, whatever sea divides them, have the same eyes and see the same visions, touching hands on the land of dreams; and in parts of Ireland, some thirty years ago, it was a custom to plant a May-tree on the dunghill by the farmhouse door, and to throw it upon the bonfire on the 'Day of the Fire Tree', in May, at the great Solar festival; in Brittany and elsewhere held on Midsummer Day.

Canon Mahé, writing of Morbihan, in 1825, says in that district trees may be seen trimmed and bent to form niches, in which crosses or images of saints are placed; and he also mentions as the seat of two famous pilgrimages our Lady of the Oak in Anjou, and our Lady of the Oak near Orthe, in Maine. In Maine, too, says an historian, there are chapels of oaks, where the trunks are enshrined in the walls beside the altar. Among many allusions to sacred trees in ancient Irish literature there is one which suggests that each church may once have had its tree: 'The tree of the church is seen from the open country, and when one goes to look for it in the oak-wood it is not found; and the sound is heard there of the bell and of the psalm-chanting, and the church itself is not found.'

Infinitely older than the church, everywhere, as Thomas à Kempis says of the Cross, you shall find the hallowed tree, standing for centuries against the attack first made on it in Europe by the early Christian missionaries.

It is only twenty years since Professor Anatole Le Braz published his collection of Breton legends, taken down from the lips of the peasants gathered round his fire; and the picture he gives of them seated in the circle of the lamplight, with bent heads and tense faces, their voices coming from every corner of the room, claiming their turn to speak, is as striking as any of the stories they are there to tell.

Loveliest of these is the 'Deux Vieux Arbres', in which two peasants, Maharit and Jelvestr, husband and wife, who have passed at death into venerable beeches, perished with the cold on the hillside, come back one night to their old home to warm themselves by the familiar fire. The young people have gone to bed, and towards eleven o'clock the son hears a slight noise outside, a rustle of trailing branches and shivering leaves:

> *Puis, peu à peu le bruit grandit, devint une rumeur pareille à celle des bois agités par la brise, et l'homme aperçut distinctement les grands ombres mouvants des deux hêtres qui s'avançaient vers la maison. Ils marchaient aussi près que possible l'un de l'autre, sur le même rang; on dit que la terre les portait, on voyait, à la lumière de la lune, briller leurs troncs argentés sous leurs feuillages immenses.*
>
> *Ils traversèrent enfin le courtil.*
>
> *Frou—ou—ou—gémissaient leurs vastes ramures. L'homme sous ses draps claquait des dents. Ils vont renverser la maison, se disait-il. Il entendait le frôlement des grosses branches contre les murs et sur le chaume du toit. Par trois fois, les deux hêtres firent le tour du logis, sans doute cherchant la porte. Brusquement, elle s'ouvrit. Et voici ce qu'il vit: son père et sa mère étaient assis, de chaque côté du foyer, non plus sous leur forme d'arbres, mais tels qu'ils étaient de leur vivant. La vieille avait relevé sa jupe—*
>
> *Le vieux lui demandait:*
>
> *—Sens-tu un peu la chaleur?*
>
> *—Oui, répondait elle.*

The time passes.

> *Dans l'âtre, le vieux disait â la vieille.*
> *—Etes vous assez rechauffée, Maharit?*
> *Et la vieille disait au vieux:*
> *—Oui, je n'ai plus si froid, Jelvestr.*
> *Sur ce, l'horloge tinta le premier coup de minuit. Les deux vieillards se levèrent, disparurent. Et alors la grande rumeur de feuillage recommença le long de la maison.*
> *Frou—ou—ou! Frou—ou—ou!*
> *Puis le bruit s'éloigna, à mesure que s'éloignait aussi l'ombre des deux arbres sous la lune.*

In the classic story of Philemon and Baucis, the old people are turned into trees as a reward for their hospitality to Zeus, but the Breton peasants are working out a long penitence in the homely purgatory of their race, not far from the friends and haunts of life. The charm of their story may owe something to the absence of the Curé who is often introduced into these legends, originally mythological, to neutralize or modify their naturalism. Nature and the ecclesiastic have never been fast friends, but in Brittany it is no use trying to throw the moon over the cliff, however much you may dislike her, and the clergy have had to take over the old superstitions as they have had to take over the old saints, of whom, says Charles Le Goffic, '*il n'y a guère trois dont les papiers soient complètement en regle*'.

Yet the idea of pain and purgatory on the tree might very well, it would seem, have come from purely Christian sources. At the taking of Jerusalem by Titus an immense quantity of trees was cut down, on which the Jews were crucified in such numbers that 'room was wanting for the crosses and crosses wanting for the bodies'. And sometime, somewhere in Palestine, a tree was planted which was carried to Calvary and replanted there.

There are legends enough of the True Cross, for the most part elaborate and artificial; but one of the eighth century, carved in runes on a cross in Ruthwell churchyard in Scotland, is of singular beauty and simplicity. The quaintness of the original, in which Christ figures as a medieval Lord or Knight and the Apostles as his vassals, cannot be suggested by a very free and condensed version of a literal rendering of the old text. In this Dream of the Rood it is the tree itself which, sighing, speaks:

> It is long since, yet I have not forgotten how I was torn up and hewn down in the wood. Strong men carried me on their shoulders until they set me on a hill. Then saw I the Lord of all men, hasting with zeal, for He would mount on me; but He forbidding it I durst

> not bow nor break. I could have felled the foeman, yet stood I fast. I trembled as He embraced me. A rood was I raised up; I bare the King but might not bow. They pierced and mocked us together, blood covered us, fearful was my fate upon that hill. I lowered myself to the hands of His friends. They laid Him down, the Weary One, to rest after His mighty strife. They made him a tomb, and singing, there they left Him, alone in the even-tide. But we [The Three Crosses?] grieving, stood yet awhile.

Sir John Maundeville, the fourteenth-century traveller, points to a 'fayre church' in Jerusalem 'toward the Weast', as the spot where the tree grew of which the Cross was made; and in the neighbourhood of Mount Zion is the 'Tree of Eldre that Judas henge himself upon for despeyr'.

On the Mount of Mamre

> there is the tree oke—that men call the dry tree. And they say that it hath been from the beginning of the worlde, and was sometimes grene and bare leaves until the tyme that our Lorde dyed and so did all the trees in the worlde, or else they fayled in their hearts or else they faded, and yet is there many of those in the world.

There are all sorts of stains on them, and all sorts of garlands; some of the stains are fresh, but not the garlands, and we are not likely to weave any more. They belong to the old gods, and for the old gods, as for the old people in the London streets, it is '*sauve qui peut*'. We really have no use for them. We have not much use for anything but machinery and science and democracy, the three-headed monster who has kicked the effete trio of the troupe, the sisters Wonder and Beauty and Stillness, out of the show.

The Renaissance revered the ancient world, the nineteenth century was moved and lit by the Renaissance; we have no patience even with the nineteenth century. The past is a stupid corpse. The inspiration of the woods, the forest voices, the fairy dancers, the mystery of things that stand against the sky—these are 'of old time'. The steeples are hidden, but not by the elms; and when the newspapers or the publishers will pay you something for a good one and quite handsomely for a bad, most secrets are for sale. We must not speak in the market-place of what happens to us in the forest, says Hawthorne—I think it is in *The Scarlet Letter*. Who was Hawthorne? There are no scarlet letters. Everything happens in the market-place. Where else? But the market-place is not real: the real things are happening in the forest still.

Near Jeanne d'Arc's home at Domrémy there was a wood in which stood a beech-tree called the Ladies' Tree, or the Fairies' Tree, famous throughout the countryside. As a child, Jeanne used to hang on its branches garlands of leaves and flowers, and dance under it with the other children. A great deal was made of this by her inquisitors—dark things were said, the garlands vanished during the night, the birds in the oak-wood fed from her lap, the wolves there would not hurt Jeanne's sheep. There was always the mystery of the Voices, to which, when they had stupefied the child of another world and burned a saint, they were no nearer.

In the course of her long trial they asked her if she still heard her Voices. Worn out with questions and learned subtleties, '*Menez-moi dans un bois,*' she said, '*et je les entendrai bien.*'

AN OLD SERVANT

AS A CHILD not much higher than her knee, I remember climbing upstairs to bed in front of her, dreading that saying which followed too often on downstairs good-nights, 'I am all behind like the cow's tail': a wretched joke which kept one awake for hours doing sums on the knots of the counterpane to prove that she could live on for years and years and was not really so very old. She was then, in fact, about fifty, with the erect swinging gait and most wonderful eyes of youth, undimmed from the day when, a girl of twenty, she had come up from her North-country village to our grandmother's London home; in time being chosen to follow her young mistress on her marriage to the less prosperous house, with its new economies and harder duties, in which we were born.

There, twenty-six years of her life were spent between the attic nursery and the basement kitchen, standing downstairs over the fire, sitting upstairs at the round table; in cooking, washing, sewing; in planning for us small treats and great careers; patching clothes and family quarrels; in an endless learning of new tasks and the making of little jests—a life of gay and monotonous and unbroken toil.

To us as children she was as fixed a part of the universe as the bath (cruelly cold in winter) into which she plunged us every morning, and the stars to which she pointed through the high window, naming some of them, in the evening sky. She slaved, worshipped, fought for, and occasionally whipped us with a calm crescendo of 'Will you? *Will you??* WILL YOU?' between the spanks; but for all that, she was not a grown-up person. She knew everything and could do everything, and she had an odd excrescence of authority; otherwise she was one of Us. At fifty she had not outgrown the absorbing conversion of lumps of sugar into 'pig's blood' over the kitchen gas, the sheer excitement of colour in a box of chalks, or the thrill of the blare of a penny trumpet. Mr Noah of the nursery ark to her, as to us, was as real a personage, and the player caught cheating at croquet in the Square an object of the same passionate and personal dislike.

On the first of the month, when her wages were paid, a large bag of tarts was bought from a grubby little shop near Covent Garden, to which a long pilgrimage had to be made—not because the tarts there were superior; on the contrary—to put fresh heart into the seedy widow who had not made the confectionery business a success; and there was a fairing for everyone in the house except the too exalted head.

In later *blasés* years, when only for her the glamour in such small things remained, the money was put on a horse or sunk in a lottery ticket, and it was she who stood to the last on the battlements of those lordly castles, built each month in Spain, before they fell.

Throughout the year her reading was limited to the Bible (herein mainly to the Book of Proverbs) and a cheap weekly comic paper; but on Christmas Eve she flung into the festooned disorder of the nursery a pile of Christmas numbers, and thenceforth walked with us, for a week or two, in the world of pure romance. Red lights gleamed from Manor House windows; ostlers bandied jests in the courtyards of lonely inns; the crack of whips and the hoofs of post-horses drowned the wheels of the crawling cab and the bell of the muffin-man ting-tinging down our long, dull street; while we glided down broad oak staircases and swore in the halls of holly-decked mansions, where above, ghosts stalked through the corridors, and below there was always dancing, or lost ourselves on the great white road outside where the snow was always falling, in a whirl of highwaymen and elopements.

She would not read herself, and did not encourage us to read, the daily papers, packed, she declared, with bribery and money-getting and slander that were no business of ours. 'He that goeth about as a tale-bearer . . . meddle not with him', she used to say when it fell to her to place *The Times* on the breakfast table; and on politics, in her presence or domain, she would have no discussion: if on stairs or in passages she overheard it, she remarked simply, 'As for lies I hate and abhor them', and passed on.

Yet as we grew older, however much she disapproved of this or that youthful escapade, she did not openly oppose or condemn it; her ideal of service was to obey, and of judgement to wait. And when she was called upon to deliver the secret note or the unhallowed bouquet, she would stand stiff-backed and sorrowful-eyed, holding it in her strong, beautifully shaped, rough hand, to 'receive instructions', with an impassive 'Very well, sir', which was not convincing. On the making of verses and the smoking of cigarettes, referred to as 'This smoking' and 'That poetry', she looked with impartial hatred, sweeping the ash and sheets of pathetically laboured MSS into her dust-pan with a gesture of indiscriminate disgust. Both practices, she told us, were 'injurious to the brain'. She believed in life with the passion and some of the recklessness of the youth she had never lost; but not in books. She worshipped work without understanding any which was not active or obviously productive, though of the making or keeping of money she had a deep and practical distrust, warning us constantly against the snare of riches, save those unsought and sent by the Lord, to which, she said, 'He adds no sorrow.'

The minimum wage would have had no interest for her: it was with the maximum of labour that she was passionately concerned; and her crowded round of cares and duties, which would have taxed the energies of women half her age, was never complete without some added responsibility, usually a protégé, for whom the hat went round. One winter it was 'an old body' who obstinately subsisted (I think at Penge) on some farcical sum per week, whom at acute personal inconvenience out of our own pitiful allowances we were forced to keep in coals till she considerately died; only to be at once replaced by a one-legged crossing-sweeper in the Gray's Inn Road, whose call for maintenance in comforters and camphorated oil (for the living leg) gave us for years no pause.

She came of very humble stock, and as a child had been for a year or two to a North-country dame-school; beyond this, she boasted, she had had no 'book learning' or any sort of education. But somewhere she had learned perfect manners, in speaking an unusual purity of accent, in writing a style that had the force and dignity of the Elizabethan; and, above all, a power of 'mastering', as she called it, any task to which she 'set her hand'.

She was always a beautiful woman, with the air and instincts of a great lady and the tact of a born diplomatist; and if by any twist of fate she had been called—as the phrase goes—to some high position, to this, too, reluctantly, she would have 'set her hand', for of her own calling, even to the badges of it, her caps and aprons, she was very proud. It was she who trained the long succession of raw girls from the country, sending them forth, when the inevitable time to 'better' themselves arrived, with an *'Ite, missa est'*, and a bright half-sovereign in their pockets. Sullen or wild or stupid or intractable they came, and tamed and sweetened they went away. She did not insist, but she was never tired, and in the end she won. If the young persons of eighteen could not be persuaded out of bed in the bitter winter mornings, the younger woman of sixty got up an hour or two earlier to 'bustle about' over the doorstep and the detested grates, till from a sense of the mere indecency of it they rose at length betimes.

And it must be said for them that, bettered beyond recognition, and flaunting scandalous millinery, from Walmer and Bath and Talbot Square they swaggered back to report themselves to the 'Old Captain'.

A long record of wisdom and devotion and uprightness must have gone to win for her the place of chief friend and adviser and, when trouble came to the house, of consoler which she came to hold. There was nothing conscious or masterful about it; it was simply the gentle, irresistible mastery of the strongest, clothed with an old-world deference. She remained 'With duty, the humble and obedient Servant' she signed herself in rare letters (some three or four a year), in which the note was always so gay and the phrase often so stately, written with difficulty, as with age her fingers began to stiffen, in a well-formed but rambling hand.

It is natural to think of her as if she had been wholly ours; but long before any of us were born she had partly kept and nursed and stored up the shrewd, rustic counsels of a much-loved mother, then stricken with some terrible disease—years dead in our time, but scarcely for a day forgotten; and that grey remote village on the hillside, which none of us had ever seen, but all the ways of which we knew so well by hearsay, was the scene, too, of her unforgettable romance. The man had been a blacksmith—this was all we knew, and that he had made it for her a sudden question of love or duty, or of this love or that. The bedridden woman could not, at most, have lain for more than a year or so between them; they were both young, but he could not wait. It was the big rusty horse-shoe hanging over her bedroom door which gave us the idea of that device for the birthday brooch and the stamping of the Christmas notepaper; after that—though little was said about it—we began to notice the special value set on anything, even a leaflet shot through the letter-box, bearing this symbol of the young man who couldn't wait.

It was her habit, here in town, to mark the seasons by a bygone calendar: to remember, walking through the London streets in spring, the carts going along the tracks, the fresh-turned furrows, the violets and celandines of the fields. Later, the first hedge roses, bees busy in summer gardens, the autumn apple-gathering, the starved birds in winter, the stiffness to the spade and the plough of the frost-bound earth, the times of flood, the market days of the old town, the Fair on Trinity Thursday, all the cherished sayings and happenings of that northern countryside which she was never to see again.

At sixty-five she looked wistfully through the frosted window panes, regretting nothing more than that she could no longer skate and slide and snowball with the 'best of us', the spirit still keen for all adventures when the flesh, which was so small a part of her, had grown infirm.

And sixty-seven was not to be the limit of her working days; she would not be spared, and no one dared to speak to her of rest. She still dusted and darned and polished and 'contrived'. No one ever had such a passion for what she called 'contrivance', and nothing pleased her more than to be called a schemer; or if one were bent on flattery, to compare her to Napoleon, who shared quite comfortably with John Wesley and Queen Victoria the niche in her temple of Fame.

Her Place of Worship (and when she used the battered phrase it raised its head again) was a Wesleyan chapel in Great Queen Street, and this was too, I believe, her favourite place of entertainment. From Sunday to Sunday she could repeat the sermon almost word for word, and ribbon for ribbon and flower for flower record the changes in neighbours' bonnets. But there and everywhere what intensely and chiefly interested her were 'the faces', closely studied and recalled long afterwards with amazing clearness; and never, she said, at best or worst seen so plainly for what they were as in 'God's House'.

'Let me look at you', she would say very gravely to the culprit brought before her in nursery days, patiently listening to his wandering story, but judging finally from what she read in his generally swollen face.

In early years the rite and reality of daily prayers were for us strictly insisted on, and 'Forgive us our trespasses' was no idle phrase when after it, each night at bedtime, we had to specify them; nor submission to God's will, when it took the form of mumps on the very afternoon when one was going to the pantomime, an easy saying. But for herself, she once admitted later, she had never asked anything of the Almighty—'As His Majesty, so is His Mercy', was all she cared to say about it—though there was one thing passionately desired at the end, for which she must have found it difficult not to ask.

It was her great wish to 'die in harness', and so, dropping one day suddenly between the shafts, she died.

On a piece of foolscap dated some years before, and signed 'With Love and Duty', she had set forth and portioned out among 'the family' her small possessions, to each one of us some carefully chosen thing. Her mother's eight-day clock, which stood in the corner by the kitchen door, her mother's tea-caddy with the inlaid roses, her own much-dented, shining mahogany work-box, the enamel medal inscribed 'Honour to whom Honour' presented to her by some pious monthly magazine, with a certificate for her last twenty-five years of 'domestic service and irreproachable rectitude of character'—'countersigned by a Minister of Religion'. This document, framed in gilt, hung over her bed, and was, with the china teapot commemorating Queen Victoria's first Jubilee, of all her belongings the most highly praised.

But a few hours after the blinds were drawn in the quiet room upstairs all these and other things had been collected, packed, and removed in a four-wheeled cab, and the funeral in every detail loudly discussed and, not without some bitterness, arranged by a band of newly arrived relations; among them the plausible greasy sister-in-law who was always taking expensive medicines and borrowing railway fares, and the heavily scented niece with the rather sunken, bold dark eyes and a willowy figure, who had once 'sat to Sant', and when not sitting to someone or other was said to be nursing an invalid gentleman at Boulogne or Worthing or Ostend. With a great display of black-bordered pocket handkerchief, they overran the house, and their moral and physical odour seemed to cling about it long after they had left it; for nearly a week they were in possession, ransacking boxes, turning out drawers, eating interminable meals, and in audible disagreement to the end about the prices and dispositions of their wreaths and crosses. I remember hoping that she couldn't see or hear them.

Within an hour of their arrival they demanded the key of what they called the 'Death-chamber', and finally claimed the exclusive right to 'follow to the grave'.

No one who knew her could think of her in either place. There was nothing there for her to do.

THE HAY-MARKET

IT IS NOT near Piccadilly: it is a place of carts and the sky. Cabs and trains know nothing of it, and on the map you will find it very small, though it is more important than Piccadilly; it is in the real world.

It is a long way from any (except, perhaps, 'St Polges' ') fountain and ten minutes' walk to the nearest monument, where a plump side-whiskered gentleman in a tight frock-coat stands affably on a panelled base of carved corn and grapes and pumpkins, emblems of bounty showered by him on the shabby crowd below, day in and day out complaining of what they pay for such things at the neighbouring shops too remote and dingy to enjoy the patronage of plump frock-coated gentlemen privileged to redeem from pedestals a thankless world. But by the grace of God there is no such person and no monument in the Market: there is a horse-trough in the centre, cutting one of the two lines of black posts marking the road off from the great stretch of cobble-stones on either side; and one clean house with a pediment freshly painted, from which the pigeons fly. And there is the British Queen at one corner looking crossways at the King's Head at the other, and opposite the British Queen the Jolly Farmers squinting round to ask the desperate Coffee Tavern at the turning into Edward Street what the Bald One owes the Mother of the Barber, with a heartless grin.

The grass shoots up through the clefts of the cobble-stones, the brown half-human two-storey houses standing back, as it were, to let it grow and watch the sparrows and pigeons congregate till the mongrel Market dogs dash out of the doorway slits to scatter them, chasing each other, like the boys when they come out of school, but faster, with wilder yelps, across the square.

'Old Mungo' (who isn't old) looks after the carts by day and 'Arry King sings over the pub (The British Queen) of nights. The Artists, on the first floor, two doors from the house with the pediment, also sing, and leer out of their windows in masks and kimonos, twanging a banjo at the passers-by. Rather false notes, the Artists; out of their own posed picture; almost everyone has a nickname, but the Market people say 'The Hartists' as they would say 'The Monkeys' or 'The Kangaroos', and the carts don't notice them.

The carts are always there: the hay-stacked carts with the empty shafts, standing like exiled ricks in a vast, strange yard; and the big two- or four-horsed drays loaded with coal sacks, meal sacks, beer casks; half asleep, pulling up mechanically at the horse-trough and the Jolly Farmers, and rumbling on, leaving nothing but empty pint-pots and mud-tracks behind them. But the hay carts which come in the early morning belong to the Market like the wind and the sky, and with these the hedge-line of the fields and the waving grasses are not far off. All year through the hay carts bring June into the Market, and June, wherever she is, has Youth at her heels with the little Book of Romance tucked under his coat. The sleek, fat pigeons, born middle-aged, have no use at all for things of that sort, no silly memories, no dream; only the everlasting problem of how to get the better of the sparrows and much too much to eat. Past the white points of the Needles, over the Island sea, the pigeons of woods and other worlds flock home in autumn, dashing themselves sometimes at the end of the journey against the pane of St Catherine's Light, dropping dazed and spent on the wet sand. The Market cockneys flutter heavily up, no farther than their narrow ledge, to roost till the morning carts, which scatter the oats from the horses' nose-bags, lumber in again.

The sparrows flying up to their one poor tree in the side street are nearer the sky, and you are nearer to it in the Market than in other places. As London grows taller and taller she gets farther and farther away from it; but here the bank of brown houses is low, the grey enclosure bare and wide; on windless days the patch of sky seems to drop a little way to roof it in. And when there is no wind in Glen or Edward or Augustus Street, which lead straight out of it, there is a wind or the spirit of a wind in the Market which seems to blow it up again; though even then you need hardly tilt your head to the clouds to see them moored up there for a moment and drifting on.

These things belong to the Market and the Market belongs to the children after four o'clock on week days, all Sundays and Saturday afternoons. Cricket goes on all over it, with or without stumps, because there are always the posts, and most of the cricketers, by the way, are not much taller. The bigger boys play a game of bump-ball from head to head: the roller-skaters have to reel away on one leg down the side streets because the paving is too rough; but there are stilts, and stilt-walkers are not as others are. No one knows till he has tried it what it is to walk a foot or two above the earth: if you could go on doing it for ever, you need envy no one, neither the angels nor the millionaires. Also you can make bonfires from knobs of coal and straw and scraps of rag and paper strewn about the Square, and, if they don't go out at once, squat round them bivouacking on a prairie.

The posts you climb continually; the horse-trough is likewise always there to sail your hat and trail your arms in, hanging on by the waist until your eldest sister sneaks up from behind, and cops you out of it by the neck—or lower down. When you are small, not more than four or five, you are reduced to making gardens on the grass of the cobble-stones with match-box sides for paths and wisps of straw for the garden trees, and ponds in the crevices with water fetched in your shoe (if it is not too holey) from the horse-trough; but it is difficult to find things really small enough for flowers. The gardeners will sometimes let you help them: their minute red hands are often chapped and always grubby, but if one happens to brush yours, you suddenly think of primroses, damp petals, gathered in some copse last spring. These are the only flowers in the Market, and the children's are the only real voices.

Hawkers bawling cauliflowers round and women telling each other Gawd's Truth on doorsteps have their stock of words of course, no voice. 'Riah, perhaps, had one that has been clogged for want of use: she seldom speaks, and no one listens to her when she does. 'Riah, the children tell you, is quite old, forty or fifty, and not four foot high: her head and hands and feet are very large; her eyes, which are dull and sticky, very small. She doesn't wash, or do anything but easy errands, sometimes getting a halfpenny tip for them, which buys a farthing's worth of cake crumbs and a barley-sugar whistle, of which the nearest cricketer or gardener can get a suck and blow. She comes out about four or five o'clock to stand in among them and watch them play: and watching 'Riah you see that she would rather like to be in some quiet kind of game herself—a youngster too.

And if you could climb up high enough, not half so high as the sky, no higher than the top of the factory chimney smoking above the sparrows' tree, you wouldn't know she wasn't.

Billy, the white cockatoo, used to watch it all indifferently from the window-ledge of No. 23, where he took his meals from a saucer or Mr Markham's hand. In the Market Billy had his Hour, and once in a rotten life, without bitterness or piercing outcries, surveyed the world—from Markham's shoulder. Billy surrendered his violent soul to a tepid young french-polisher who liked him moderately, but was only 'minding' him for six months, and took him back at the end of it to the doddering spinster (skirt hand and Markham's Aunt) at Bethnal Green. The next news of Billy was that he had bitten her savagely and was dead.

The wind has sown the grass beyond the cobble-stones; there are tufts of it in the cracked pavement of Augustus Street, the Market's scarred and withered limb, where the smoke-blackened stucco peels and falls off in flakes all round the blistered curve. Cats doze, men smoke silently, and women discuss them with great frankness at the Market windows, heads and shoulders hanging out.

In Augustus Street the thin cretonne curtains, stiffened with dirt, are carefully drawn, and no one knows what goes on behind them. Perhaps, as Markham's Aunt said of Billy's death, 'Better so.'

Walking down Augustus Street one evening, towards dark, two figures came out of one of the houses just in front of me at the Market end. A tall, stout woman and a tiny child holding on to her skirt, trying to keep up with her and chattering, in a rather tired treble, like a chirpy little sparrow, as they went along. Suddenly the woman stooped and struck the child, with a thickly spoken 'Now go and make yer bl—y 'appy life miserable and stop yer bl—y jaw!' The child stumbled and caught at the woman's skirts again, and they went on, a big shadow and a little shadow, moving unevenly in the dusk across the Square.

The Square was full of voices and sharp sounds: dogs yapping, the clatter of boots on the stones, the clash of shrill and piping voices, small black shouting shadows scudding across the thin sheet of blue mist, with the row of ghostly hay-stacked carts beyond.

A few yards from the Jolly Farmers a girl was standing in a doorway looking out at it. A woman with a red puffy face and a jug in her hand pushed past her out of the blackness of the passage behind and began talking noisily. 'You mark my words. 'E'll knock 'er silly before 'e's done. Wot's 'Erbert after orl? Not much. She always said she'd 'ave 'im, the dirty ——! I wouldn't let it brike yer, Mibel!' The girl said, 'Cawn't yer let it alone?' and the woman shuffled off, in loose felt slippers, to the Jolly Farmers, muttering 'A bit of muck like that!' and shuffled back two minutes afterwards wiping her mouth with the back of her hand to say it more noisily over again. The girl said, 'For Gawd's sake, let it alone!' and stood on, staring into the Market.

A COUNTRY BOOK

RICHARD JEFFERIES wrote *The Story of My Heart*, a wild, wearisome, awful chronicle of a heart too large to find a home on earth, which yet never reached as far as heaven, and so wandered on, with widely-opened but sun-blinded eyes upon its endless way. But the book of which I am thinking is a better story, with much in it also of this strange man's heart. When first I read it many years ago, it set my own heart beating, for I felt I discovered in it an undreamed of universe. It seemed almost like a new friend who brought to me thoughts I had never known and showed me things I had never seen. Yet some people call it a dull book—perhaps because it is so faithful and must be read faithfully line by line, or perhaps because they do not love its theme. And yet this cannot be; for everyone loves the country—and it is a country book which teaches one to look at Nature, not as a great picture but rather as a living world, where life is orderly and sweet and for the most part peaceful—with a sweetness and peace and order to which we cannot reach.

It has a simple title, 'Field and Hedgerow', but it tells of many things beside the hedges and the fields. It should have for motto a line of Byron's, 'Oh that my words were colours!' for there is colour on almost every page of it, the myriad colours of Nature and the more mystic colours of man's mind. The tint of this man's mind was sadness, though the tint of Nature—which above all other things he loved—is joy. From a blade of slender grass which dare not grow too high lest the wind should snap it, or the smallest speck upon an insect's wing—'that singular shadow-painting', to the clouds—those 'fleets of heaven which sail on and on and know no haven', he watches tirelessly the minute and mighty pageant, and it is marvellous as we read to find how much he saw. 'What is the colour of the dandelion?' he asks, 'not yellow, nor orange, nor gold.' And so he turned to books to find it. There was much about assorted wools and soldiers' uniforms, but 'the dandelion remained unexplained'. 'So many, many books—and such a very very little bit of Nature in them.' He found from the dandelion that there were 'no books' to teach the names and mysteries of beauty, only 'five thousand books to unlearn'.

'It seems', he says, 'as if the chief value of books is to give us something to unlearn. I hope in the days to come future thinkers will unlearn us and find ideas infinitely better.' 'Yet the spirit of the earth and sea, the soul of the sun—this never dies; this I wish not to unlearn.' This was his learning and he was a great teacher. The sky was his book and the yellow pages of the wheat 'like an ancient illuminated manuscript—in gold, gules, blue, green; with foliated scrolls and human figures—quaintly drawn and bold'. The poppies are a 'barren race', 'Lords of the July field, raising up a brilliant blazon of scarlet heraldry out of nothing. They are useless, they are bitter, they are allied to sleep and everlasting night'; yet the genius of colour is in them and 'they are saved'. It has always seemed to me, he looked at the gipsies somewhat after the manner of the poppies—they are alien, they are lawless, but they have the genius of strength in them and they are saved.

'The gipsy loves the crescent moon, the evening star; he was born on the earth in the tent, and he has lived like a species of human wild animal ever since.' 'Are they the oldest race on earth?' he goes on to ask, 'and have they worn out all the gods?—all the hopes and fears of the human heart in tens of thousands of years, and do they live merely quiescent to fate? No living faith—so old—so very very old'—they have worn out 'even hope in the future and merely live quiescent to fate, like the red deer'. Where the gipsies settle they impregnate the place; gipsy names and types of gipsy faces find their way at length into the village which has been haunted by them for a century, and holds a gipsy fair. He is an observer of faces—though he loves them less than beetles' wings and the woodbine leaf, and the pigeons who when the birch-trees redden cannot keep silence any longer. The farmers have 'new hats and jackets, but the same old faces'. The stout old man with a body 'as rotund as a full sack of wheat' has a new hat but the same old face. 'Could his great-grand-father have been dug up, and set in that barn door, he would have looked just the same, so would the sacks and the wheat and the sunshine.' In modern country pictures the old lines, he avers, are smoothed away, the people are put into attitudes, but such pictures are not true. 'Country people are the same now as when the old artists honestly drew them—sturdy and square—bulky and slow. The Wind, the Rain, Frost and Heat have beaten up their faces into rude repoussé work', and the painters nowadays should remember that and mark it, and paint the old faces and also the new hats. They do not read, he says; perhaps because of the books which have such a 'very very little bit of Nature in them', and out of doors it is all there.

'A barnyard chanticleer and his family afford more matter than the best book ever written.' And they have the slow up-springing of the wheat to watch and the greenness of the mowing grass, chicks and 'enamelled eggs', and the veined branches of the elms. 'Black type on white paper is but flat surface after these.' Surely no one who ever loved a book could read it in the country and shut his eyes to the greatest volume of them all. The only leaves there are of million hues of green, the simple romances of the birds are sweeter than the most intricate romances of mankind, the voice of the insects as Jefferies noted it, is itself a scientific treatise, and poetry is everywhere. 'Sweet, will you, will you kiss—me—dear?' he says the chaffinch sings. The chaffinch may have been his favourite, for there is a poem about him at the end of the book, beginning with the old story 'kiss me dear'. There is no music like the music of the birds. In 'Hours of Spring' he sings about their song, 'sweetness of dew and rifts of sunshine—all that is delicious and beloved of spring-time' is expressed in it. But they are not always singing; the chaffinch has other than sentimental moods and calls loudly, says Jefferies, for 'ginger-beer!' The rooks make speeches—as one can well believe after the wicked wonderful story of them in Troy Town! The wind is bad for birds as doubtless it means a scarcity of prey. The robin has to fight for his territory, since if he trespasses he is driven out by other birds. The thrushes herald the approach of summer by their early singing, and the starlings tell the time of year 'as accurately as the best chronometer at Whitehall'.

'How happy the trees must be to hear the song of birds again, after the silence and the leaflessness, to feel them busy at the nest-building!' The promise of spring and the pageant of summer twitters and sweeps and glows and hums through the first quiet pages, till later, the tenderness and glory takes colour and sound and shape before us, and the very scene is there. The beginning of things—the birth of beauty, little by little comes into view; the grass springs and the larks begin to sing, the lambs to bleat and the first butterfly to dart across the roadway. It is the waking of the world, the cry 'to arms' for every living creature from the dreary frostbound earth. Summer is, I believe, the time for which we are waiting all year long, and when it has gone we wait for it again, and so on till summers are no more. 'The Makers of Summer' are written in this book—or rather they creep and fly and start from it—an amazing crowd, clothed in a thousand hues, humming a hundred songs. Insects bring the summer as surely as the flowers—more surely than the birds or sunshine, Jefferies says. They are 'the details that make the groundwork of a summer day. One swallow does not make it—one wasp does.' This world of wings rivals in brilliancy the world of flowers and is the link between the flowers and the birds. But for the birds, it is said, these insects might literally eat us up; they are so minute, we hardly notice them, and yet so innumerable that we can hardly find a spot the size of a wafer whereon one is not. In 'Some April Insects' the communities of ants are compared to 'a hundred Londons' and these creatures are said so to accommodate themselves to Nature, that they have reached 'a species of millennium'. 'Are they then'—it is a fanciful query—'more intelligent than man?'

All the essays are not so charming or suggestive as 'Hours in Spring', 'Nature and Books', 'The Winds of Heaven', and 'July Grass', but the most detailed or most 'dull', as, for instance, 'Summer in Somerset', will break off suddenly in its close analysis to tell of the highwayman and his mare, and the way a poor sheep-stealer was tracked by a little girl who found ashes upon his floor, or the tale of the smugglers who taught their horses the words of command backward with a view to the revenue men.

'The Country Sunday' is a somewhat cynical treatment of an exquisite subject, a curious, interesting scene; including the pastor whose simple manners needed no spoon, and the village folk only too glad to welcome a miracle, under any denomination, if it would but bring them a shower of gold. There is too much pomade about it, too little tenderness perhaps, and it cannot be true that such roses bloomed unseen. Jefferies did not love the bells and he could not bear the sight of a steeple and the sense of God, as we know it, was never his. He looked for 'something higher than a god', and little wonder! never found it. 'No thought that I ever had', he cries elsewhere, 'has satisfied my soul', although his soul was steeped in the knowledge and love of God's creation. This was the tragedy of his life. I know no pathos like that which underlies the first and latest pages of this book. Every blade of grass and the wild free creatures of the woods were his—'my pets' he calls them, and yet when he could no longer walk among them and mark their changes in his book they sprang and chased their mates quite careless of his absence. 'I wonder to myself how they can all get on without me, how they manage bird and flower, without me to keep the calendar for them. For I noted it so carefully and lovingly day by day.' It is like the cry of a father whose children have forgotten him; he watches them from his invisible dwelling and wonders again and again 'without me how does this lark today that I hear through the window know that it is his hour?' This cry breaks from the opening page and from the closing one resounds a sadder echo, 'No one else seems to have seen the sparkle on the brook, or heard the music at the hatch or to have felt back through the centuries. No one seems to understand how I got food from the clouds, nor what there was in the night nor why it is not so good to look at it out of the window.' They turn away their faces, the things he loved so deeply. 'And perhaps in time I shall find out—when I pass away—that as a matter of fact, there never was any earth.' 'Never was such a worshipper of earth,' he cries in the story of his heart, and as we read the record of that worship we feel that it is true. They have put a bust of him in Salisbury Cathedral; they should rather have cut his name on the bark of some gigantic tree, and if he must have an epitaph, there seems but one for him—the utterance of a man who loved the nature that he worshipped with a tamer fire:

> I hearing get, who had but ears,
> And sight, who had but eyes before;
> I moments live, who lived but years,
> And truth discern, who knew but learning's lore.

This 'Field and Hedgerow' is or should be too a book for Londoners, for it is not like a portfolio of pastoral sketches to be hung in the drawing-room of one's mind, but rather like a branch of sweet-briar or a breath from a field of new-tossed hay, which sends the veritable fragrance and freshness of the country into the chamber where one wakes. It wakes one too from pavement dreams—those thoughts that come sometimes in cities, of the weary length or terrible brevity of life, setting forth as it does the illimitableness of Nature, its slow and steady beauty to be contrasted with the haste and tinsel of the street. It fills the mind with a sense of the loveliness and greatness of unnoticed things. It seems almost a book of eternity, where the grass waves and the roses bloom for ever, where the winds clash like cymbals and birds sing—untouched by the pangs of labour and untroubled by the fret of time. It holds what George Eliot called the 'exquisite stillness of the sunshine', and the tale, as Mrs Browning somewhere says, of 'summer days that scarce dare breathe they are so beautiful'. It shows 'all things reposed but man, so busy with his vulgar aims', reminding man—though its author meant not thus to remind him—that whether his aims be mean or great, there remains, even in this world, the haven of God's unspoiled beauty—and 'beyond our restlessness His rest.'

Play

THE CHINA BOWL

The living room of a fisherman's cottage in Cornwall some forty years ago. A heavy old door leads straight out on to the beach; over the mantelpiece hangs an antique looking-glass, and beside it is a faded sampler in a frame. A large family bible rests on the chest of drawers, a glass box—and the china bowl.

David, the owner of the cottage, a tall dark man, is standing by the window cutting fish for bait. Rachel, his old mother is sitting by the hearth mending a net . . . her coarse, brown fingers moving swiftly to and fro over the strands. . . .

Outside, a heavy sea is running. . . .

RACHEL: Be any boats gone out today?

DAVID (*at window*): What be thinking upon, Mother. 'Tis blowing half a gale,—boats couldn't put out sich a day. Though they lobster pots be ready for takin' up long since.

RACHEL: 'Tes dirty, sure.

DAVID: And yesterday 'twas comely weather and the gulls coming back down the coombe.

RACHEL: The sea be cruel hungry all times.

DAVID: Yes. Even when it do look so smiling.

RACHEL: Wasn't a sea like this that took your father. Was a quiet night, but no stars shining, I mind it well; and about half arter nine a breeze sprung up a'most as sudden as it fell. We was sitting heer when old Abe comed shouting in and called us out; and theer we saw it, close in shore, out 'pon the rocks, a girt ship like a city 'twas, with all her lights; jest like a shining lighted city, and then—'twas gone!

DAVID (*comes in*): And when the lifeboats was got out, 'twas 'most too late?

RACHEL: They couldn't see; for all it were so still, 'twas dark as Doom, they heard 'em screaming, poor souls! But they couldn't find 'em, not till daylight. Father brought one man in, and theer was a little maid, not mor'n seven, standing 'pon the deck and waving her little arms; a girt wave washed her over to him, and he caught her, and lost her, and caught her again, and then they two went down together.

DAVID: And was washed in together.

RACHEL: And they was all laid out, the ladies in their jewels and watches and gold chains and all, up in the church theer, with the men.

DAVID: Old Abe do tell of it.

RACHEL: He and me is the only ones left that saw it and he been bird-witted ever since.

DAVID: He heard the cry of her as she went down.

RACHEL: Won't never go no further than the cross-roads now because he says he hears the voices.

DAVID: Yes, I heard him say he hears the voices on the road at night.

RACHEL: And my two boys—that were a gale up Channel. You'm the only one left me, David, the last of all my children and the best.

DAVID: Don't 'ee sit thinking on they things, Mother.

RACHEL: I do think on 'em. I be getting an old woman now, close upon eighty year, and I reckon I think more on the things that be gone and done with. 'Tis the old people's way.

DAVID: Think of the children that's maybe coming. 'Tis pretty work to watch they playing and blinching round the door.

RACHEL: Times and agen I do think of Jenefer; and of nights when the wind be blowing simmee I hear the latch click and fancy her's come home.

DAVID: Her won't come now, Mother. 'Tis over late; mor'n thirty year since her went away.

RACHEL: But if her did, you'm not the man to judge her, Davy?

DAVID: Nay.

RACHEL: The sampler there—'tis all I have left of her. 'Jenefer Parris, aged 13. March, 1844.' Look at they figures, so clear as print, and the little house, marvellous like to a house, it be, and Adam and Eve a'standing, all prinked up beside it. Her done that in the winter nights, sitting heer by this same fire. 'Was a wild maid even then; but you was never a riotous lad, not like the others. A parcel o' times they was very plaguen. Father did like to hear 'em racket; he said that racketting lads make the bravest men. But I doubt it, no I doubt it. I mind 'ee, David, when 'ee was a lad, brave and quiet and different from the rest.

DAVID: 'Twould be fine and peaceful to be a lad again.

RACHEL: Will be no peace for 'ee in this house till I be out of it, poor lad! And Susannah would be finely pleased to see me carried upalong for the last time.

DAVID: Don't 'ee say that, Mother.

RACHEL: You do know it. Forty year we lived together, you and me, Davy, and I done everything for you and you for me; and now her won't so much as let me mend a shirt of your'n, or darn a sock, or set a pan on the fire for 'ee.

DAVID: 'Tis to save 'ee trouble, Mother.

RACHEL: 'Tis to make a mock of me, a grey old woman eating your bread and sitting lazy with folded hands that was always fain to do for 'ee. 'Tis to break me, Davy. If so be as her could her would blind me so as I couldn't see thee and deafen me so as I couldn't hear 'ee, and stop my heart so as it couldn't beat for 'ee. Her wants to have 'ee for herself alone.

DAVID: 'Tisn't so bad as that. And 'twill pass surely; maybe when the little one comes her'll be different. I do hope it. Love be a powerful strange thing, and strong as death, so the Book do say.

RACHEL: And jealousy, that be cruel as the grave. If I could fend for myself, and go—

DAVID: No, Mother, this be your home so well as mine; most all of the things in it be your'n. 'Tis the house that Father brought 'ee home to and where all on us was born. All your life you haven't looked out to see from no other windy than this heer, nor gone out and in by no other door. 'Twouldn't be rightly home to 'ee elsewhere.

RACHEL: Not without you, Davy. You'm all that's left.

(She drops the net and takes his hand.)

You've always been brave and good to me, son.

DAVID: And you to me.

(The door latch lifts and in comes Susannah, a tall, red haired, very handsome woman of twenty-three, a beautiful primitive rather savage creature)

DAVID: You'm back then, Susannah. What have 'ee got theer?

SUSANNAH: A picture.

DAVID: A pretty one?

SUSANNAH: Yes, sure. 'Tis my portrait. Miss Maxwell done it. And I giv'd six and ninepence for the frame. Ziah Mitchell down to the shop wanted me to give eight shilling for it, but I wouldn't. 'I'll keep my eight shilling and you can keep the picture', I told her; so her stood out and I stood out, for three weeks and more, but I've agot it now, at the price I said.

DAVID: What did her say?

(She starts unwrapping it.)

SUSANNAH: Her said 'If'ee had waited another week 'ee could have had it for nothing, because I couldn't have put up with a face like that theer staring at me another Sunday? 'Happen you never look in the glass?' I asked her. 'Why for? she said. 'Because if 'ee do', I said, 'I reckon you could put up with anything.'

DAVID: Her's as God made her, poor soul.

SUSANNAH (*comes in*): The spiteful toad! There—what do 'ee think of it?

DAVID: 'Tis a terrible fine frame.

SUSANNAH: You'd ought to like the face in it. 'Tis what they calls a study. Miss Maxwell done it for a picture her calls Dalilah, though her do say there were never a Dalilah painted with thicky skin and hair.

DAVID (*looking at it carefully, all his movements are slow and ponderous*): 'Tis like 'ee and 'tisn't like 'ee. The face be you'm but the look behind it be mighty strange. I suppose 'twouldn't be properly a picture if 'twas too similar to life.

SUSANNAH: Simmin' to me, 'tis similar to life.

DAVID: Couldn't her call it something else? Dalilah baint a pleasin' name to go by.

SUSANNAH: And why?

DAVID: Her weren't a pleasin' maid.

SUSANNAH: I thought her was. Happen Miss Maxwell will change it, 'twouldn't hurt the picture.

DAVID: And will 'ee look like that in the other picture.

SUSANNAH: Yes, sure, but bigger and more upstanding, and theer be a man in it.

(She crosses the room and takes down Jenefer's sampler.)

I'll take this old sampler down from the wall here—'tis so old an' ugly—and put my picture heer. I be going to fix it heer. Give it to me, David.

DAVID (*mildly*): May so we'll find another place.

SUSANNAH: I'm minded to put it theer. 'Tis the place I've settled for it. Miss Maxwell said this were the only light to show it up and theer I mean for it to go.

DAVID (*still mildly but firmly*): I'm not wishful to cross 'ee, Susannah, but that piece of work has been theer a matter of nigh upon fifty year and us would miss it if 'twas shifted; it must bide.

SUSANNAH (*comes back her eyes flashing*): 'Tis a pretty thing to be so set on! Should have thought 'ee wanted nothing to mind 'ee of her that done it. I tell 'ee straight I never could bide it about the place. Be you so set upon calling everyone to mind your sister and her shame?

DAVID: Was but a child when 'twere adone, and if God do please her's but a child again. So us do think of her.

SUSANNAH (*scornfully*): You was brought up a good Methody, David; did they teach 'ee to make so light of sin.

DAVID: They teached me to make something of forgiveness.

SUSANNAH: Mayst leave that to the Almighty.

DAVID: Not if the Almighty have a'left it to me.

SUSANNAH: You'm powerful friendly with the Almighty all on a sudden.

DAVID: That's but silly talk.

SUSANNAH: Thank 'ee for telling me that I talk silly. And if I do, I be only follering your blessed Bible and answering foolishness to them that speaks it.

DAVID: Theer's other words in it than as that.

SUSANNAH: If 'ee will have it, the naked truth is that I've got no patience with the precious holy Book, wheer 'tis only all they loose and sinful and wasteful women that's made so much on, they with five husbands and seven devils and more lovers than they can count; and we told we baint to cast the stone!

DAVID: Read better than that, Susannah.

SUSANNAH: I read what's wrote; and so far as I can see if the world baint to be littered up with 'em and Sabbath school prizes for the wickedest, 'tis for me that have lived clean and honest and walked the other road to take and cast it.

RACHEL: And if 'ee do, 'twill throw itself back against 'ee sure; maybe someday to strike a child of your'n with eyes so bright and clear as you'm and the same shining hair.

SUSANNAH: Like enough, if there's evil blood in the poor babe. It won't be mine.

DAVID: What's took 'ee, Susannah?

SUSANNAH: Give it to me. Give me my picture.

DAVID: You'm not to hang it theer.

SUSANNAH: And why?

DAVID: Because Mother'll look to see it where it have always been.

SUSANNAH (*turning upon him suddenly, her face ablaze*): Be this my house or her'n?

DAVID (*he flinches before her but at last says firmly*): It be mine, and I be master in it.

SUSANNAH: Who be mistress?

RACHEL: Say no more, David. (*She rises and moves away.*) I'll take it to my own room.

DAVID: You can bring it back, Mother.

RACHEL (*quietly and unresentfully*): I would sooner take it away.

(*Rachel goes, closing her bedroom door behind her. Susannah and David face each other, David grave, Susannah at first defiant but suddenly melting she goes towards him, touches his arm and looks down at him with dangerous sweetness.*)

SUSANNAH: Why did 'ee wed me, David, if 'ee meant to make me only half a wife? There was lads and many that would have had me, and turned their kin to doors for me.

DAVID: I do know it.

SUSANNAH (*caressingly*): Will 'ee give me the place that's mine, or will 'ee put another woman in it?

DAVID: I never done that.

SUSANNAH: Think of this minute past, and which did 'ee put first?

DAVID: Reckon I'm new to the ways of women, twist and twine this way and that, I can't catch hold on 'em. I be only a dull slow man, Susannah.

SUSANNAH: You was finely hurried to have me, David, and if so be as I don't please 'ee after all, why didn't 'ee take more time to look around the maid you was so mazed to wed?

DAVID: Simme women do take some looking round. 'Tis like this heer: now 'tis ice and next 'tis fire, and then 'tis up and oft like a gale to sea. There was a time when I wouldn't have nought to say to things like they. They tried to get me but I wouldn't. You have agot me, and that's all about it now.

SUSANNAH (*smiling*): Maids be so slippery as fish, so they do say, and yet the men be catched by 'em.

DAVID: Clean off.

SUSANNAH: Do 'ee think 'ee have got me?

DAVID: I be main loth to doubt it.

SUSANNAH: What would 'ee have felt like if I'd said 'No'?

DAVID: 'Most like a boat with a split keel, tossing out yonder in the dark. 'Twould have been the end of day-light, simming to me.

SUSANNAH: You was terribly set on me.

DAVID: A man most is terribly set upon his life when he is like to lose it.

SUSANNAH: 'Tis bad work when it do come to that.

DAVID: 'Tis bad work sure, when a man be past his prime and the maid in flower and all the young lads clamouring to her, 'Will 'ee have me?' and me with all my mouth-speech gone.

SUSANNAH: You never had much of it to lose.

DAVID: I never wanted it afore.

SUSANNAH: And now you can use it fine and loud against me.

DAVID: I never done that.

SUSANNAH: Not when you hurted me as you done this same minute over the picture theer?

DAVID: You hurted me.

(A pause)

SUSANNAH: I'll set the tea then.

(Susannah crosses to a cupboard and takes out cutlery, etc. Starts laying the table.)

SUSANNAH: I got a devil, David.

DAVID: We all got devils. I seen a many and all sorts, and terrible bad ones, in my time. I seen 'em standing beside quiet men, on dark nights out to sea. I seen 'em in 'most every pretty woman's eyes, but that be natural. The woman was the first to make friends with He.

SUSANNAH: 'Twas a He anyways.

DAVID: Theer be nothing for to show that the serpent weren't a female serpent.

SUSANNAH: If her had a'been, her'd have given the apple to Adam and not to Eve.

DAVID: 'Tisn't right to make game of they things, but if we got devils we'd ought to quieten and bind 'em down, not loose 'em to go prancing round like the show horses at a fair.

SUSANNAH: You could bind and cast out mine if 'ee a mind to, you'm the Lord God and all to me. If I did know that 'ee loved me first and last and put no one afore me or beside me, and I was the only woman in the world for 'ee.

DAVID: You'm young, my dear, and you got no patience; 'tisn't over long to wait. Where be the matches?

SUSANNAH: Beside your arm. I've no patience with your patience. You'd sit patient like a stuffed bird on the chimney piece, waiting for someone to take 'ee down and dust 'ee, and never moving till the day of Doom.

DAVID: If 'ee'd knowed trouble and loss, like Mother.

SUSANNAH (*passionately*): 'Tis trouble enough to love 'ee as I love 'ee. (*Recovering herself.*) And I could have had more than one handsome lad. I never told 'ee afore, but I could have had the curate, up to Gorran.

DAVID: Poor silly calf.

(He strikes a match and lights a pipe.)

SUSANNAH: So he be, but he'd have made a lady of me, and put the wedding in the Parish Magazine and all; and he won't have no one else.

DAVID: Us'll see that come theer's a maid that will have he.

SUSANNAH (*comes in from table*): But I loved 'ee, David. I love 'ee more than any man and all the Gods theer be. I love the mark of your girt wet boots on the stones, and the nets when you be drying 'em, and your shadow on the wall. And times when you'm out of nights and the wind be raving and the waves breaking thunderous in to shore, my heart stops beating and I get up out of bed and go to the windy and call out to 'ee over the black water.

DAVID: I've heard 'ee sure.

SUSANNAH: No, David, you'm one of they that don't hear nothing, nor see nothing. Men be like that. But I've stood theer by the windy till I were mazed and froze, and all the world did melt away like as if theer was no one in it but you and me, and there was no more boats and no more houses and no more lights and no voices and no faces, only your face so white and strange out theer in the black raging night. I've thought I've lost 'ee.

DAVID: Poor maid. Why didn't 'ee mind they words on the stone of the girt grave up yonder in the Churchyard, 'He came, He drew me out of many waters'?

SUSANNAH: But He drawed them dead and drowned. They was all dead swollen men and women, dressed up so fine in silks and jewels, and talking and laughing as they went down. And that were a quiet night.

DAVID: Should have had the little bleating parson. Won't drown hisself in nothing deeper than cups of tea.

SUSANNAH: Should I? Should I, David? Will 'ee give me the place that's mine?

DAVID: What do 'ee want? To fix the picture?

SUSANNAH: Yes, and to do whatever else I have a mind to in the home you've brought me to.

DAVID (*going*): Do what 'ee please, my dear, and don't 'ee think of they whist things no more. 'Tis late for we to be sweethearting thicky way, more than four months wed.

SUSANNAH: I can put up with it—(*she pushes him away smiling*). Theer, go out and cleanse thyself, I be going to set the tea. (*Front door opens.*)

DAVID (*by door*): 'Tis blowing up worse if anything. I'll beach the boat up higher before full tide.

(*Door shuts. Susannah lays the tea things. Inner door opens.*)

SUSANNAH (*inoffensively*): Where be going?

RACHEL: To fetch some milk.

SUSANNAH: I've got enough.

RACHEL (*coming in*): Will want some more if boats go out tonight.

SUSANNAH: They won't go out.

RACHEL: If the wind drops.

SUSANNAH: It won't drop. Hark 'ee to it. And you'll sleep through it.

RACHEL: I lain awake so many nights, I do sleep now. And Davy's home.

SUSANNAH: For all the fuss that's made of David, you'd think he was different from other men. But at the root they be all the same.

RACHEL: I always thought him different. Why did 'ee choose him then, when 'ee might have had a younger lad, if all do seem the same to 'ee.

SUSANNAH: I suppose in a score of pilchers, some be bigger and better than the rest.

RACHEL: Sure enough; he is a better man, he were a better lad. None of the other lads was like him.

SUSANNAH (*sharply*): He might so well be a saint in a painted windy to hear 'ee talk, but he be just a man, and at the root they be all the same.

RACHEL: Not to me, Susannah. He be my son.

SUSANNAH: And he be my husband.

RACHEL: 'Tis the Lord's will that every woman's son will come to be another woman's care, but once He have a'given her a son, even the Almighty can't take him away.

SUSANNAH (*bitterly*): And a wife be different?

RACHEL: If so be as you have a son, Susannah, maybe you'll come to see it.

SUSANNAH (*comes in from table; deliberately but without violence*): I see fine that there can't be two women in a man's house and in his life and he to shift see-saw up and down, first with one and then the other, without there be trouble for them all. Come soon or late, he'll have to choose atween the two.

RACHEL (*gently*): 'Tisn't sense for to put it that way.

SUSANNAH: 'Tis the way I put it.

RACHEL: Yes, Susannah. (*Goes to door.*) I'll go for the milk . . . happen we'll want some more if boats go out tonight.

(*Front door opens, closes.*)

SUSANNAH (*takes up the portrait from a chair and looks at it; to herself*): 'Tis my portrait—an' I be mistress here. I'll hang it where I chose . . . and that's on the wall theer . . . whatever they say!

(*She hangs it up.*)

That's done! An' proper fine it looks.

(*Knocks on door.*)

(*Enter Miss Maxwell, a well-dressed woman, about thirty, with a good deal of manner. She shakes hands affably with Susannah.*)

MISS MAXWELL: Good evening, Susannah. You're looking charming.

SUSANNAH: I can't help that.

MISS M: I thought I'd call to see whether . . . . Ah! So you've hung it there! The very place for it—how nice of you to put my poor little sketch in the place of honour! Did I suggest it? Then it was because I thought you *ought* to have the place of honour. Really, it looks rather well.

SUSANNAH: David says 'tisn't like me. But he says 'twouldn't be properly a picture if 'twas too similar to life.

MISS M: There's something in that. There's the artist's temperament, of course.

SUSANNAH: What be that? The part of the picture that isn't like?

MISS M (*comes in*): Oh, well, it's just what I see and other people don't. But you know I'm coming down in the spring with the big picture on purpose for you to sit; and that's going to be an immense success. Everyone who has seen the sketch is asking me who Dalilah is. But I keep it a secret, or Tregarveth would be besieged by people—tiresome young men in knickerbockers—bringing down canvases to take you away on, and then what would your husband say?

SUSANNAH: He's out to the fishing most days. And he's nought but a girt sleepy child. He wouldn't notice nothing. The men do see what the women want 'ee to.

MISS M: I wish they did.

SUSANNAH: Don't they to London?

MISS M: Not always.

SUSANNAH: Then you don't take the proper way with them.

MISS M: We take all sorts of ways.

SUSANNAH: There bain't but one. If they're very plaguen a kiss will always finish 'em.

MISS M: But you know a great many London women, as you call them, have given up kissing.

SUSANNAH: What's wrong with it?

MISS M: They don't believe it's the right way.

SUSANNAH: Have they found another?

MISS M: They're looking for it.

SUSANNAH: May so well go home.

MISS M: Oh! you belong to the Dark Ages! But you won't desert me, you won't sit to anyone else?

SUSANNAH: Why for not?

MISS M: Well, you know, it would spoil my picture, and then I discovered you, didn't I?

SUSANNAH: I were discovered again last night.

MISS M: No? Who?

SUSANNAH (*rapidly*): A female-looking gentleman with long hair and a round green hat and yellow skin and a flat nose and puffed up mouth and rabbity legs and a maid's ribbon round his neck and a white umbrella.

MISS M: Teddy Barclay! But he can't want you, he likes ugly women.

SUSANNAH: He didn't say so; if he do, can have post-mistress with her bulged out eyes and turned in feet, or Vicar's wife, so like a mule in a maiden's hat.

MISS M: What did he say?

SUSANNAH: That's telling.

MISS M: Don't sit for him, there's a dear; he'd make a perfect fright of you. He always does.

SUSANNAH: That's what he said you would.

MISS M: How nice of him! And so he's caught you? Teddy!

SUSANNAH: I couldn't sit to a popinjay like he, no more than I could sit to a boggart in a turnip field. I couldn't keep a straight face afore him. If a man's to stand staring at me and me at him for hours together, he's got to be a proper man.

MISS M: Why didn't you tell him so?

SUSANNAH: I did.

(*During this scene Miss Maxwell has been unobtrusively examining the things in the room, particularly the armchair and looking-glass. She now comes to the china bowl, and inspects it carefully.*)

MISS M: What a charming bowl this is . . . so quaint . . . this old china bowl. Do you know, the very first time I entered this room—and what a charming room it is! I said to myself, I positively must have that delicious bowl, and I shall be really broken-hearted if I can't. I shall indeed.

SUSANNAH: I don't see nought in the old bowl.

MISS M: No? But of course you are going to say it's a family treasure or something dreadful of that sort, and that you can't possibly part with it.

SUSANNAH: How much would 'ee say 'twas worth?

MISS M: Oh! I don't know; I daresay it's not really valuable, only I've taken such a fancy to it, and it is, isn't it, don't you think, rather useless, and a little bit in the way? I would give ten shillings for it.

SUSANNAH: Ten shilling.

MISS M: And that would buy you a lovely hat.

SUSANNAH: Isn't too much money in this place for hats or any sort of finery, with a teasy old woman to house and keep.

MISS M: Oh! but you ought to have pretty things, you are such a beautiful person—aren't you?

SUSANNAH: I shouldn't buy hats with it.

MISS M: No?

SUSANNAH: I been cooped up heer all my days like a crab in a pot, and I want to see the world.

MISS M: That costs a good deal.

SUSANNAH: Thirteen and fivepence, theer and back.

MISS M: ?

SUSANNAH: To Plymouth. David been theer once, but he comed back all mazed. A terrible giddy place, so they do say, six and seven people looking in to shop windeys all to one time and cars running about the streets and circuses and all.

MISS M: Of course you ought to go to Plymouth, and if you let me have the bowl—

SUSANNAH: How much did you say for it?

MISS M: Ten shillings.

SUSANNAH: I wouldn't, and I be sure David wouldn't, part with it under twenty.

MISS M: That's a good deal. Shall we say fifteen?

SUSANNAH: Say twenty.

MISS M: Then it's a bargain.

(She takes out her purse and puts down the money on the table.)

MISS M: There.

(She goes over to the looking glass.)

That's rather a pretty glass too . . . over the mantelpiece. . .

SUSANNAH: So folks say; old Steve to Gorran have got the brother of it.

MISS M: You don't know if he wants to sell it?

SUSANNAH: I don't know that he do, but a gentleman comed down last summer and took a conceit for it and offered for to give him a girt black and gold one twice the size and new for it; he had it theer all waiting in a cart outside; and when Stevie'd looked at it he called him in, very soft and civil, and said, 'Sit 'ee down, sir', and then he cried out to him all on a sudden to open his mouth, and he said, 'They be an old ancient yellow and mixed lot of teeth you got. I tell 'ee what, you come along right off with me to Helston and I'll have 'em drawed for 'ee and give 'ee a brave new set I got in my pocket, was my brother's, all cleaned up, with beautiful pink gums and all; a bit raspy to the roof at first, maybe, but all so like as peas and so white as milk.'

MISS M: Oh! I don't want the glass, and the bowl's another story, isn't it? My man is outside with the pony-cart, and if you don't mind he could take it now?

SUSANNAH: I'll car' it out to him.

MISS M: Oh, that would be kind of you. Then I mustn't keep you from your tea.

(Susannah takes the bowl and is going out with it when Rachel enters.)

RACHEL (*to Susannah, sternly*): What be doing with that bowl?

MISS M (*suavely*): Susannah has just parted with it—to me; I admired it so much; I hope you don't mind—

RACHEL (*to Susannah*): What's the meaning of it?

SUSANNAH (*sullenly*): You did hear; I've parted with it and that's true.

(The two women face each other, Rachel amazed, a terrible sense of helplessness creeping over her, trying to straighten her bent body. Susannah defiant.)

(*The door closes.*)

RACHEL (*slowly and distinctly*): It wasn't your'n to part with.

(Susannah laughs harshly. Rachel turns towards Miss Maxwell with quiet dignity.)

The bowl be mine, and my dead husband brought it back to me from foreign lands the year that us was wed. 'Twas used to christen my first child, the one that died almost so soon as he seen the light. It have a stood theer 'pon the Book nigh upon sixty year; and I would so soon part with my right hand. What have 'ee got to say?

SUSANNAH: 'Tis I, not she, as have a'got the saying; and I say I've sold it and the price of it lies theer.

RACHEL: Wasn't it enough for 'ee to try and steal my son from me, but you must make away with a bit of a keepsake that were mine afore ever you was born?

MISS M: This is very distressing; I'm afraid—I see—naturally I didn't know—but of course if this is so, Susannah will release me—

SUSANNAH: I don't. (*To Rachel.*) And I have David's word for it. He gived me leave to do whatever I'd a mind to in the home that's his and mine. (*To Miss Maxwell.*) Call yon man—no, I'll take it out to him.

MISS M (*going*): But really, Susannah—perhaps, in the circumstances. . . .

SUSANNAH (*by door*): 'Tisn't over pleasant for 'ee heer. I'll settle it, if you'll step outside.

(*David enters. He looks from one to the other, sees the money on the table, and turns to Susannah.*)

DAVID: Wait, Susannah— do 'ee bide here a minute. Put that bowl down—put it down I say.

(*She hesitates but finally puts the bowl on the table.*)

What's the meaning of it? This money on the table?

SUSANNAH (*sullenly*): You can see.

DAVID: Take that damned money to her that it belongs to, and give back to Mother the thing that's her'n. (*Susannah does not move.*) Take it—I say.

(*A long pause.*)

SUSANNAH (*savagely*): Let your mother take it. 'Tis her work to make trouble in this house and set 'ee again me. Let her take it or let it bide, I say.

DAVID: Do as I bid 'ee.

(*Susannah laughs. David steps forward and raises a threatening arm.*)

DAVID: Will 'ee do as I bid 'ee? Or else—

SUSANNAH: No.

RACHEL (*fearfully*): No, son—don't 'ee strike 'er—don't 'ee!

(*Rachel tries to throw herself between them, but before she can do so, David strikes Susannah, who staggers back and steadies herself against the wall. David is going out, when she stops him with a gesture.*)

SUSANNAH (*almost in a whisper*): Don't move, man! Stay theer. You'd best take notice of 'em , for they'm the last words I've a' got to speak to 'ee. You've choosed the wrong woman, David Parris, to serve as 'ee've a served me this same minute. (*She raises her voice and ends loudly.*) Hark 'ee—never will I mend or clean or do for 'ee again. Never will I hold speech with 'ee or look at 'ee, or take that hand of your'n, or lie beside 'ee so long as us do live. And never, mark 'ee, David Parris, never shall the child that's to be born, so long as I can keep it from him, hear his father's name. I cast'ee off. You'm patient, but I'll outlast 'ee, I'll outlast 'ee; God judge atween us, David Parris, I've a'done with 'ee.

(*She flings open the door and holds it back erect and breathless. David stands motionless, with bowed head.*)

DAVID (*brokenly*): So be it, Susannah, so let it be.

(*Susannah goes out. David sits down dazed at the table, his head in his hands.*)

DAVID: . . . so let it be.

RACHEL (*dispassionately and straightening herself up*): Theer be only one thing for to do. I must go, David, and her'll come back.

DAVID: Let a' be, Mother.

RACHEL: I'd oughter have gone before. And I can fend for myself fine. I baint done yet. Mother were hale and doing at eighty-one.

DAVID: Her won't come back.

RACHEL: And Sarah Yeo'll have me, sure. Her've got a tidy little room and wants looking after terrible bad, poor soul. Was saying only the other day—

DAVID: I sim I want some looking after. When a man takes to striking women—

RACHEL: You'm roadling, man. You baint the first that has been fo'ced to show you'm master.

DAVID: If a man can't master hisself, he'm a brute. I reckon, and not properly a man.

RACHEL: And they that calls out for the brute in him, what's they?

DAVID: I be all in a fog. I can't see straight—nor think straight—

RACHEL (*going to cupboard and taking out teapot*): Let it all bide a bit and have some tea. Kettle's on the boil. I'll wet the tea . . . let it bide a bit, Davy lad.

DAVID: I couldn't touch a screed of it.

RACHEL: Then best go upalong and tell Susannah I be going to Sarah Yeo's tonight.

DAVID: I couldn't. I couldn't, Mother. (*He gets up heavily and moves to the door.*)

RACHEL (*anxiously*): Wheer be going then!

DAVID: To take the boat out.

RACHEL (*alarmed*): You mustn't, lad, sea be too high for 'ee to fight it.

DAVID: I must fight something.

RACHEL (*putting a hand upon his arm*): Don't 'ee, Davy, don't 'ee. For my sake . . . if you love me . . . not in this sea. I'll go, David, and her'll come back.

DAVID (*shaking her off rather roughly*): Let 'a be, Mother. I must go.

(*The door opens. She calls to him over the sound of the sea.*)

RACHEL: I can fend for myself. I baint done yet. . . !

(*The door slams. The old woman starts crying in a dry, broken way. Someone knocks on the door, then Miss Maxwell opens it and comes in.*)

MISS M: I came back to tell you how dreadfully sorry I am for all this—this misunderstanding. I'm afraid it all comes of breaking the tenth commandment.

RACHEL: You've broke a man's heart, and turned him from his home.

MISS M: Oh no! I hope it's not as bad as that.

RACHEL: He've struck her, and she've left him.

MISS M: But she'll come back.

RACHEL: Susannah baint a woman to be struck.

MISS M: He struck her? Poor Susannah!—really that's rather dreadful. I thought he was such a nice quiet man.

RACHEL: He never spoke a hard word or did a harsh act in all his days afore.

MISS M: And over such a little thing, a piece of china! A china bowl—surely—

RACHEL: The money's theer; you can take it and the bowl too if you've a mind; I never want to look at it again.

MISS M: Very well. If you would prefer it. It all seems rather unnecessary.

(Miss Maxwell takes up money and is about to go.)

MISS M: I'm sorry. Good-bye, Mrs Parris.

RACHEL: Afore I was married I were in service up to the great house; maybe you know it?

MISS M: Oh yes! I know Lord Vivian. Why?

RACHEL: It were his father then. 'Tis a grand place, marvellous like to a palace 'tis, and crowded up with all sorts of gimcracks, books and that, and chiney and that, and pictures scores and scores on 'em all in gold frames upon the walls. But all the years that I were theer it never took me to want any of they things. I never wanted 'em. There's handsomer bowls nor this up theer, a parcel of 'em. Happen you asked his lordship to sell 'ee one of they?

MISS M: That's different isn't it? I happen to want this bowl.

RACHEL: Yes, sure. This be only a poor bleak room with nothing in it to take your fancy but the old bowl, the only pretty thing we got to mind us of him that's gone and hand on to our children.

MISS M: I see. Of course if I'd known you looked at it like that—

RACHEL: Why shouldn't us? To we they things is home and long quiet thought and all that's left of the days when us was young. To you they'm just another ornament to take and boast on and show up in your fine houses. You like old ancient things?

MISS M: I simply love them. I have a passion for them. I collect them, you know.

RACHEL: Haven't you none of your own?

MISS M: China? Oh yes, rather a fine collection, but I'm afraid that's the collector's vice, the more one has, you know, the more one wants, but I suppose I can't expect you quite to see our point of view.

RACHEL: 'Tis plain enough. We'm poor folk and you'm rich folk, you'm born to buy and we'm born to sell. And, so bad seasons, when times is hard and bread scarce, and us don't know nothing of the valley of 'em, you come a'poking and peering round, and out with a few shillings to cheat 'em out of we.

MISS M: Cheat is an ugly word, Mrs Parris.

RACHEL: It's an ugly thing. Will 'ee put your hand on the Bible theer and swear you never cheated?
(A pause.)
It's the word that frights 'ee, not the meaning of it.

MISS M: Possibly.

RACHEL: And you'm not alone in that. I seen many a gentleman shouting lies at the top of his voice, till he was hoarse, to catch votes for Government from they poor silly fishermen, and terrible upset when he be called a liar. And many a woman playing the harlot, with pink rosy cheeks, turn white when she be called the name.

MISS M: The word is more horrible than the thing.

RACHEL: Is it?

MISS M: It is, but I don't know why.

RACHEL: 'Tisn't the name things go by that'll be set down against us at the last.

MISS M: I wonder? But about politics, you know, you're wrong; these gentlemen are simply working for you. They—

RACHEL: Don't look to me like gentlemen, they looks more like cheap-jacks with long tongues and large pockets, working for their living, and soft places; and stirring up everything for more and more soft places, which first or last us has to pay for. All us wants is to be let alone.

MISS M: Dear Mrs Parris, I can only say how sorry and vexed I am to have caused all this trouble in your home.

RACHEL: I've no home now.

MISS M: No, really, aren't you taking everything too seriously? I feel sure it will all come right. (*Going.*) These little tiffs have a habit of smoothing themselves out you know.

RACHEL: Wish 'ee good-day.

MISS M (*glancing through window*): Oh! Oh dear! There's a boat ashore!

RACHEL: A fishing boat?

MISS M: Yes—over there on the rocks! But it can't be a Tregarveth boat—none of them have gone out today. It must have drifted. It's breaking up there on the rocks, and oh!—I'm afraid—I'm afraid—there's a man in the sea—a body—in the sea. Yes how dreadful— There's a man drowned.

RACHEL (*repeating dully*): Theer's a man drowned.

MISS M (*nervously coming back*): You'll let me stay here a few minutes, won't you? till—I—I'd rather not see it. I shouldn't sleep—

RACHEL: Theer's a man drowned.

MISS M: Oh! The sea's dreadful, isn't it? It gets so frightfully on my nerves sometimes. I always sleep with a night-light by the sea. *(Enter Susannah, throwing the door open violently and holding it back.)*

RACHEL: Theer's a man drowned.

SUSANNAH: I know! David.

MISS M: David? Your husband! Oh, how dreadful. Poor Susannah.

SUSANNAH: 'Tis no business of mines. They can car' him home to his mother's, that be the place for him—I told 'em; they can car' him theer.

(Door shut.)

RACHEL (*looking beyond Susannah at the door*): Davy! Davy!

SUSANNAH (*coming in; with slow distinctness*): Yes, they'm bringing him along; but I didn't come to look at a dead staring man. I didn't come to claim him though he be mine, not your'n. I comed to have a last word with 'ee, Rachel Parris, and to take a last look at the woman who've killed her son. Be afeared the dead'll rise to give me another blow? There is none left to strike for 'ee or speak for 'ee. You be alone with me. You'm fo'ced to hear what I be going to tell 'ee, and 'tis words to think on. Mark 'em, Rachel Parris. David do owe his death to 'ee this day. 'Twas easy work to part we, that were soon done, but 'twere the finish of him. 'Twasn't sich easy work for he to bide with 'ee. He couldn't bide. You was the one that made a brute of him, jest for a piece of painted cloam; that were the price of wife and child, for David, and 'tis to pay it he lies theer. 'Twas I that sent him to his death, so they'll be saying. They'm wrong. The Lord be witness that were left to thee.

RACHEL (*crouching fearfully*): Susannah. . . .

SUSANNAH: Go out and look at him. Mayst take thy fill of glazing at the last of all they sons, but never think that he comed back to 'ee. He knowed so well as I what you'd a'done for him, and if he loved 'ee once 'twas over then. 'Twas over when 'ee took the light from they blue staring eyes of his. I were the only light of 'em, times and again he telled me so, I were the light and you the darkness of his life. He minded it, I tell 'ee, night and day. His heart were gone from 'ee afore his body. He leaved 'ee wi'out a word and he comed back to me. Body and soul you had a'lost him, and if so be as the dead do rise and theer be judgement, neither in this world nor the next will he have part nor lot with thee.

Appendix

A REMINISCENCE OF PRINCESS MATHILDE BONAPARTE

BORN MAY 27TH, 1820: DIED JANUARY 2ND, 1904

WHEN staying in Paris three years ago with an aunt, who for years had been one of Princess Mathilde Bonaparte's intimate friends, I went frequently to her hotel in the Rue de Berri.

The daughter of Jerome, ex-King of Westphalia and youngest brother of Napoleon, and Caroline of Wurtemberg, Princess Mathilde was niece to the great Emperor, and through her mother was connected with the Imperial House of Russia—a relationship that stood her in good stead during the unhappy years of her married life.

She was born at Trieste in 1820, by which time the Napoleonic dynasty had crumbled utterly away; its founder was a prisoner at St Helena, and the members of his family were scattered in exile over divers parts of the world. In 1840 she married Prince Anatole Demidoff, the owner of the marvellous collection of art treasures in the San Donato Palace in Florence, but the marriage was from the first an unhappy one, and after a few years a separation took place.

Princess Mathilde settled in Paris during the last days of Louis Philippe's reign; and, under various governments, she lived there till her death in January last. When, after 1848, Louis Napoleon became President of the Republic, it was she who acted as hostess for him, and did the honours of the Elysée. Later on Napoleon III, who in his younger days had been deeply in love with his cousin, created her an Imperial Highness with an appanage, and in all affairs of ceremony she came second only to the Empress.

Throughout the eventful period known as the Second Empire, she played a leading part. When it, too, came to an end, amidst black ruin and despair, Princess Mathilde went for a short time into exile, but when the Republic was again established, she returned to Paris and, abjuring politics, gave herself up to the enjoyment of society, particularly that of those distinguished in art and letters.

Her *salon* soon became a centre—the only one of real importance in Paris—for all that was literary and artistic in a city famed for those qualities.

By her wit and beauty and her genuine love of art in all its forms, as well as by the advantages of her wealth and position, she was able to attract and gather round her all the eminent men of the day. To read the list of her friendships, and the names of those who frequented her *salon*, is to study the history of French art and literature during the past thirty years.

The brothers de Goncourt—to mention a few names only—Flaubert, Sainte-Beuve, Théophile Gautier, Renan, Alex. Dumas *fils*, Taine, Edmond Giraud, and the venerable painter Hébert, who survives her, were among her intimate friends during the seventies; later on appeared Bonnat, Detaille, Yriarte, Guy de Maupassant, Coppée, Sardou, Pierre Loti, Hanotaux, Henri Lavedan, Frederic Masson, and hosts of others more or less celebrated. Persons of distinction from all parts of Europe were also to be met at Princess Mathilde's, for, wide and catholic in her tastes and sympathies, she knew how to respond to any call that was made upon her.

She was as benevolent, too, as she was artistic, and amid all the pleasures of her crowded life, she had perhaps none greater than that of helping, out of her abundant means, those whose talents were greater than their opportunities. Her charities and her kindly deeds were innumerable, and it is not surprising that, loving human intercourse as she did, she should have been to the last surrounded by hosts of friends, as well as by those who looked to her for assistance.

When I saw Princess Mathilde first, a year after she had celebrated her eightieth birthday by a great reception—at which she wore a low dress for, in spite of her great age, her shoulders and arms were still beautiful—the glories of the past were over, the light of her *salon* had waned. The great men who once adorned it were but names inscribed on the rolls of art and literature; the friends of her youth had most of them passed 'the door of darkness through'. Of her contemporaries still surviving, but few in the ordinary course of nature could have boasted her unimpaired faculties, and the zest for society still possessed by one who had played a brilliant part in it all her life, and to whom it had become as second nature. If, however, the crowds of former days had vanished, a constant stream of visitors still flowed through the Princess's hospitable doors. There were many sons and daughters of former friends—themselves middle-aged persons with sons and daughters of their own—many persons eminent in the Paris of today, together with a sprinkling of young and rising men, for she was still quick to recognize talent, and possessed the faculty, rare in old age, of making and keeping new friends.

Of these friends many dined or breakfasted regularly with her on fixed days of the week, for at neither of these meals was she ever alone. My aunt had a standing invitation to dinner on Fridays, and so long as I was with her the Princess kindly included me in it.

I well recollect the first time I accompanied her. Princess Mathilde dined at half past seven; so, driving through the great doorway opening direct into the Rue de Berri, just before that hour we found ourselves in front of a low white house forming the opposite side of a courtyard. Passing in, our cloaks were taken from us in a white painted hall, tall doors on the right were thrown open, and we were shown into a long ante-room, hung with many pictures—as indeed was every corner of the house.

Its rich decorations of crimson and gold made a warm background for a stately row of marble busts of the Bonapartes on the right. At the farther end, beyond a crimson curtain, was gathered a little knot of people, and on a sofa against the wall—also on the right—sat the Princess.

As we advanced she rose to receive us.

I shall never forget the impression her small figure, bent with the weight of years, but full of dignity, made on me. Prepared as I was to be interested in her—remembering her near relationship to the colossal figure round whom the most striking period in French history centres; her close association with the swift, fleeting brilliancy of the Second Empire, and with all that was great in French art and literature for many past decades—it was yet her own intense personality, and the extraordinary force of character that stamped every line of her rather rugged face, and looked out of her keen dark eyes, that awoke a special feeling of sympathy.

One saw at a glance that the fires of her life though sunk low were still glowing, one realized instantly that here was one who had gone through life in no mere superficial mood: that she had both keenly suffered and keenly enjoyed was written plainly in the traces left by Time upon her face, and also in the quick sympathy of her expression.

Strictly beautiful Princess Mathilde could never have been, for her features were cast in too masculine a mould, but she must always have been among those who, apart from social rank, stand out in a crowd, distinguished from the common herd by the high courage of their bearing and the force of their presence.

Her dress—always the same when I saw her in the evening—was rather curious. She wore a rich white brocade skirt, and a transparent lace body over a black silk 'slip', cut low in the round fashion of early Victorian days, and with short sleeves. Over her shoulders was draped a white China silk shawl, and round her neck hung seven graduated rows of magnificent pearls. [The necklace given by Napoleon to her mother, Princess Caroline, on her marriage.] Her hair, still dark, was parted in front, while across the top of her head a thick plait made a sort of coronet. It was drawn high up at the back, emphasizing her strong, determined profile. Once or twice I saw her in a lace cap which, as it softened her features, was infinitely more becoming. I can quite believe that, did she choose, Princess Mathilde could make herself formidable. As I saw later on, she was very open in the expression of her likes and dislikes, and her prejudices were certainly strong, which made those who did not know her well somewhat in awe of her. To me she was invariably kind and gracious.

On its being announced that '*Son Altesse Impériale était servie*', the Princess rose, and taking the arm of one of the gentlemen present led the way to dinner. We followed through a great square reception-room decorated with palms and hung with pictures as if for an exhibition, and up a shallow flight of steps into the dining-room—comparatively small, lined with dim old tapestry, and lighted only from above. In one corner stood a statue of Napoleon surrounded by palms.

Princess Mathilde seated herself at the farther side of the large round table facing the entrance, through which she looked down into the great *salon*, and of course during dinner was helped first. We ate off gold plate; there were many servants in the green Imperial liveries; and the centre of the table was adorned by a large silver gilt Imperial eagle encircled by five small ones. But in spite of a certain amount of ceremony there was no stiffness or formality. The guests were nearly all intimate friends or acquaintances, and the conversation was free and general. The Princess, as a rule, did not take a large share in it during dinner, but she was constantly appealed to, and nothing seemed to escape her observation.

Afterwards we all returned, in the same order in which we had come, to the room where we had previously been. The large *salon* was only used for receptions. The Princess seated herself in her customary place on the sofa, and, it must be owned, generally fell asleep. The company gathered round a large table in front of her, on which were books and the current numbers of magazines and illustrated papers, and talked in low tones, until, the Princess waking up, conversation once more became general. She was keenly interested in politics, and in the news of the town, and her friends seemed to vie with one another in bringing her the latest information on all subjects. Her criticisms and remarks were always interesting: they were so spontaneous and trenchant, sometimes, indeed, cuttingly severe.

The *loi des associations* was then under discussion in the *Chambre des députés* and shortly after speaking at length in its favour, M. Waldeck Rousseau, the premier, had fallen dangerously ill with an abscess under the tongue. All Paris talked of his condition and discussed his sufferings.

'*Il est puni, où il a péché*', was all the Princess's comment.

There was a masculine force about her judgements which made them striking, even if they had not been expressed with a rather startling directness. In their variety and sagacity, they bore witness to the activity of her mind, and to her great experience of public and private life. On hearing her talk one could not help thinking that she must have inherited more than a touch of her great uncle's extra-